Batch Control Systems: Design, Application, and Implementation

Batch Control Systems: Design, Application, and Implementation

Thomas G. Fisher, P.E.

Resources for Measurement and Control Series

Instrument Society of America

INSTRUMENT SOCIETY OF AMERICA
67 Alexander Drive
P.O. Box 12277
Research Triangle Park
North Carolina 27709

Library of Congress Cataloging-in-Publication Data

Fisher, Thomas G.
  Batch control systems / Thomas G. Fisher. --
    p.   cm. -- (Resources for measurement and control series)
  Includes bibliographical references.
  ISBN 1-55617-131-5
  1. Process control -- Data processing.   2. Process control-
-Automation. .   I. Title.   II. Series.
  TS156.8.F573 1990
  660'.2815--dc20

90-5176
CIP

*This work is dedicated to
the memory of my granddaughter,
Dana Leigh Fisher,
March 1, 1990–March 2, 1990.*

So Small, So Sweet, So Soon

Contents

Preface

Process engineers have usually selected batch operations when product quantities are small, reaction times are long, feedstock supplies and market demands are uncertain, manufacturing procedures are likely to change, or a large variety of small volume products will be produced. Batch operations have definite advantages when there is a need to manufacture small amounts of particular products or to have the flexibility to change output mix quickly and with little waste. To be effective, the batch control system must also be flexible to allow the manufacture of the different products.

Although advanced technology and improved production techniques have caused a reduction in hardware prices, the same is not true with application software. The cost of application software has become a major consideration in automating batch processes.

Batch automation can be difficult because there are no standards in the batch control area. This lack of standardization can cause the following problems:

- It is difficult for users to effectively communicate their requirements to vendors because of the terminology problems.
- Batch control systems are difficult to configure, and switching from one vendor's software to another can be a nightmare.
- There is not a universal model for batch control systems, which makes it hard to use the same recipes at different plant sites or divisions within a corporation.
- Operator interfaces are different from manufacturer to manufacturer and sometimes from system to system from the same manufacturer.
- There is no standard documentation method for batch control systems.

• It is difficult to integrate devices from different vendors into one batch control system because of the proprietary communications, proprietary operating systems, and so on.

The International Purdue Workshop on Industrial Computer Systems, Special Applications Programming Committee TC-4, worked for several years on a design tool kit that would provide standard terminology for batch process control. This terminology, combined with a structural model that defines the relationships among equipment and processes, was intended to make it easier to develop batch control systems. This would then allow a user to compare batch systems from different vendors for his or her application.

Similar work has been done by the NAMUR Committee in Europe. Their goals were to reduce the cost of developing application software as well as the amount of time needed for development by enabling shop floor personnel to construct valid control instructions directly from the process instructions. The NAMUR Committee realized that the achievement of this goal could not be allowed to interfere with the security of the batch control system. Their concepts required the use of pretailored modules that could be used by shop floor personnel who were trained in their use and interconnection.

Both of these committees are now inactive. However, ISA's SP88 Batch Control Systems standards committee was chartered to begin its work in October 1988. Its purpose is to provide standards and recommended practices, as appropriate, for the design and specification of batch control systems as used in the process industries. It's output to date draws heavily from the Purdue TC-4 and NAMUR work. The scope of this committee's work is:

1. To define a standard functional model or set of models that describes the batch processing plant and the types of control needed for batch processing: production scheduling, recipe management, batch management, sequential control, regulatory and discrete control, and safety interlocking;

2. To define terminology that is specific to batch processes and batch control systems and that will encourage understanding between manufacturers and users;

3. To provide a standard data structure for batch systems that will simplify data communications within the overall batch architecture (This implies a close coordination with ISA's SP72 and SP50 standards committees. Actually, the framework is a result of MMS [Manufacturing Message Specification]. SP88's task will be to define the batch-specific requirements for messaging.); and

4. To develop guidelines for a standard batch control language to simplify the programming and configuration tasks necessary to implement batch and to simplify the task of communicating between the various components of a batch control system.

Note: It is not the intention of the SP88 committee to generate code but to establish guidelines or a framework for batch-specific languages.

Developing a standard of such magnitude and importance is no easy task. To help guide its way, the SP88 committee has set eight major goals for the standard:

1. Improve communications between users and vendors through common terminology and structure.
2. Reduce the life-cycle engineering effort for batch applications.
3. Allow ease of recipe development and updating.
4. Provide for transportability of recipes.
5. Reduce manufacturing's dependence on system experts, e.g., recipe configuration straightforward enough that it may easily be done by a process engineer or chemist and not require a system specialist.
6. Flexibility—separation of functionality from hardware.
7. Provide batch control system guidelines for implementation and use.
8. Meet the functional needs of users.

But the real challenge of SP88 can be summed up by its own mission statement:

> To make the standard(s) comprehensive enough to be of value and accomplish its goals, yet flexible enough in the right areas to allow control systems manufacturers to be innovative. They (the standards) must be sophisticated enough to apply to the most complex batch processes, and be able to collapse to fit the simplest of them. They must give guidance to achieve understanding and uniformity without being restrictive and cumbersome. They should apply equally as well to a plant that is run manually as to one that is fully automated.

However, in today's world of global business, the importance of international standards cannot be denied. So the SP88 Committee mapped out a strategy to produce an internationally accepted standard and submitted the following new work items to the Industrial Electrotechnical Commission (IEC):

1. Batch control systems—models and terminology
2. Batch control systems—data structure and guidelines for languages

These work items were voted on and accepted by IEC at their June 1990 meeting in Chapel Hill, NC. This means that SP88 will lead this work in the international arena.

The importance of standards to the development and design of batch control systems is emphasized throughout this book.

Thomas G. Fisher
Chardon, OH
September 1990

About the Author

THOMAS G. FISHER, P.E., has more than 20 years of experience in control systems and instrumentation and is currently Manager of Control Systems Technology in the Process and Quality Management Division of The Lubrizol Corporation. He holds B.S. and M.S. degrees in Chemical Engineering from Grove City College and West Virginia University, respectively. Tom is a Fellow Member of the Instrument Society of America. He has been active for several years in ISA's short course program.

About the Book

This book on *Batch Control Systems: Design, Application, and Implementation* is the outgrowth of a short course the author has been teaching for ISA for several years. The short course material is constantly being updated to keep it in line with current technology in the batch control systems area. In the past few years, that has taken a considerable amount of time because there has been, and continues to be, a lot of changes in vendors' offerings in this area. There has also been a significant amount of work around standards for batch control systems. This book is current with today's (1990) technology and is current with the work of ISA's SP88 Batch Control Systems standards committee at the time of this writing. The technology is going to continue to evolve; SP88 is going to continue to evolve its standard. So this book is really a snapshot in time at this particular point in the development of batch control systems.

It appears that the trend in industry is a move toward standards-based control systems. Now that the work of SP88 has been moved into the international arena, the importance of user involvement in this work becomes even more critical, so that the eventual standard(s) will meet the needs of the user community.

This book is divided into four parts: Batch System Basics, Batch Control System Structure, Batch Control, and Batch Control System Design. Part I, Batch System Basics, is intended to introduce the reader to batch processes, to point out the differences between batch and continuous processes, to acquaint the reader with some of the inherent control problems associated with batch processing, and, very importantly, to acquaint the reader with the terminology associated with batch processes and batch control systems.

Part II, Batch Control System Structure, introduces the reader to the concept of a hierarchically structured batch control system. A model for batch control that has been developed by SP88 is compared with some of the current CIM (Computer

Integrated Manufacturing) models that currently exist. This batch model is not a physical architecture model; it is a functional model that is intended to show what functionality is needed at the various levels of the hierarchical structure. Further models are introduced to show the control activities that are needed to implement batch control systems. Finally, the importance of standards is discussed, and the author's viewpoint is given on the direction these standards will take.

Part III, Batch Control, describes in detail the six essential control activities that the batch control system designer will encounter. These are Safety Interlocking, Regulatory/Discrete Control, Sequential Control, Batch Management, Recipe Management, and Production Scheduling. If there is one chapter in this book that really needs further definition and development (SP88 is currently working in this area), it is the chapter on Batch Management. This is a control activity that people have recognized in the last few years as being absolutely necessary to batch control systems. Some vendors now include batch management packages in their control systems. However, this may be the area in which there is the most difference between vendors' offerings. This chapter is an attempt to put some organization into this control activity; it is not intended to be the final word.

Part IV, Batch Control System Design, introduces the reader to some of the complexities involved in designing and implementing batch control systems. A push is made to use top down design techniques as a more structured method for developing the control requirements for the system. Hardware is discussed from both a functionality and a reliability/availability standpoint. Finally, chapters are included to give the reader some guidance in specifying and justifying batch control systems.

It would have been advantageous to be able to hold off on this book until SP88 could complete its work. However, standards take years to develop, and this subject couldn't wait that long. Hopefully, the viewpoints expressed here will not deviate too substantially from the final work of SP88.

Acknowledgments

The first group of people I need to acknowledge is my family, my wife Shirley, my sons Gary and Jeffrey, and my daughter Rebecca, for the patience they have shown over the years with the massive amounts of time I have been away from them. This actually spans quite a few years, starting from my initial work in designing batch control systems and work with engineering contractors on detailed design through participating in start-ups of these units in various parts of the world. Much of this work involved spending a considerable amount of time away from home, but it did provide the necessary background needed to develop a course and start teaching that course on Batch Control Systems. The short course provided the necessary foundation for writing this book, but there have been many changes between the contents of the short course notes and this book. Again, that has meant spending a lot of time in my office, surrounded by papers, away from my family. They have supported my efforts in these areas, and I truly appreciate and need that support.

The second group of people I want to acknowledge are those who reviewed my preliminary manuscript and made many suggestions for improvement. I have tried to incorporate as many of their comments as possible into the final manuscript. They are: Don Dodd—DuPont, Steve Duff—Moore Products Co., Paul Merlenzie—SAC Company, Tim Shaw—Texas Instruments Inc., and Evan Whitmer—Honeywell Inc.

The third group of people I need to acknowledge are the students in the short course on Batch Control Systems I have been teaching for ISA for several years. They have provided valuable comments on the contents of the short course and some needed direction. Their questions during the teaching of the short courses have provided impetus for developing better methods for explaining the course content and better methods for presenting the course. I hope that shows up in this book.

Finally, I want to acknowledge the input I have received from the members of SP88. Much of their input is included in this book. I particularly want to express my gratitude to Rick Mergen, Chairman of SP88 and a fellow Lubrizol employee. We have spent countless hours discussing the intricacies of batch control systems. Rick has provided me with a place to go to discuss new ideas and concepts related to batch control systems, particularly those that have not yet been addressed by SP88. The output of those discussions can be found in many places throughout this book.

Part I
Batch System Basics

1

Introduction to Batch Control Systems

Introduction Industrial manufacturing processes can generally be classified as continuous, discrete, or batch. How a process is classified depends on whether the output product from the process appears in a continuous flow or in discrete batches or quantities.

In a continuous process, product is made by passing materials through different pieces of specialized equipment; each of these pieces of equipment ideally operates in a single steady state and performs one dedicated processing function. The output product from a continuous process appears in a continuous flow.

In discrete manufacturing, products are traditionally manufactured in production lots (a group of products having common raw materials and production histories). In a discrete manufacturing process, a specified quantity of product moves as a unit (group of parts) between workstations; each part maintains its unique identity. One of its useful features is the ability to audit quality economically and answer the growing demand from customers for traceability.

So what is a batch process? Shaw (Ref. 1) gives the following definition of a batch process:

> A process is considered to be batch in nature if, due to physical structuring of the process equipment or due to other factors, the process consists of a sequence of one or more steps (or phases) that must be performed in a defined order. The completion of this sequence of steps creates a finite quantity of finished product. If more of the product is to be created, the sequence must be repeated.

Batch processes are discontinuous processes. Ingredients are sequentially prepared, e.g., mixed, cooked, reacted, finished, and then packaged. When the ingredients are combined in the proper proportions and exposed to the required process conditions for the necessary times, the process usually results in an acceptable product. Batch processes are neither discrete nor continuous; however, they have characteristics of both. From a control standpoint, a major distinction between the types of processes (continuous, discrete, and batch) is the frequency of starting the manufacture of a new product. Staples (Ref. 2) provides a comparison of the characteristics of the three types of processes, again from a process control perspective (see Table 1-1).

Products in a batch process may be made in one or a few vessels. These vessels are often taken through several operations in which multiple processing functions are performed. The significance of a batch's characteristics extends beyond the batch's completion. Products from a batch system usually have a unique identity. This means that particularly good (or bad) batches can be isolated, and the historical information from these batches can be used to optimize control parameters for subsequent batches.

Batch manufacturers are now facing the same demands from customers for product traceability and quality assurance. A need for better data collection and processing in batch control systems is resulting from the effects of government regulatory agencies, such as the Food and Drug Administration. This traceability can be an extremely important concept when considering manufacturing and control objectives.

Batch Control Systems
Control systems themselves are either regulatory, discrete, or sequential. So, what is a batch control system?

A batch control system provides for multiproduct production through recipe processing by controlling variables in the regulatory control, discrete control, and sequential control domains.

At the present time, most batch control systems are implemented with relatively straightforward control strategies. Even where programmable controllers, distributed control systems, or process computers are used, the implementations tend to simulate the same tasks traditionally performed using relay logic and analog controllers.

The monitoring capabilities required for batch control applications differ from those found in regulatory control for continuous processes. Since batch processes are dynamic by nature, they have many transient events to be monitored. This transient data can be a valuable tool for process optimization, but greater amounts of computational power are required in the control system to

---

TABLE 1-1
Comparison of Continuous, Discrete, and Batch Control Characteristics

	Continuous	Discrete	Batch
Product Frequency	Weeks	Seconds	Hours
Lot Sizes	Large	Small	Medium
Labor Content	Small	High	Medium
Process Efficiency	High	Low	Medium
% Discrete/% Analog I/O	5:95	95:5	60:40
Type Control System	DCS	PLC	Various

capture and process this data than might be necessary for purely regulatory control.

The versatility of a batch control system generally determines its effectiveness in batch applications. A typical batch control system must handle pulse and other discrete inputs as well as analog signals because of the wide range of sensors and actuators likely to be encountered. Typical functions that must be performed are (Refs. 2, 3, and 4):

1. Implementing feedback control of flows, temperatures, pressures, and levels, as well as advanced control strategies.

2. Performing logic for interlocking, including safety interlocks that are needed to protect personnel, equipment, and the environment from the harmful effects of hazardous chemical processes.

3. Performing calculations for tasks such as heat balancing.

4. Providing batch sequence control that involves mixing ingredients, heating, waiting for the reaction to complete, cooling and discharging the resulting product, etc. This requires flexible logic and sequence handling capabilities to accommodate the large number of processing alternatives, and recovery from unplanned and failure conditions. This results from the large number of process vessels, pumps, motors, valves, limit switches, etc., that are typical of batch processes.

5. Scheduling and tracking the operation of multiple processing units.

6. Charging materials into batch tanks or reactors. This includes metering the materials as they are charged, whether by weight or volume, as specified in each recipe.

7. Adjusting set points of process variables (temperature, pressure, level, flow, etc.) as required. This includes ramping set points up or down and holding set points for a prescribed period of time.

8. Transferring materials at the completion of the process operation.

9. Detecting end of reaction conditions whether that be by laboratory analysis, temperature, viscosity, etc.

10. Reporting information regarding batches produced on a batch, shift, daily, or weekly basis.

11. Keeping the operator aware of process status and making sure he or she is capable of interacting with the recipes and with the sequential, regulatory, and discrete controls.

12. Maintaining complete information (recipes) required for manufacturing each product, or grade of each product, including names and amounts of ingredients, temperature and pressure set points, ramp rates, processing times, and sample points.

Making all these different functions work together is the key to an effective batch control system.

The hardware and software necessary to control continuous processes are well within the scope of current technology. Operators are expected to monitor the process and to intervene only if abnormal circumstances are detected. This may leave the operator with little to do, needing to take action only when the process is in a transient rather than a steady state. This transient state may be due to external disturbances, grade changes, or set point adjustments that have upset the system or the start-up or shutdown of units.

Control, equipment as well as practice, is more highly developed for continuous than for batch processing. This was mainly because economic incentives were traditionally more apparent in improving the efficiency or capacity of high-volume plants, such as are found in continuous processes. Today, there is an emphasis on upgrading controls for batch processing to take greater advantage of the flexibility of these plants and to improve the cost effectiveness and safety of short production runs.

Types of Control

The essential elements of a batch control system are the regulatory, discrete, and sequential control functions that combine regulation of continuous variables and control of discrete devices according to some predetermined operating sequence. The regulatory, discrete, and sequential control functions are defined as follows:

1. Regulatory control—Maintaining the outputs of a process as close as possible to their respective set point values despite the influences of set point changes and disturbances.

2. Discrete Control—Maintaining the outputs of a process to a target value chosen from a set of known stable states.

3. Sequential Control—A class of industrial process control functions in which the objective is to sequence the process through a series of distinct states.

In addition to monitoring and controlling process conditions, batch controls must coordinate sequences of events and closely control the timing and progress of process events. Many batch applications require significantly more sequential and discrete control than regulatory control.

As a further complication, all control systems require safety systems that act independently of sequential, discrete, or regulatory control functions. Safety systems are the control functions that prevent abnormal process actions that would jeopardize personnel safety, harm the environment, or damage equipment.

The Hardware/Software Problem

For years batch process applications have been the targets of numerous control system vendors. In the past, control vendors from the process and discrete worlds have force fit their systems into batch applications. As technologies have evolved, both worlds have enhanced their batch process capabilities.

Adequate solutions exist for pure discrete applications. This is the traditional stronghold of programmable controller (PLC) vendors. Pure analog applications, such as are usually found in continuous processes, are the stronghold of distributed control system (DCS) vendors. Batch control applications tend to fall between these two application areas, and neither of the above solutions is optimal.

DCS vendors have pushed their systems down into batch applications from the analog side. These systems maintain the superior analog capabilities and advanced programming power of typical DCS systems, but they may be slow and expensive when performing discrete control. Large batch process applications tend to fall into the domain of DCS systems. DCS systems are expensive, but they are a good solution when the application requires advanced control techniques and extensive reporting and recipe-handling requirements.

PLC systems, which are good at simple discrete control, have migrated upward from the discrete side. Batch applications are now employing these controllers because of their speed and the perceived lower cost. PLCs are also considered to have better environmental protection than DCSs. Although PLCs may, in fact, have better temperature specifications than most DCS systems, this alone does not provide true environmental protection. Environmental protection implies things such as resistance to corrosive atmospheres. Although the environmental protection built into PLCs may make them suitable for mounting on the factory floor of an automotive plant, it is probably not suitable for mounting the PLC on the factory floor of most chemical plants. Programmable controller manufacturers are now offering increasingly sophisticated input/output options, data display options better suited to batch process operators, and communication and support with general-purpose computers for complex data processing functions. Some of today's PLC offerings can control analog values equally well as discrete. However, many PLC systems lack the programming power to handle applications that require higher quantities of control loops, especially if advanced process control techniques are necessary. Advanced math and reporting capabilities that are easily performed by DCS systems are also difficult to implement in PLCs that offer only relay ladder logic programming techniques. But PLCs have the obvious benefit of low cost; and, in the past, many control compromises have been driven by this overriding factor.

The hardware and software issues in batch process control have not been resolved. Krigman (Ref. 5) puts it into perspective:

> Hearing the drums in what they perceive as the jungle out there, control instrumentation vendors of all shapes and sizes claim to have discovered the lost world of batch processing. Based on this insight, they are touting distributed and other systems that are somehow supposed to be optimized for the batch environment. This usually means that a network has an interface for one of the more popular programmable logic controllers. It also means that somewhere in the software, someone has appended a section of table-driven operations and has labeled the corresponding portion of the data base "the recipe".
>
> Unfortunately, hardware and software packages of this type do not address the real issues of batch process control. We're worrying about strategies to accommodate an operation that is transient rather than steady state, plant equipment that is used for varied rather than dedicated purposes, and loads that are uncertain rather than predictable. And we're trying to understand our operations well enough to

conceptualize the coordination of control functions encountered at different levels of the plant hierarchy—the routing and sequencing associated with material movement and vessel interlocks, the regulatory action involved with maintaining set point conditions in unit operations, and the decision support essential to handle production management problems such as equipment failures or changes in feedstock quality.

Ladder logic graphic interfaces, standardized loops on menus, and pre-engineered alarm sequences are not going to help with this work. The real question is whether they can even be helpful later on, or whether they hinder progress by making it ever so convenient to continue building digital systems that simulate the electromechanical and the electronic and pneumatic analog equipment they replaced.

The following are some of the problems a user is likely to encounter with the current offering of batch control systems:

1. The operator interfaces being supplied in batch applications are essentially the same as those used in continuous systems. The displays now being used in distributed control systems are really just substitutes for the indicators, recorders, and graphic panels of electronic and pneumatic days. They have proved to be reasonably effective in the continuous processing environment because a picture of current conditions is enough to characterize a plant in equilibrium.

These interfaces do not meet the needs of batch plants because of the assumption of static process behavior. The operator in a batch plant needs to know more than just the present state of conditions in the process; she or he needs to have some idea of where the unit has been and where it is going in the future. The real problem is how to best convey the information to the operator so that it realistically represents the dynamics of the transient batch process. This problem is not being addressed by control system vendors today.

2. There is no agreement on how to best distribute the control hardware and software to achieve the most cost-effective combination of performance and reliability.

3. Reliability and recovery from control system errors has not been addressed properly. The state of a batch process cannot be determined solely from measurements at a particular instant. Therefore, restarting a batch after a control system failure may be difficult unless the total history of the batch is known.

4. There is no accepted standard representation of the batch system. Without this, it is difficult to talk about the requirements of a system or how to program the procedures into the new digital systems. And without a standard structure, batch process control programming can be a nightmare. Programming is complex even for single-product applications, because these often comprise many batch stages and multiple units with intermediate storage.

5. The ideal software package for batch control has not been developed yet. Languages such as FORTRAN or BASIC are not effective for complex batch applications, and systems based on relay ladder logic are not well accepted in the

processing industries. However, a number of vendors now offer specialized software for batch process control.

Future batch control systems will have to be more sophisticated if they are to meet the increasing demands of factory automation.

EXERCISES

1.1 List some characteristics of continuous processes that are also typical of batch processes.

1.2 Give some reasons why simply combining ingredients in the proper proportions and exposing them to the required process conditions for the necessary times doesn't guarantee acceptable batch product.

1.3 Why do most batch control implementations tend to perform just the same tasks that have traditionally been performed using relay logic and analog controllers?

1.4 Discuss why the need for safety devices and interlocks complicates batch control implementations.

1.5 Give some reasons why a combined DCS/PLC control system may have advantages for batch applications.

1.6 Why can't the state of a batch process be determined solely from the current values of process variables?

REFERENCES

1. Shaw, W. T., *Computer Control of Batch Processes*, EMC Controls, Inc., Cockeysville, MD, 1982.

2. Staples, R. A. C., "Cost Effective Batch Control System Using Programmable Controllers," ISA/87, Paper #87-1129.

3. Blickley, G. J., "Batch Process Controls Using Programmable Controllers," *Control Engineering*, July 1984.

4. Urmie, M., "Programmable Controller for Batch Processing," *Measurements & Control*, December 1982.

5. Krigman, A., "Batch Process Control—Sweet Dreams or a Nightmare?" *In Tech*, October 1985.

2

Batch Control System Terminology

Introduction   Discussion of batch control systems is often hampered by lack of a standard language. If the parties involved in discussing these systems don't speak the same language, then meaningful communication is difficult. Those who have tried to communicate using a translator know how difficult that process can be. Batch processes and their control systems are fields where different industries and vendors have created their own languages.

    Progress in batch process control has also been hampered by the lack of a standardized structural model in conjunction with standard terminology, i.e., a language in which problems can be described, formulated, compared, discussed, and solved (Ref. 1). There is no equivalent to the block diagram used in regulatory control in the area of batch sequencing.

    The first step of this effort is the development of a batch control model. This is a set of common attitudes about how the different elements, tasks, and recipes of a batch are related, similar to the way loops and blocks are related in regulatory control (Ref. 2). In this model, there is a separation among the elements of the control system so that a control description can be written for a variety of different products, operating on a variety of process equipment, but following the same generic sequence of operations. The quantities required for each product may be declared independently from the procedural elements and the equipment dependencies. The model also allows any or all of these items to be bound into the procedural elements as well if this flexibility is not needed.

Production Equipment   Any representation of a batch processing system must account for equipment. The unit model shown in Figure 2-1 provides equipment structures at the production and control levels.

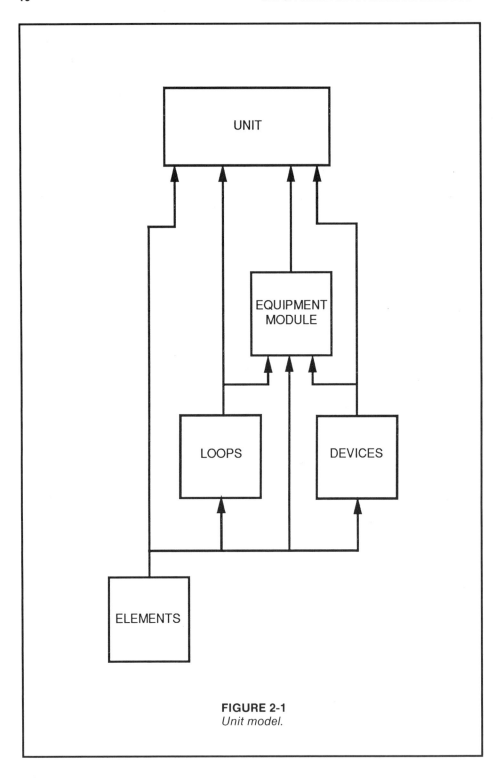

FIGURE 2-1
Unit model.

Element An *element* is a piece of plant equipment having an active function such as measuring or manipulating a physical variable. An example might be a temperature sensor that provides an input to a control system only for logging purposes.

Loops A *loop* is a combination of two or more elements or control functions arranged so that signals pass from one to another for the purpose of measurement and/or control of a process variable. An example might be a loop comprising a thermocouple, a transmitter, a controller, and a control valve. The same loop might have the transmitter and the controller configured in digital hardware/software and would then include any necessary input and output hardware. Simple single-variable loops use one process measurement to produce commands for the particular final control element with which it is paired. Complex multivariable loops utilize signals from a number of sensors to compute commands that may drive several actuators simultaneously. Loops are the primary control entities at the functional level in continuous processes; they are also encountered in batch applications. For example, a loop might be used to regulate the flow, temperature, or pressure in a vessel on the basis of a ramped set point.

Devices A *device* is a combination of elements associated with finite state conditions, e.g., an automatic block valve complete with solenoid valve, pneumatic actuator, and limit switches. A device can assume one or more states; for example, a solenoid valve can either be open or closed. A device can also provide feedback indicating its state. Commonly, feedback is provided by elements such as limit switches, which indicate the state of specific devices in the field.

A simple device might detect the closure of a single contact and operate a relay to energize the associated motor. Complex sequential or combinatorial devices are also possible, which utilize signals from multiple sensors and produce commands for a number of actuators in series or simultaneously. For example, some of the more common examples of devices found in most batch processes include the following:

1. Motor starters with no feedback verification and a single on/off contact to operate them
2. Solenoid valves with a single open/close contact output to operate them
3. Motor starters with separate, momentary on and off contact outputs to operate them
4. Solenoid valves with separate, momentary open/close contact outputs to operate them, e.g., a dual-coil solenoid valve
5. Motor starters (as above) with a feedback signal indicating that the motor is running
6. Valves with one or two open/close feedback signals to indicate actual valve position
7. Multispeed agitators with separate contact outputs for speed selection

Equipment Modules An *equipment module* is one functional group of equipment typically centered around a major piece such as a vessel, heat exchanger, filter, etc., including loops, devices, and elements, to accomplish a task in the operation of a process. This set of loops, devices, and elements can be treated as a single integrated control object and can be set in one of several states or values. An example might be a complete liquid delivery system composed of a jacketed vessel, pump and flow control, and several discrete valves (which may also be devices).

Equipment modules are often associated with equipment that is shared by a number of other pieces of equipment. For example, a hot oil heater that is used to provide high temperature heat transfer fluid to any of several reactors would probably be considered an equipment module. An equipment module may or may not actually contain any of the raw materials that are used to make a batch of product.

One of the primary reasons for creating loops, devices, and equipment modules is to allow for controlled access of the associated equipment. The second reason is to make the operation of the equipment simpler. For example, an operator can maintain the level in a vessel by watching the level and manually adjusting the feed valve. This operation can be simplified by putting in a controller where the operator merely sets the desired level on a set point dial. When an operator wants to close a large, motor-driven valve, he can monitor the open/closed feedback signals and actuate the manual switch until he sees the signal verifying that the valve has closed or an excessive amount of time has gone by. However, a computer can take this over from the operator so that he could just indicate "close valve."

The loops, devices, and equipment modules integrate the various instrument functions to the point where the combination performs a process-oriented rather than an equipment-oriented control task. Examples are: (1) set point stations in feedback loops that allow operators to change processing targets, and (2) parameter adjustments in devices that may permit changes in production limits. The loop, device, or equipment module is defined by a standardized higher-level interface that conveniently defines both human and computer control. For example, the set point in a faceplate is a convenient point of entry of both human commands and computer supervisory control. These interface capabilities are extremely important when more complex combined loops and devices are used, e.g., multivariable loops, combinations of sequential devices, and complex mixtures of both loops and devices. They allow supervisory actions to be formulated in terms of simple process objectives, e.g., "fill tank" rather than all the individual equipment-oriented checks and actions.

Unit A *unit* is a collection of associated elements, loops, devices, and/or equipment modules that perform a coordinated function. This may be a group of interrelated pieces of processing equipment, such as a vessel for containing the product being processed, valves for controlling flow to or from the vessel, heating or cooling equipment, and, perhaps, support vessels. It includes the plant equipment associated with all or part of a particular process. The unit is connected to the control system, through its valves and other actuators, and is followed by the control system through various kinds of sensors. From the point of view of the control system the actuators and sensors constitute the main interface to the process. The unit is the primary object for automatic control of the batching system. Units operate relatively independently of each other.

In a single-product, single-stream process, there may be only one unit. But a unit may also be one of several equipment groups involved in making a particular product. The boundaries of a unit can also change as pieces of equipment in the plant are reassigned to meet varying production demands.

EXAMPLE 2-1

Problem: A simple batch process is shown in Figure 2-2. It consists of a weigh tank that is shared by the two batch reactors, the reactors themselves, and a storage tank that is shared by the two reactors. Classify the equipment in this system based on whether it is an equipment module, unit, device, etc.

Solution: The weigh tank, since it is shared between the two reactors, would probably be considered an equipment module. The reactors themselves would be classified as units. The storage tank, like the weigh tank, is shared by the two reactors and would generally be considered as an equipment module.

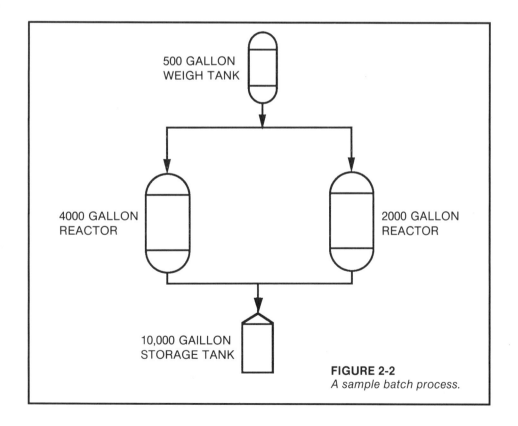

FIGURE 2-2
A sample batch process.

Processing Actions   A representation of a batch processing system also requires means to specify the actions being performed on the raw materials to yield the final product. These actions tend to be hierarchical; five different levels of activity are shown in the procedure model in Figure 2-3. They may be executed in sequence, in parallel, or as alternatives to one another.

Procedures   At the highest level is the *procedure*, which is the part of the recipe that defines the generic strategy for producing a batch of product. Procedures define and order the actions to be performed and the associated control requirements necessary for making a general class of products in the batch process. Procedures are at the top of the processing action hierarchy because they specify how classes of products will be made in the batch system.

Operations   Within the procedure, an *operation* is an independent production activity, consisting of phases, that is carried to completion in a single unit. The operation is the sequential analog of the unit operation in continuous process. In a

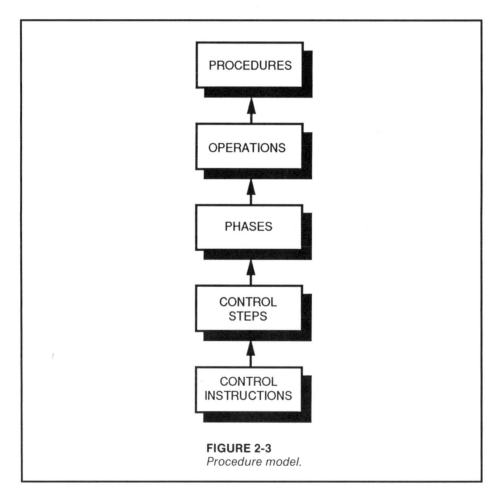

FIGURE 2-3
Procedure model.

continuous process, each unit performs one operation. In a batch unit, several such operations may be carried out. And in a multiunit batch system, each unit may carry out one or more of the operations for making the product.

Some basic operations have a fundamental significance in process technology, especially in the manufacture of materials produced in batches. These basic operations are employed in identical or only slightly modified form in the manufacture of various products. In this manner, the basic operations are independent of the product manufactured, such as:

- charging,
- reacting,
- distilling, and
- neutralizing.

Phases A *phase* is an independent process-oriented action within an operation. The phase is defined by boundaries that constitute safe or logical points where processing can be interrupted. For example, it may be necessary to allow operator intervention to change an ingredient or to direct finished product to a different downstream vessel. The sequence under which phases are performed constitutes the batch operation. In practice, phases will usually be selected as the smallest groups of actions that can be sufficiently decoupled from the rest of the operation to meet the criterion for external intervention.

For example, if the operations in a particular reactor system were CHARGE, REACT, and PUMPOUT, then the corresponding phases might be as follows:

Operations	Phases
Charge	Add Ingredient A
	Add Ingredient B
	Mix
	Add Ingredient C
React	Heat
	Add Ingredient D
	Hold
Pumpout	Cool
	Transfer

It is sometimes convenient to distinguish operation boundaries that permit long-term or indefinite intervention from phase boundaries that can accommodate only short-term supervisory interactions such as parameter changes.

Control Steps *Control steps* are the lowest level terms within a phase that describe an event or action that is of interest to the operator. This lowest level term will probably involve one or more direct commands to final control elements. Control steps will usually be specified by single *control instructions* in programs written in high-level languages. Control instructions are the smallest independent expression of control. A control instruction is the most basic expression of the batch language executed during the processing of a control step. As an example, the control steps involved in the "Add Ingredient A" phase of the "Charge" operation discussed above might be:

Open Valve A
Check Weight In Weigh Tank
Close Valve A

The language being used would determine the actual control instructions needed to accomplish these equipment-oriented actions.

The control steps that constitute a phase will definitely be equipment- or site-specific. Furthermore, these control steps are altered only infrequently, usually in conjunction with modifications to the production equipment.

Process Management
A representation of a batch processing system should also include provisions for supervising and managing the batch plant. This includes means for specifying products and means of production. The elements that are included in the proposed model serve this purpose (see Figure 2-4) (Ref. 3).

The term *recipe* is used in virtually every batch production facility. However, the meaning of the term varies considerably. The recipe is the complete set of data and operations that define the control requirements of a particular type or grade

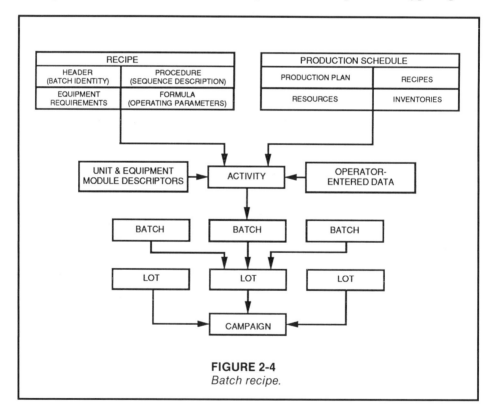

FIGURE 2-4
Batch recipe.

of product. Specifically, it is the combination of procedure, formula, header, and equipment requirements.

Formulas are sets of parameters that distinguish the products defined by procedures. Formulas may include types and quantities of ingredients, along with information such as the duration and the magnitude of process variables. They may affect procedures. The recipe concept simplifies generating different products or grades using an established procedure.

Headers provide information about the purpose, source, and version of the recipes, such as recipe and product identification, originator, issue date, etc. *Equipment requirements* specify the type and size of equipment needed, materials of construction, etc.

In some plants, a recipe may have a further level of generality to accommodate processing in any of several batch units. The specifications that particularize the recipe for the assigned batch unit are the *unit and equipment module descriptors*. Examples might be Reactor T-101, Filter F-305, etc.

There may be an additional need for *operator-entered data*, e.g., partial batch sizes or customer data. The combination of a recipe, unit and equipment module descriptor, operator-entered data, and a schedule for when the product should be produced applied to a process unit to carry out actual production is referred to as an *activity*, and it results in a batch of product. In more complex processes it may be desirable to break the formula, unit and equipment module descriptor, and the operator-entered data each into pieces. Each piece may be entered at a different time, allowing the production decisions to be distributed in time.

A *batch* is the product produced by one execution of a recipe.

Where several separate batches have been made from a common source of raw materials and using the same recipe, the accumulation of all of the batches is called a *lot*.

If further grouping is done, i.e., if the batches in a lot are blended to compensate for changes in feedstock or other processing conditions, the complete production run between recipe changes is a *campaign*.

EXAMPLE 2-2

Problem: A recipe is being sent out from corporate headquarters to various manufacturing plants. Would the procedure that is included in the recipe contain operations, phases, and control steps?

Solution: No, a recipe sent out to various plants is normally considered a generic recipe that is not specific to plant equipment. So this recipe would include only operations and phases. Control steps are very site-specific. For example, even though one of the phases in the procedure is to "Add Ingredient A" and applies to all plants, different plants may use different equipment to add ingredient A, e.g., a weigh tank versus a flowmeter. The equipment-specific instructions, the control steps, would be different for a plant that is charging ingredient A by weigh tank than for a plant that is charging ingredient A by flowmeter.

EXERCISES

2.1 How would you classify a group of equipment that contained loops, devices, and elements?

2.2 Can a loop have more than one set point?

2.3 Assume that a batch process was classified as one large unit. What would be the reason for classifying equipment within that unit as equipment modules, loops, devices, and elements?

2.4 Should an operator normally interact with the batch recipe at the phase level or at the control step level?

2.5 Is there a reason for having different levels of recipes in a corporation?

REFERENCES

1. Bristol, E. H., "A Design Tool Kit for Batch Process Control: Terminology and a Structural Model," *InTech*, October 1985.

2. Bristol, E. H., "A Model and Terminology for Batch Control," Minutes, 1985 Spring Regional Meetings, International Purdue Workshop on Industrial Computer Systems, May 9, 1985.

3. Mergen, R. J., "Batch Control Systems Standards, An Update on ISA/SP88," December 18, 1989.

3

Characteristics of Batch Processes

Introduction   Continuous processes are being used to produce many products that were originally produced by batch processes. One reason for this is that batch processes have typically been labor intensive, and dedicated and experienced operators have been necessary to produce products with consistent quality. Although the technology has been available for many years to allow accurate automatic control of continuous processes with a small labor force, this has not been true for batch processes. Fortunately, this condition is now changing.

Distributed control systems and programmable controllers have been available for years, but they have been primarily involved in the control of continuous processes and discrete parts manufacturing plants. That is because those were the plants that produced the largest volume of products, and that is where the development money was spent. Now a considerable amount of development money is being spent on hardware and software to control batch processes. Control systems are now being introduced with structures that allow the user to define his/her batch control system utilizing the terminology presented in Chapter 2. This change in emphasis from continuous processes to batch processes reflects the movement toward flexible specialty chemical processes and biochemical processes (both tend to be batch processes) in this country. In fact, some think that batch processing may be the salvation of American industry. This is because batch plants provide the capability to compete in markets for small volume specialized production against countries that have cheap labor and protectionist trade policies. In the past when all the attention was placed on larger commodity-type chemical plants, the demand did not exist because those plants are primarily continuous.

Batch processes in the chemical industry manufacture products by processing raw materials under controlled conditions. This involves adding materials in proper quantities at controlled rates and at desired points in the sequence, while maintaining exacting temperatures and pressures within the process. The rate of temperature change is controlled by heating, by cooling, by the charge rate of one of the reactants, etc., depending on the type of reaction encountered. A catalyst is often present to initiate and/or maintain a rate of reaction.

In most cases, the maintenance of set point temperatures and/or temperature profiles is very important in achieving the highest quality product and improved yields, as well as plant and personnel safety. Steam, cooling water, and other utilities for the reactors are shared by a number of reactors. The capacity of these shared units needs to be considered so that the demand for the various utilities can be met. The completion of a batch is determined by a number of techniques such as heat input/output calculations, monitoring of the pressure drop across a vent valve, temperature monitoring, motor current drawn by agitators, operator experience, laboratory analysis, or, sometimes, pure guess.

Batch vs. Continuous Processes
Industrial chemical processes are designed to produce a desired product from a variety of starting materials through a succession of operations. Figure 3-1 (Ref. 1) shows a typical situation. The raw materials undergo a number of physical treatment operations to put them in the form in which they can be reacted chemically. They then pass through the reactor or series of reactors where they are changed chemically. The products of the reaction then undergo further physical operations, i.e., filtration, purification, etc., to obtain the final desired product.

The process in Figure 3-1 may be continuous flow, batch, or a combination of the two. Since it is possible to have both batch and continuous flow operations within the same process, it is best to look at the individual unit operations when discussing the type of processing.

Continuous processes normally operate at or close to steady state. The values of process variables should be essentially static at any point in the process. There should be no accumulation of material in the equipment; no change in composition of the exit streams; and the composition at any one point in the system is unchanged with time. Control systems for continuous processes work to minimize fluctuations in these process variables caused by external disturbances, e.g., a change in composition of a feed stream or set point changes. They usually do this by increasing or decreasing existing flows of material or energy. They are most economical when large quantities of material are to be processed and the same product will be made for a long period of time.

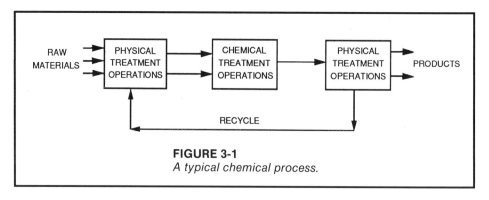

FIGURE 3-1
A typical chemical process.

A batch process, on the other hand, is transient under normal conditions. It involves a sequence of phases carried out on a discrete quantity of material within a piece of operating equipment, usually a vessel. Material and equipment are generally changing state at any particular point, so the assumption of steady-state operation is not valid. Batches of product are transferred from one piece of process equipment to another, requiring the automatic start-up and shutdown of this equipment; the equipment may be idle between batches. The same equipment may be used to make many different products.

Since the batch process is characterized by change, the positions of the process equipment also vary with time. For example, a valve may be open or closed, and a motor may be on or off. Control loops are used for a period of time in one mode, and then the mode is changed. A flow controller may be used in an automatic mode to regulate the flow into a reactor vessel. Once the proper quantity of material is charged, the flow controller might then be switched to a manual mode and the valve closed.

There are a wide variety of batch processes in the chemical industry; however, certain characteristics are common to all of these processes. Typically, batch processes are used to manufacture a large number of products. Within each product are often a number of grades with minor adjustments. There may be dramatic differences between different products. Since frequent product and process changes are a way of life in batch processes, they must be flexible and allow relatively easy process adjustments.

Process utilities such as steam and water are from common headers and may have the capabilities to support only a portion of the plant requirements at any given time. Shared equipment, such as process utilities and common process units (e.g., storage or preparation tanks), are another characteristic of batch processes.

Some key differences distinguish a batch process from a continuous process (Refs. 2 and 3):

1. Discrete loads of raw materials are usually fed into the system for a batch process.

This differs from the continuous feed of materials found in a continuous process.

2. Each batch of material being processed can be identified throughout a batch process, because each batch is kept separate from all other batches being processed.

In most continuous processes, raw materials cannot be uniquely tracked.

3. Each batch of raw material can be processed differently in the various pieces of equipment in a batch process. The same equipment might be used to produce different products or product grades.

In continuous processes, raw materials are usually processed in an identical fashion.

4. Batch processes proceed in a sequence of phases through the system. These phases are a function of the process and the product being produced, not of the control technique used. Movement of a batch from one piece of equipment to another can occur only when the operation in that equipment is complete and the

next piece of equipment is ready to receive the material. This means that communications must occur between the control systems on these different pieces of equipment.

In continuous processes, materials flow steadily from one piece of equipment to the next.

5. Batch processes use large quantities of two-state devices, such as automatic block valves. These on/off control requirements contribute to the difficulty and complexity of the control system application, since many on/off functions must be performed during each phase of the process. This can lead to problems, such as:

- processing phases not performed in correct sequence,
- processing phases not performed at the correct time or for the correct time duration,
- incorrect material addition, and
- incorrect quantity of material added.

A continuous process tends to use continuously modulated valves. Although pumps and motors are also used in continuous processes, they are not typically cycled on and off as they are in batch processes.

6. Batch processes generally have recipes associated with each batch of product that is made, and the same equipment might be used to produce many different products or product grades. These recipes direct the processing of the raw materials into final product.

Continuous processes usually operate under the same recipe for large periods of time.

7. Batch processes generally require more sequential logic; this is part of the normal operating mode of the batch process.

Although sequential logic is sometimes used with continuous processes, it is typically used only during the start-up or shutdown of the system. These are used infrequently. An example is the purging and ignition sequences that a fired heater goes through on start-up and shutdown.

8. A batch system uses a number of regulatory control loops that operate within the phases of the process, e.g., temperature control during the heating phase. Although these may be the same regulatory control loops that a continuous process uses, the discontinuous nature of the batch process causes many unique control problems with these loops. This has been the cause of considerable difficulty in batch control systems. The integral action of regulatory controllers, i.e., controllers that contain the integral or reset control mode, causes the algorithm to wind up when not in the operational phase (e.g., during heatup from a low temperature to a higher temperature) when the regulatory control action is not required.

Although it is possible to have windup problems in regulatory control loops in continuous processes, they are not typically part of the normal operation of the system.

9. Batch processes often include the processing of phases and steps that can fail, so special failure routines to be executed in that event are also included.

When a failure occurs in a continuous process, the process is usually shut down.

Batch Process Classifications
Batch processes can be classified both by the number of products they make and by the structure of the process facility (Refs. 4 and 5).

The number of products is typically the number of individually identifiable chemicals, substances, or items produced. A batch process can be single-product, multigrade, or multiproduct. A single-product batch process produces the same product in each batch. The same *operations* are performed in each batch using the same amounts of raw materials. Many single-product plants have been converted to continuous processes.

A multigrade batch process produces products that are similar but differ only in formula quantities. The same *operations* are performed on each batch, but the quantities of raw materials and/or processing conditions (e.g., temperature) are varied, i.e., the *procedure* remains the same, but the *formula* is changed.

The multiproduct batch process produces products utilizing different methods of production or control. The *operations* performed, the amounts of raw materials, and processing conditions may vary with each batch, i.e., both the *procedure* and *formula* are changed.

The difficulty in automating a batch process is greater for a multigrade process than it is for a single-product plant. The multiproduct batch process is the most difficult of the three types to automate.

Batch facilities can also be categorized by the structure of the process facility. The two basic types of batch structures are series (single-stream) and parallel (multistream); however, many batch processes combine these two structures to give a series/parallel structure. A series structure is a group of units through which a batch passes sequentially (see Figure 3-2); it could be a single unit, such as a reactor, or several process units in sequence. In this system, two different recipes could be executing at the same time. The parallel structure is shown in Figure 3-3; the series/parallel structure is shown in Figure 3-4. With both the parallel and series/parallel structures, several batches may be executing at the same time. Several batches could be performing the same operation.

The batch process classifications by product and by structure can be combined in a matrix (see Figure 3-5) to show the degree of difficulty in automating these various combinations. The multiproduct, series/parallel batch processes require the highest degree of sophistication in control equipment to achieve effective batch control.

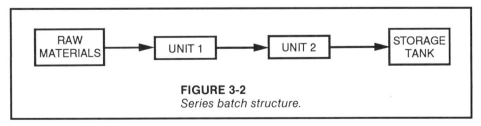

FIGURE 3-2
Series batch structure.

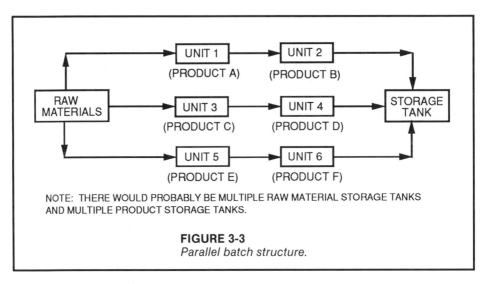

NOTE: THERE WOULD PROBABLY BE MULTIPLE RAW MATERIAL STORAGE TANKS
AND MULTIPLE PRODUCT STORAGE TANKS.

FIGURE 3-3
Parallel batch structure.

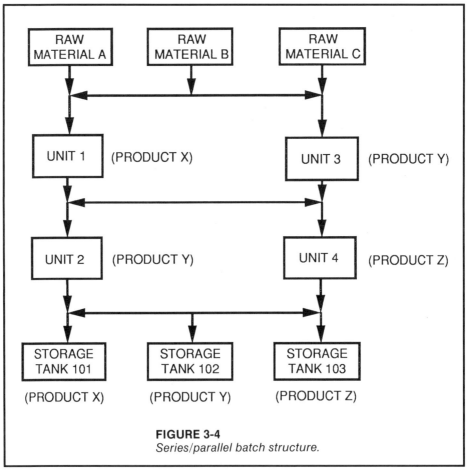

FIGURE 3-4
Series/parallel batch structure.

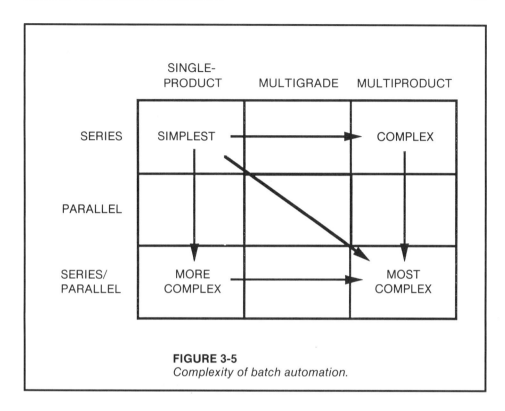

FIGURE 3-5
Complexity of batch automation.

Dealing with Common Resources

When more than one batch unit is interested in the status or use of a resource, the resource is designated as a common resource. Common resources are almost always present with parallel and series/parallel batch process structures. A resource may be either exclusive-use or shared-use (see Figure 3-6). Note that this is the same batch process shown in Figure 2-2.

Exclusive-Use Resources If the resource is designated as exclusive-use, only one unit may use the resource at a time. The weigh tank in Figure 3-6 is an example of an exclusive-use resource. It can be used by only one reactor at a time. This means that some mechanism must be put into place to prevent both reactors from trying to use the weigh tank at the same time. Also, the batch scheduling system must take this exclusive-use resource into consideration. If one reactor is waiting for the use of the weigh tank, that reactor is idle and is not making product, which has a negative effect on equipment utilization.

Another problem presented by the exclusive-use type of common resource is associated with the use of distributed control systems. Distributed control systems are used to "distribute" the risk of a control system failure. If one controller fails, it does not shut the complete process down. Control systems associated with exclusive-use resources may need higher reliability to prevent such shutdowns.

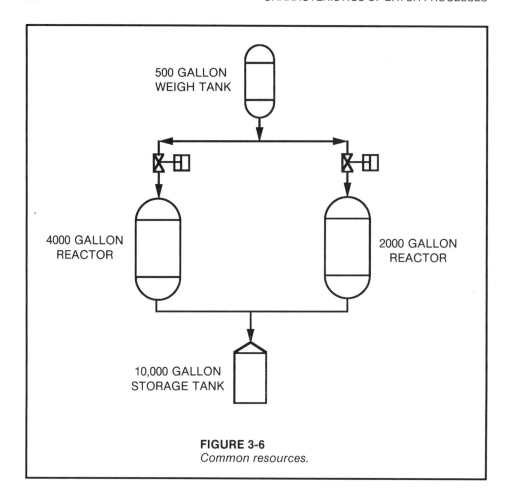

FIGURE 3-6
Common resources.

EXAMPLE 3-1

Problem: In the batch process shown in Figure 3-6, the following four microprocessor-based digital systems are provided:

- One for the weigh tank
- One for the 4000-gallon reactor
- One for the 2000-gallon reactor
- One for the storage tank

Which microprocessor-based system contains the automatic block valves between the weigh tank and the reactors?

Solution: The weigh tank controller must be interfaced to the controllers on the two reactors to tell the reactors that the charge of that particular ingredient is complete and to know when another charge is needed. The limit switches on the two inlet valves must be interfaced with the controllers on the weigh tank and the two reactors. Another ingredient cannot be charged to the weigh tank unless these valves are both proven closed. In this case, the valves would probably be put into the control system where speed was the most important. For example, the weigh tank controller monitors the amount of material charged to the reactors. When the amount charged equals the preset amount dictated by the recipe, the weigh tank controller closes the automatic block valves. To avoid overcharges on shutoff, speed is very important to the weigh tank controller. This means that the block valves should be part of the input/output (I/O) system of the weigh tank controller. This avoids the time delays involved with sending a "valve close" signal outside of the weigh tank controller to another device, e.g., through discrete outputs, a serial interface, or a data highway.

Note that this means that the reliability of the weigh tank controller is now critical to the operation of the batch plant, since neither reactor can operate without the weigh tank controller in operation.

EXAMPLE 3-2

Problem: Since the weigh tank controller, the 4000-gallon reactor controller, and the 2000-gallon reactor controller all need information on the position of the two automatic block valves that feed material into the reactors, should the limit switch inputs be taken into all three of these controllers?

Solution: It is normally good practice to avoid multiple inputs of limit switches, process variables, etc., into different control systems. As in the example above, these inputs should normally be taken into the control system where speed is of the most importance and then that information provided to other control systems as necessary, e.g., via a data highway. This avoids the cost of multiple inputs and the problem with keeping documentation of multiple inputs up to date.

EXAMPLE 3-3

Problem: Another option would be to define this system as only one unit and use only one controller. What kinds of problems does this create?

Solution: If the batch process is complex and involves a lot of process equipment, the size of the one control system becomes much more unwieldy. It could also greatly increase the complexity of the programming and make it more difficult for more than one designer to work on the program at the same time. And, of course, reliability is also a major concern with this type of system. Achieving higher reliability now means that the whole control system must be considered — not just one small part of the control system.

Shared-Use Resources If the common resource is designated as shared, several units may use the resource at the same time. The shared common resources in Figure 3-6 are the storage tank, the common piping from the two reactors to the storage tank, and the utilities (e.g., steam and cooling water) that are used to heat and cool the reactors. The mechanisms associated with the use of an exclusive-use resource are not required in this case. However, care must be taken so that one unit does not shut off or deactivate a resource while other units are also using it or that the capacity of that resource is not exceeded by one of the units. In Figure 3-6, if the capacity and head of the pump on the 4000-gallon reactor are large in relation to the pump on the 2000-gallon reactor, it may not be possible for both reactors to pump to the storage tank at the same time.

EXERCISES

3.1 What are the advantages of being able to have a unique identity associated with each batch of material processed through a batch process?

3.2 Why does changing both the procedure and the formula in a multiproduct batch process make this much more difficult than for a multigrade process where only the formula is changed?

REFERENCES

1. Mergen, R. J., "Introduction to Batch Control," ISA Cleveland Section Symposium on Batch Control Systems, May 1982.

2. Shaw, W. T., *Computer Control of Batch Processes*, EMC Controls, Inc., Cockeysville, MD, 1982.

3. Martin, P. G., "Computer Control of Batch Processes," *Measurements & Control*, September 1984.

4. PS Sheet Application Note AP4:020 (A), "Introduction to Batch Processing," Fisher Controls, August 23, 1982.

5. Smith, C. L., "Integrated Management and Control of Batch Production Facilities," Seminar Hosted by Texas Instruments, Cleveland, OH, December 16, 1986.

Part II
Batch Control
System Structure

4

A Hierarchical
Batch Model

Introduction   An integrated plant control system has distinct decision-making levels; commands and information flow automatically between these levels. The number of levels differs from one application to another, and the definition of what takes place at each level varies also. Batch control systems lend themselves well to such a hierarchical structure. The model that was developed by the National Institute of Standards and Technology (NIST), formerly the National Bureau of Standards (NBS), for their Automated Manufacturing Research Facility (AMRF) (Ref. 1) is an example of a hierarchical structure (see Figure 4-1). It divides the organization into five discrete levels, with each level building on the less complicated functionality of the level below it. This is part of their attempt to develop a generic model for real-time production control that can be used as the basis for system design and the interfaces between systems.

The NIST model is very similar to the CIM (Computer Integrated Manufacturing) Reference Model developed by the International Purdue Workshop on Industrial Computer Systems (Ref. 2). An example of the Purdue CIM Reference Model for an industrial plant utilizing continuous processes, such as in the petrochemicals industry, is shown in Figure 4-2. The only difference between this model and a model that applies directly to discrete parts manufacturing plants is the nomenclature used within the boxes. The Purdue CIM Reference Model does not extend to the *equipment* level, although it is intended to apply to all industries. The Purdue model is also intended to apply to a plant entity, and, in general, does not cover *corporate management*. However, this model can be extended to cover an industrial company with multiple plants (see Figure 4-3) (Ref. 2).

The International Organization for Standardization (ISO) under their Working Group 1 (Ref. 3) is also developing a CIM Reference Model (See Figure 4-4) (Ref. 2). The ISO model extends beyond the facility to the corporation. ISO intends to use their model as a means for helping develop needs for additional international standards to facilitiate the field of CIM (Ref. 2).

Figure 4-5 compares the above models and shows the control function intended for and the responsibility assigned to each level.

31

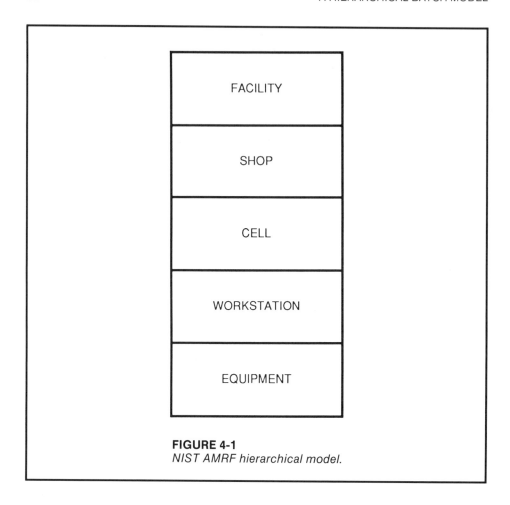

FIGURE 4-1
NIST AMRF hierarchical model.

The names associated with the various levels in these models tend to be based on the typical industry in which the model is used. The design of these models is usually based on three guidelines (Ref. 4):

1. Levels are introduced to reduce complexity and limit responsibility and authority.

2. Each level has a distinct planning horizon that decreases as one goes down the hierarchy.

3. Control resides at the lowest possible level.

Every control module within these hierarchies must react to inputs in essentially the same way: input commands from its superior are decomposed, status feedback data from subordinates is processed, and new outputs in the form of commands and status are generated (see Figure 4-6) (Ref. 1).

Many people view these models as strictly physical models, where each level represents a physical piece of computer or control equipment. That view may hold true in some applications. However, it is better to view this model as a functional

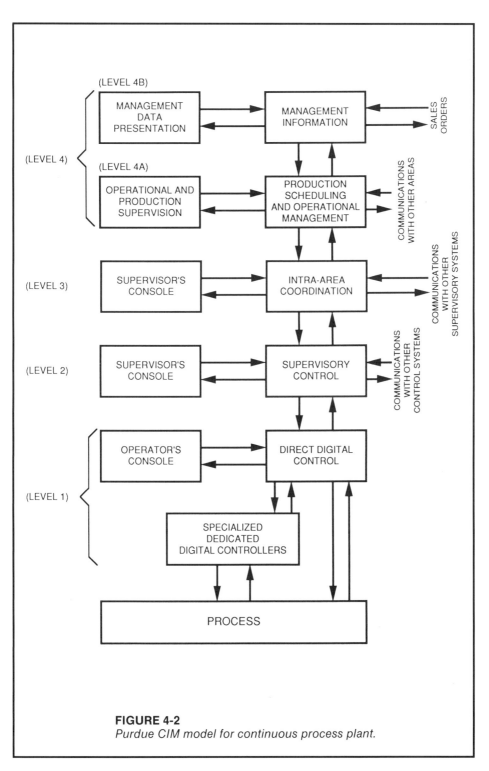

FIGURE 4-2
Purdue CIM model for continuous process plant.

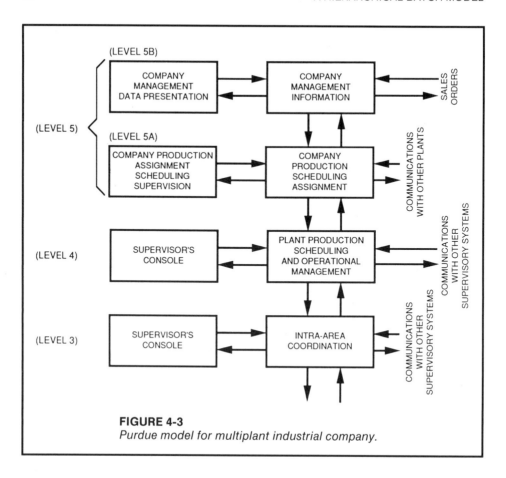

FIGURE 4-3
Purdue model for multiplant industrial company.

model, where each level defines a level of functionality, and then define what is typically accomplished at each level. Not all applications will require every function, or they may require a very simple version of that function. Then hardware and software can be selected to provide the necessary functionality needed for that application. This may result in some levels being combined, which means that the model may get collapsed into less than the number of levels shown in these various models.

An information management service is needed to support this real-time control system, and it must provide for the storage and retrieval of various types of data and the reliable transport of that data from one control process to another (Ref. 1).

Communications
A system of integrated communications is needed to tie these various levels together and provide for the *transport of data*. But this communication must take place both horizontally and vertically. That is one of the dangers of this type of structure, particularly when it is shown in the form of a pyramid (Ref. 5). The layers of functionality are defined as concentrating centers

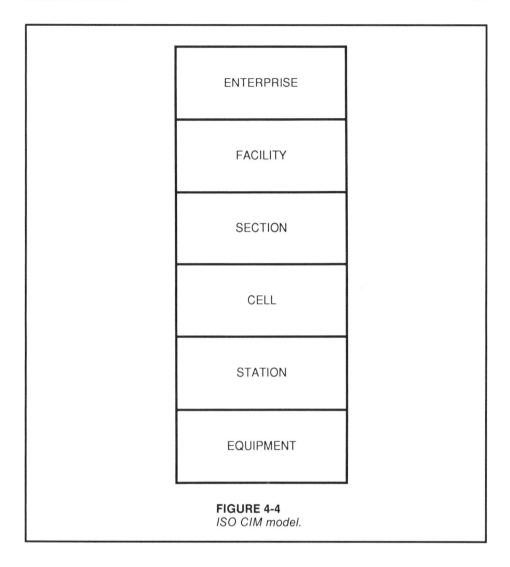

FIGURE 4-4
ISO CIM model.

of information, from the factory floor to top management. The danger is that this architecture is configured only for the convenience of data gathering; it may ignore the actual flow of the manufacturing process. For example, two supervisory stations at the cell level often need to communicate with each other; this requires horizontal communications.

Another critical factor in communications is the speed required at these various levels. At the process control level, high speed communications are required because the equipment must operate in real time. The further up the hierarchical structure, the less communications speed becomes a factor. This means that different types of networks are needed at different levels of the structure.

The topic of communications is covered in more detail in Appendix A.

NIST MODEL	PURDUE MODEL	ISO MODEL	HIERARCHY	CONTROL	RESPONSIBILITY
Null	Null	6	Enterprise	Planning Production	Achieving the mission of the enterprise and managing the corporation.
5	4	5	Facility/Plant	Scheduling Production	Implementing the enterprise functions and planning and scheduling production.
4	3	4	Section/Area/Shop	Allocating and Supervising Materials and Resources	Coordinating production, supporting the jobs, and obtaining and allocating resources to the jobs.
3	2	3	Cell	Coordinating Multiple Machines and Operations	Sequencing and supervising the jobs on the shop floor and allocating resources to the jobs.
2	1	2	Station	Commanding Machine Sequences and Motion	Directing and coordinating the activity of the shop floor equipment.
1	0	1	Equipment	Activating Sequences and Motion	Realizing commands to the shop floor equipment.

FIGURE 4-5
Hierarchical model comparison.

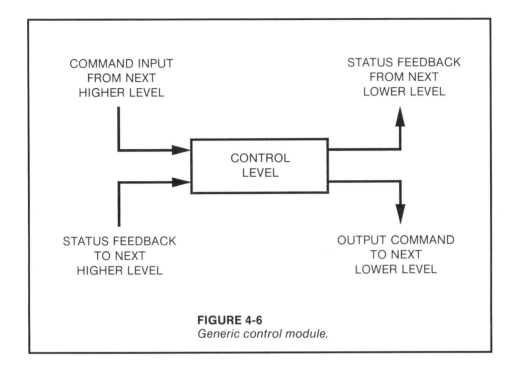

FIGURE 4-6
Generic control module.

Database Management Systems
The management of data is a key ingredient in these types of control systems, so that the *storage and retrieval of various types of data* is accomplished by all the components in the system. The database management system provides shared data to all manufacturing processes; it should do this in a timely, accurate, and completely transparent manner (Ref. 6).

The topic of database management systems is discussed in detail in Appendix B.

A Batch Model
The terms that identify each level of the hierarchy in the models previously discussed have a definite connotation for discrete manufacturing systems (NIST and ISO models) and for a continuous process (Purdue model). However, they don't hold as much meaning for batch control systems. Figure 4-7 shows a similar model, with seven levels, but with each level identified by a term that is hopefully more indicative of batch systems (Ref. 7). Also identified in Figure 4-7 is the overall purpose of each level.

Loop/Device-Element Level The first level holds the real-time devices that interface directly with the process. These devices are generally referred to as measurement devices and actuators. Most applications require some mix of discrete (usually two-state) devices and regulatory loops, although batch applications tend to be heavy on the discrete devices.

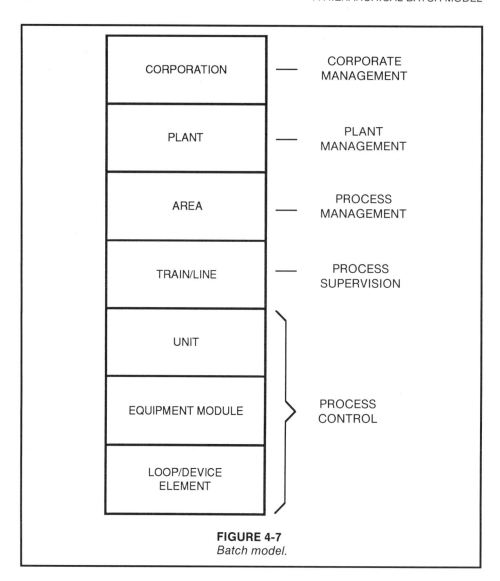

FIGURE 4-7
Batch model.

Equipment Module Level The second level is the equipment module level. This process interface level also holds the real-time devices that interface directly with the process. Equipment modules are made up of combinations of loops/ devices and elements, along with the necessary process equipment, e.g., piping, valves, pumps, etc.

Unit Level The third level is the unit level. The elements, loops, devices, and equipment modules at the first two levels are combined and coordinated at this level.

The first three levels are the *process control levels*. Measurement and control of the real-time devices, e.g., temperature sensors, pressure switches, solenoid valves, control valves, etc., are accomplished at the process control level and could involve single or multiple programmable controllers (PLCs), single-loop controllers, the multiple-loop controllers in distributed control systems (DCSs), etc.

These loops, devices, and elements either generate inputs to the control system or accept outputs from the control system. This requires basic communication between plant floor equipment, such as sensors and actuators, and higher-level control devices, such as programmable controllers (PLCs) and single-loop controllers.

The process control level consists basically of regulatory and discrete controls, with the type of control being dictated by the type of field devices with which they are interfaced. The controls that interface with discrete field elements and devices are referred to as discrete controls. The controls that interface with analog field elements and loops are referred to as regulatory controls.

Regulatory controls, such as PID loops on level, pressure, temperature, and flow, must provide control of items specified in a recipe, e.g., tight temperature control, exact composition control, etc. Discrete controls handle the opening and closing of valves, turn timers on and off, start and stop pumps, etc. From a safety perspective, the interlocking of discrete devices is a critical concern and must be a real-time element of control at the process control level.

Train/Line Level The fourth level is the train/line level. Train/line is a collection of one or more associated units and equipment modules, arranged in serial and/or parallel paths and used to make a complete batch. Here, the emphasis switches away from real-time control to supervisory control. Large PLCs are sometimes used at this level. Other alternatives are distributed control systems and minicomputers. Personal computers have some potential for use in this area as their speed and power increase. These systems usually coordinate multiple PLCs, single-loop controllers, multiloop controllers, and various other types of controllers installed at the process control level.

The coordination of multiproduct, series/parallel processes is performed at this *process supervision level*. The working batch recipes exist at this level.

Area Level Planning and management functions are implemented at the area level. An area is a collection of one or more associated trains/lines that may be related because of geographical location, because they make related products, or because of resource considerations. The various trains/lines that constitute the area must be operated in a harmonious manner so as to produce the desired product from the batch. Thus, batch management is a principal control requirement at this *process management* level. Batch management includes functions such as dynamic batch scheduling; production reporting; and recipe selecting, editing, and downloading. Batch management is discussed in more detail in a later chapter. This is the highest level in the plant where real-time response should be a significant issue.

Plant Level Strategies are developed and complete plant functions are directed from the plant level, where a plant is defined as a collection of one or more areas on a common site. This fifth level in the batch hierarchy is *plant management*.

Production scheduling, inventory control, and cost accounting programs are incorporated at this level. Computers at the plant level accept production requirements downloaded from the corporate information system and generate facility production requirements and schedules.

Corporation Level At the top of the structure is the corporation level. A corporation is defined as an organization that coordinates the operation of one or more plants. This level interfaces the plant control systems to corporate management information systems (MIS). The MIS computer handles such things as billing, order, and account handling. It also provides the data for corporate management to make strategic decisions that impact the future of the company. Therefore, these systems often need access to current process information and plant management data. The information needed at this *corporate management* level is available at the top level of the batch model.

EXERCISES

4.1 Why is horizontal communications at the various levels (e.g., area to area, equipment module to equipment module, etc.) an important consideration in the design of a batch control system?

4.2 List additional activities, e.g., SPC, that would normally take place at the train/line level.

4.3 In addition to the need for different types of communications systems at the various levels, why is there also a need for different types of database management systems at these various levels?

4.4 Why should there be no need for direct inputs and outputs at the train/line level in the batch model?

REFERENCES

1. Jones, A., and C. McLean, "A Proposed Hierarchical Control Model for Automated Manufacturing Systems," *Journal of Manufacturing Systems*, Vol. 5, No. 1, 1986.

2. Williams, T. J., ed., *A Reference Model for Computer Integrated Manufacturing (CIM)*, Prepared by CIM Reference Model Committee, International Purdue Workshop On Industrial Computer Systems, ISA, 1988.

3. CIM Reference Model Working Group, ISO/TC184/SC5/WG1, *Technical Report on CIM Reference Model*, July 1987.

4. Jones, A., and A. Saleh, "A Multi-Level/Multi-Layer Architecture for Intelligent Shop Floor Control," *IJCIM Special Issue on Intelligent Control*.

5. Catalano, M. A., "Intelligent Supervisory Stations More Than a Window on the Process," ISA/85, Paper #85-0084.

6. Davis, W. J., "Real-Time Optimization in the Automated Manufacturing Research Facility, " NISTIR 88-3865, U.S. Department of Commerce, October 1988.

7. ISA/SP88-1989-3, Minutes of SP88 Batch Control Standards Committee Meeting, August 30, 31, and September 1, 1989.

5

A Control Structure for Batch Systems

Introduction   Batch process automation extends over a hierarchy of functions, as discussed in Chapter 4. The main purpose of the batch model (see Figure 4-7) is to give users a framework from which they can decide what functions are needed for their applications. The resulting functional model then gives users and suppliers a common ground for communication in the development of optimal solutions.

When a batch automation system is designed, it is very often based on a hardware concept using a hierarchical model devised to meet the individual needs of a user or manufacturer. These structures are generally fine for describing the overall architecture of a control system, but they are effective only when the needed functionality of the control system is already known. Without this knowledge, this approach ignores the essential functions of how the process is run, where the batch data is stored, and how the plant is scheduled.

A structure is needed that better defines the specifics of the control system, e.g., where do the safety interlocks reside, how do the safety interlocks interface with the rest of the batch control system, how do the regulatory controls and sequential controls communicate, etc.? To date, distributed control systems and the offerings from programmable controller manufacturers have primarily addressed the distribution of control functions in a horizontal manner: the control requirements are segmented so they can be implemented in some number of microprocessor-based controllers that all perform the same general types of functions.

This type of approach may be suitable for the continuous process industries, which was the primary target market for the initial distributed control systems. In batch production facilities, however, the critical issues are those associated with vertical distribution. The control system must be structured in a manner that reflects the requirements for control at the various levels of the organization. The result is a hierarchical control system that starts with the safety interlock functions on the plant floor and ends with corporate MIS (management information system).

The Control Structure

Rosenof proposed a structure for batch processes that fits this requirement of vertical distribution (Ref. 1). With Rosenof's structure, the control system was divided into levels, where a level represented an extent of control and covered the entire process. Each of the levels had an operator interface along with unique or shared hardware and software. This did not mean that there would be a proliferation of operator interfaces; the same operator interface would be used for a number of levels. It did mean that the system had to be designed to allow the operator to intervene at any level. His design approach allowed different hardware/software systems for different levels.

A Control Activity Model

That same approach is taken with the *control activity model* shown in Figure 5-1. This model shows the general control activities of the entire batch control system in a hierarchical manner from the sensors to the business planning level. Each level of the control activity model is defined below (Ref. 2).

Safety Interlocking—The control functions that prevent abnormal process actions that would jeopardize personnel safety, harm the environment, or damage major equipment.

Regulatory Control—Maintaining the outputs of a process as close as possible to their respective set point values despite the influences of set point changes and disturbances.

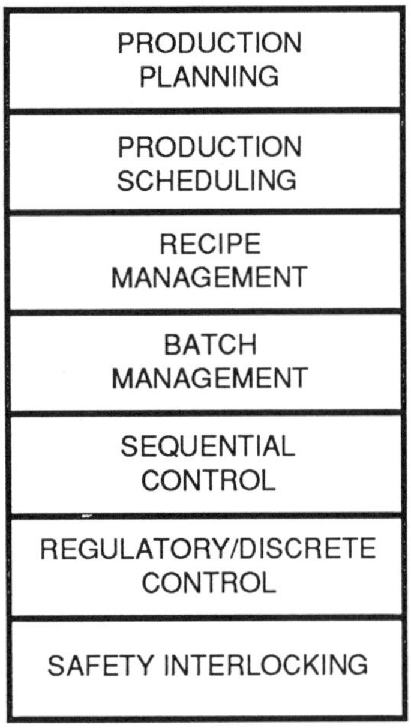

PRODUCTION PLANNING
PRODUCTION SCHEDULING
RECIPE MANAGEMENT
BATCH MANAGEMENT
SEQUENTIAL CONTROL
REGULATORY/DISCRETE CONTROL
SAFETY INTERLOCKING

FIGURE 5-1
Control activity model.

Discrete Control—Maintaining the outputs of a process to a target value chosen from a set of known stable state(s).

Sequential Control—A class of industrial process control functions in which the objective is to sequence the process through a series of distinct states.

Batch Management—The activity that:

- selects a control recipe and transforms it into a working recipe,
- manages resources necessary for batch execution,
- initiates and supervises the execution of the batch, and
- collects and manages batch data.

Batch management is discussed in more detail in Chapter 11.

Recipe Management—The activity that includes creating, editing, storing, and retrieving basic, master, and control recipes and interfaces with the production scheduling and batch management activities. The various types of recipes are discussed in more detail in Chapter 12.

Production Scheduling—An activity that accepts inputs such as the production plan and, based on a scheduling algorithm, develops a production schedule that typically includes the following:

- Batches/amounts to be produced
- Target trains/lines to be used
- Time targets
- Production disposition
- Resource constraints

Production scheduling is discussed in more detail in Chapter 13.

Production Planning—An activity that accepts inputs such as customer orders and, based on a manufacturing strategy, develops a production plan that typically includes the following:

- What is to be produced
- How much is to be produced
- Where it is to be produced
- When it is needed
- How it is to be packaged

Further discussions on the production planning activity are beyond the scope of this book.

Detailed Control Activity Model   These general control activities from the *control activity model* may be further decomposed to generate specific control activities that can be more easily mapped into the various levels of the batch model. The *detailed control activity model* is intended to provide this decomposition for the regulatory/discrete control level and the sequential control

level. It breaks the regulatory/discrete control level into: *manual control, process interlocking, basic regulatory/discrete control,* and *advanced regulatory/ discrete control* levels; it breaks the sequential control level into *automatic recipe execution* and *manual sequential control* levels. See Figure 5-2.

A level doesn't depend on any higher level for the performance of its functions. It might receive commands from an upper level, such as "Open Valve A," but this level will continue to function even if the upper level fails. The higher level cannot be used unless this level is operational. For example, the batch process should not run, even in the MANUAL mode, unless the safety interlock system is in operation. These rules apply to the interface between all levels.

The detailed control activity model also shows the interaction between the various levels and the role of the operator interface. Although an operator interface is shown at each level of the model (see Figure 5-3), these are not all independent operator interfaces. It simply means that the operator must have the ability

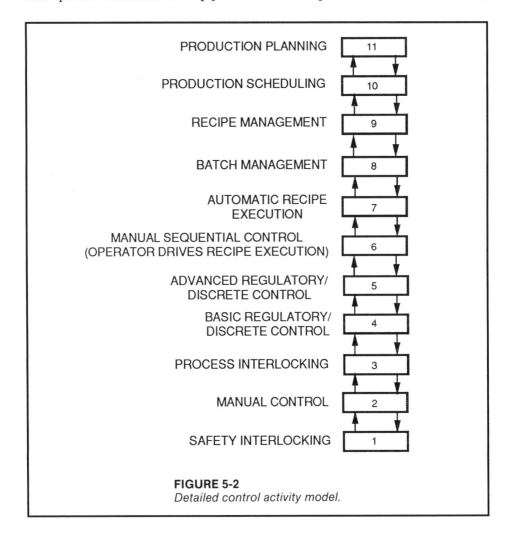

FIGURE 5-2
Detailed control activity model.

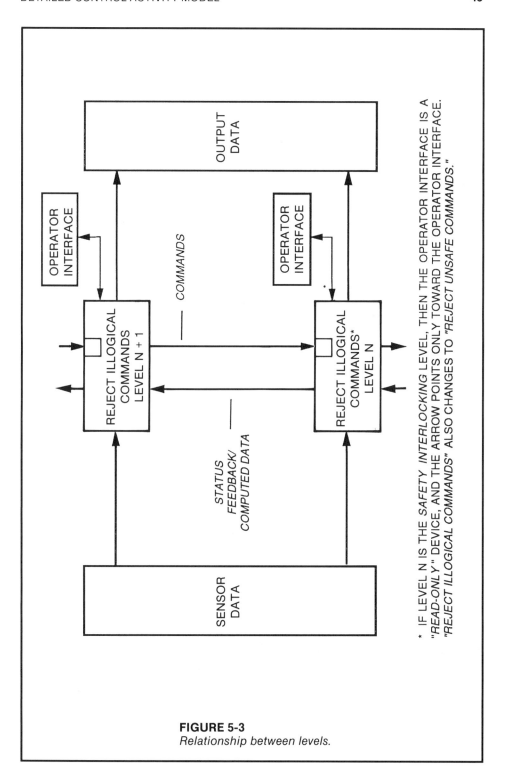

FIGURE 5-3
Relationship between levels.

to interact with each of the control activities. The operator interface allows the operator to stop the command from the higher level and enter that information directly. This capability is necessary in case the upper level fails and the lower level continues to run. For example, at Level 4 (basic regulatory/discrete control) the operator may need the ability to switch a regulatory control loop from "remote set point" to "local set point" and to enter a specific set point. This may be because Level 5 fails, and this level is supplying set points to regulatory control loops at Level 4 based on an optimization routine. As Figure 5-3 shows, a lower level has the ability to reject a command from a higher level if it considers that command illogical (rejects unsafe commands at Level 1).

Note also that at Level 1, the operator interface is a "read-only" device. It can only monitor the operation of the safety interlocking level. It does not give the operator the ability to bypass the safety interlock system.

Figure 5-3 also shows that data can come into the system at any level. However, if that data is needed at more than one level, it must enter at the lowest level where it is needed and then be transmitted up to the higher level. Outputs can be generated at any level.

The "zero" level, not shown here because it is not a control activity, is the process. Emphasis should be given during the process design phase to making the process itself as inherently safe as possible. This involves examining the process to see what changes can be made to make the process safer, e.g., by using a less hazardous material for the reaction, by using a more dilute concentration of a particular material, by reducing the quantity of a hazardous material that is stored, etc. Because there are always possibilities of control failure at any level above this one, process equipment must be designed with appropriate safety margins to minimize the consequences of such a failure. This implies the use of thicker pipe walls and vessel walls in some applications.

Safety Interlock Level

Level 1 is for safety systems that protect personnel, equipment, and the environment (some consider these as *first-level safety systems*). The sensors, interlocks, and output devices communicate with the operator through the use of indicating lights, switches and push buttons, and annunciators. This level includes redundancy and fault tolerance as necessary and independence of safety functions from control functions to ensure that the process is maintained in a safe condition regardless of failures or errors at higher levels (Ref. 1).

This level should be physically separate from all other levels. This means that a separate piece of hardware/software, including operator interface, should be used to implement the safety interlock system. It also means that all the critical inputs and outputs, along with the safety interlock logic, would be totally contained in the safety interlock system. It does not mean that the safety interlock system should not be integrated into the rest of the batch control system (e.g., the basic process control system), such as by a data highway. However, when the safety interlock system is integrated into the basic process control system, special precautions must be taken to make sure that the communications network cannot corrupt the integrity of the safety interlock system. This means that other devices on the network can only *read* information out of the safety interlock system; they can never *write* information to the safety interlock system.

In fact, if the safety interlock systems utilize a programmable controller (PLC), it would be preferable if the program could be put into read-only memory so that it is difficult to make changes to the interlock system. The engineer or technician who is configuring the batch control system should not have configuration access to the safety interlock system. Although this level does have an operator interface, this interface does not provide the operator with the ability to bypass first-level safety devices.

Manual Control Level   Level 2 provides manual control. Because the operator can run the batch process in MANUAL, the plant can be operated to actually make product without any higher levels operational. It may not be possible to make the quality of product ultimately desired, but the plant can be operated. It will also be operated safely, because the safety interlocking level must be fully operational.

The safety interlocking level prevents the operator from placing the plant in a dangerous condition. For example, at this level an operator may have a switch that can be put into the HAND position to open an automatic block valve, but that HAND position must not bypass the safety interlock system. However, it would be able to bypass the signal from the sequencing system that calls for the valve to be closed (see Figure 5-4). This manual mode may be implemented through a CRT-based workstation, individual stations, or a combination of the two.

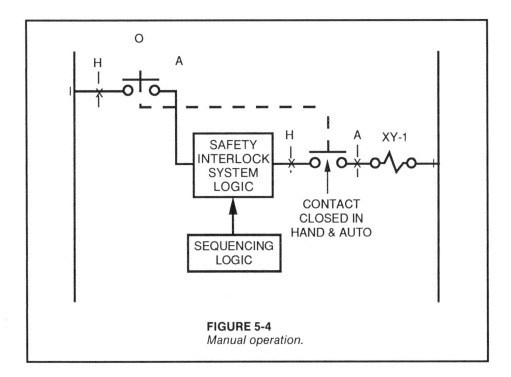

FIGURE 5-4
Manual operation.

Process Interlocking Level Level 3 also has interlock logic, but at this level the system is protecting product quality or preventing minor equipment damage; this level is not intended to protect personnel, the environment, or major equipment. At Level 1, a reactor may be shut down if its temperature exceeds a high limit value, because this could cause a runaway or decomposition that could eventually injure personnel, damage major equipment, or harm the environment. At Level 3, the pumpout from a reactor may be stopped if the valves on the pump discharge are not lined up to the correct destination. This could cause the product to be ruined if the transfer is made, although it probably doesn't pose a safety hazard. (Note: combining some materials can cause a first-level safety problem, and those systems would be included in Level 1.)

Regulatory/Discrete Control Level Automatic control is implemented at Level 4. The operator generally uses the same control stations as for Level 2 (particularly for regulatory control loops), but now controllers are placed in the AUTOMATIC mode so that they attempt to control the process to some specified set point.

Advanced Regulatory/Discrete Control Level Loops are combined at Level 5 to implement advanced control systems. Cascade control systems, feedforward control loops, and override control systems operate, and logic systems turn plant equipment on and off, as required, to coordinate the operation of plant equipment. Optimization routines are implemented at this level.

Manual Sequential Control Level Sequential control is added to the plant at Level 6. However, here the operator is manually driving the execution of the recipe. The logic for implementing the phases is built into the control system; the operator is simply initiating phases.

Automatic Recipe Execution Level Level 7 is the limit of direct process control. This is fully automatic sequential control. The operator simply asks the system to "Make a Batch of Product B."

Levels 1 through 7 of this structure are directed toward controlling the process. In batch applications, this is a combination of sequential, regulatory, and discrete controls; routine process logic; monitoring; interlocks, exception-handling logic; and recovery logic. The primary goal is to ensure reliable operation of the batch process, including, in some cases, complex cleaning procedures for production equipment.

Batch Management Level Level 8 is the management of batch production. In its simplest form, this means providing information to an operator that all the materials and equipment required to process a batch are available. A primary function at these levels is to maintain some form of equipment history logging for preventive maintenance, not so much to prevent downtime, but to prevent it from occurring while a batch is in process. However, the most important requirements are dynamic scheduling and recipe handling, which provide the ability to switch production processes efficiently between products or grades of products.

Recipe Management, Production Scheduling, and Production Planning Levels Level 9 and 10 involve area and plant management: Level 9 is the establishment and maintenance of recipes; Level 10 is the scheduling of a sequence of batches. Level 11 represents corporate demands for production from the plant.

The Level of Automation

The user must determine how much the batch production system will be automated. Although the user may decide to design a system that can be expanded to add higher levels or include other plant areas at a later date, the user may also decide to put in a system that doesn't have those capabilities. However, the user must define control requirements at all levels, because all of these control activity levels must be implemented if the batch process is to perform its function. Production goals must be set, batches must be scheduled, and recipes must be followed and maintained, whether this is done manually or automatically by the system.

Each of these levels has corresponding human monitoring and intervention requirements. When a level is not automated, the necessary displays and manual controls are needed to effectively manipulate lower levels. Where automation exists, these controls are needed to monitor that level and intervene in the case of failure. It is important for the operator to know what phase the batch is in and when he or she may intervene. This is particularly true during an upset. For the batch plant this includes knowing the current state of process variables, but it also includes knowing the position in the batch program. It should also include a recorded history of how the process arrived at that state.

Advantages of This Approach

Rosenof notes the following advantages of using a batch control system that is structured in this manner (Ref. 1):

1. A safer control system, because the batch process never runs without the safety interlocking level operational
2. More straightforward engineering, because once a top-down design is complete, engineering starts with the safety interlock system and progresses up the hierarchy
3. More straightforward start-up of the system, because start-up proceeds in the same manner as the engineering with the safety interlock systems being checked out and put in service first
4. A system that can be started up quicker, if necessary, while still incorporating all the necessary safety functions, because all levels of the hierarchy do not have to be functional to safely make product.

Comparison with the Batch Model

Figure 5-5 shows a possible mapping of the control activities from the detailed control activity model into the batch model. Obviously, different mappings are possible, depending on system configuration and company philosophy. In some cases, the control activity may be distributed across several levels of the production model. For example, there is

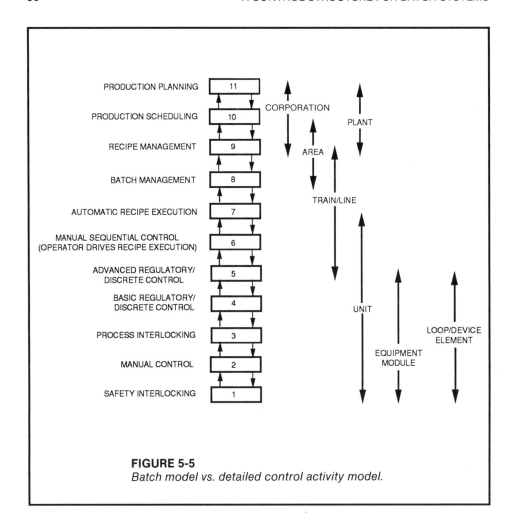

FIGURE 5-5
Batch model vs. detailed control activity model.

overlap between some levels with production scheduling and recipe management. This is because production scheduling and recipe management also follow a hierarchical structure. Different types of scheduling are applied at different levels; different recipes also exist at different levels.

EXERCISES

5.1 Explain why the manual control level of Figure 5-2 can safely bypass the process interlocking level.

5.2 At what other levels of Figure 5-5 would you expect to see overlapping of control activities?

5.3 At what level of Figure 5-2 would you expect to find statistical process control (SPC) implemented? Statistical quality control (SQC)?

5.4 What is the minimum number of operator interfaces permissible with the structure specified by the detailed control activity model? Where would they be used?

REFERENCES

1. Rosenof, H. P., "Successful Batch Control Planning: A Path to Plant-Wide Automation," *Control Engineering*, September 1982.

2. ISA/SP88-1989-MM-5, Minutes of SP88 Batch Control Standards Committee Meeting, December 6, 7, and 8, 1989.

6

The Role of Standards in Batch Control Systems

Introduction   The need for standards in batch control systems has become more apparent with the increased emphasis on quality combined with pressures to automate to stay competitive. Two good reasons for applying standards in the batch process industry are to reduce user costs and to promote understanding.

The dream of many plant managers of having a plant that is completely automated, from order entry to delivery of the product to the customer, is more easily realized in a continuous process plant than in a batch process plant. In a continuous process plant, generally only one or two products, or grades of product, have to be manufactured. Meeting customers' requirements may be as simple as changing the plant throughput to match customers' demands or making adjustments to specific process parameters to change product grades.

The issues are considerably more complex in a batch process plant (Ref. 1):

1. Generally, many more products, and grades of products, are being manufactured in the batch plant, which may have been the reason a batch process was chosen over a continuous process in the first place. Certainly, there are common resources being shared by different units within the batch plant.

2. Much of the "recipe" in a continuous process is actually built into the piping. Material flows from one piece of equipment to the next; specific unit operations take place in each piece of equipment. Usually the only variables that can be varied are certain process parameters and the feed rates to the process.

3. Batch processing, however, is done in discrete stages; instructions of what to do next are determined by how a quantity of material is processed in the system (procedure). Process variables, e.g., temperatures, pressures, flow rates, etc., and charge quantities may also be changed by instructions (formulas). The combinations of procedure and formula, along with other information about the batch identity and equipment requirements, are called recipes (see Figure 6-1) (Ref. 1).

53

RECIPE	
HEADER (BATCH IDENTITY)	PROCEDURE (SEQUENCE DESCRIPTION)
EQUIPMENT REQUIREMENTS	FORMULA (OPERATING PARAMETERS)

FIGURE 6-1
Recipe structure.

Batch processing derives its power from the ability to make many different products, or grades of products, in a limited amount of multipurpose equipment using recipes to define the process. Because recipes are nothing more than instructions, they are easily changed, which allows batch plants to be very flexible. However, this also causes additional challenges. For example, who should have the ability to change a recipe? Should a company be able to use the same generic corporate recipe from one plant site to the next? When a corporate recipe is changed, how is that change implemented throughout the organization? Obviously, specific guidelines for recipe management and recipe handling must be instituted. Different companies will use different techniques. However, it is clear that if a corporation wants to duplicate a product from one batch train/line to the next, or from one plant site to the next, without the customer noticing any difference in the products, the same recipe must be used in all cases. This concept of a generic "corporate recipe" is illustrated in Figure 6-2 (Ref. 1).

User Requirements for Batch Control Systems
When users have applied control systems to batch processes in the past, they have had little choice but to accept what process control manufacturers have had to offer. This meant that the application was driven by the availability of current hardware/software offerings instead of by the application. Process control vendors have been slow to respond to user needs in batch control systems. This, coupled with the limited flexibility of many of these systems, has prompted some users to design and produce control systems of their own, based on custom software and general-purpose computers. However, the cost of development and the ongoing cost of support of these systems is very high (Ref. 2), and this approach has been taken only by large users of batch control systems.

Many users are looking for flexible batch control systems that incorporate the following features:

1. An easy way of defining a batch control system
2. An easy method of configuring a batch control system, i.e., a standard batch language

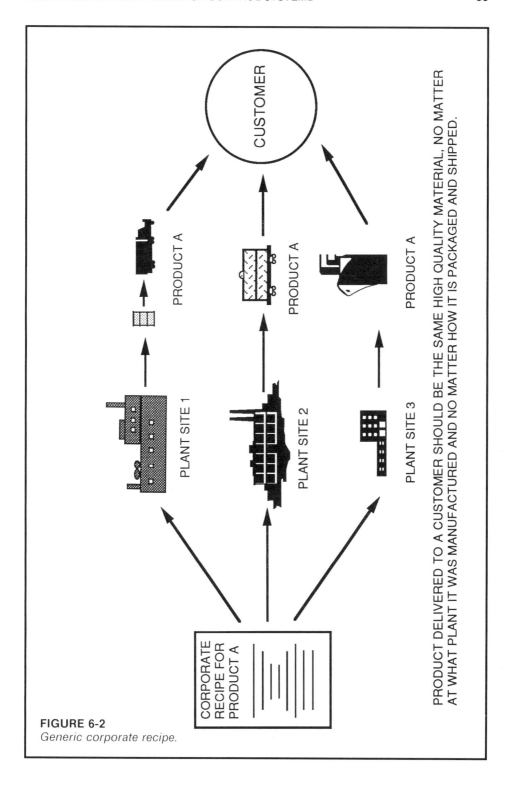

FIGURE 6-2
Generic corporate recipe.

    3. Interoperability in a multivendor environment
    4. Compatibility of data between various hardware/software systems
    5. Portability of applications, i.e., the ability to move programs to different
hardware/software platforms
    6. Consistent user interfaces

Defining a Batch Control System

Making the definition of a batch control system easier implies having standard terminology and a set of models for batch control and a standard sequence diagraming technique.

Terminology The task of defining a batch control system, even when dealing with just the various departments within the same company or plant site, can be a challenging job. This task becomes even more difficult when the people in these different departments are not using the same terminology. When agreement is finally reached within the company or plant site, then these requirements must be transmitted to a process control vendor, an engineering contractor, or to a systems integrator. Additional confusion usually results at this phase of the project because of these same terminology problems.

    ISA's SP88 standards committee is addressing the problem with terminology by building upon the work of the Purdue TC-4 committee and the NAMUR committee, and by using other national and international standards, codes, and recommended practices as appropriate.

Models It is difficult to develop standard terminology when there are no standard models available to define batch control systems. The starting point for these models should be a model that defines the structure of a batch process plant from a functional viewpoint, not from a physical viewpoint (see the batch model in Figure 4-7). Then each individual plant or organization must decide how this model fits into its batch system. Additional models are needed, e.g., a control activity model that defines the control requirements for batch processes (see the control activity model in Figure 5-1).

    ISA's SP88 standards committee is also addressing this aspect, using the work that has come out of the National Institute of Standards and Technology (NIST), the Purdue Workshop, and other national and international standards, codes, and recommended practices.

Sequence Diagraming Technique It has always been difficult to define the sequential requirements of a batch control system in a manner that doesn't require a computer programmer background or control systems engineering background to understand what the system is trying to accomplish. Verbal descriptions are often inadequate, because it is difficult to show all the interactions among the various components of the batch system. Therefore, standard sequence diagraming techniques are needed (sequence diagraming techniques are discussed in more detail in Chapter 10).

Ease of Configuration
In general, it takes far too much time to config-
ure today's batch control systems. The resulting documentation of the application
program is also often inadequate and difficult to follow. The following are some
features that are needed to minimize the configuration time and to allow the
resulting program to be more understandable (Ref. 1):

1. The sequence diagram is directly used in the batch program (or, at the
very least, a direct conversion is available). This minimizes the rework of having
to redo the sequence program in the same or a different language.

2. Configuration may be done on line or off line using an engineering
workstation (general-purpose computer). This workstation should have the ability
to configure all components in the batch control system, even those of different
manufacturers. Note that a different software package is needed to configure the
safety interlock system to provide the necessary separation between the safety
interlock system and the basic process control system.

3. Data has to be entered only once. The user should not have to enter any
data more than once. This means that if an input point is configured for use in a
regulatory control loop, it should not have to be reconfigured for use in discrete
control or sequential control applications.

4. Graphical-based configuration is used where possible. For example, regulatory control loops are configured by drawing the loop diagram using function
blocks and by answering menu questions to choose the necessary options for each
function block. Sequences are configured using a technique such as sequential
function charts. Interlocks are configured using ladder logic or function blocks.

5. Configuration is self-documenting. This requires that the system be capable of generating reports that fully document the application program. This
includes a graphical representation of control loops, sequences, and interlock
logic.

Interoperability, Compatibility, Portability, and Consistent User Interface
Today, more and more users also want interoperability,
compatibility, portability, and a consistent user interface across their plant automation systems. To get these features, they want as many standards as possible.
With the use of standards, there is less training, lower training costs, fewer
logistics problems, higher volumes of the same kind of item, simpler repairs, and
fewer use of specials. The massive investments made in training people will not
have to be made each time a new computer with a different operating system is
installed.

Open Systems
Open systems promise to provide the answer to the prob-
lems of interoperability, compatibility, portability, and a consistent user interface.
This open systems approach to batch process automation allows companies to
select the equipment they want and that which is optimized to meet their specific
needs. It helps to build the systems needed for a particular application and frees a
manufacturer from dependence on any one vendor. This lets customers truly own
their own systems.

Formal standards are essential as a basis for open systems.

What is meant by the term *open* and how does a user judge the *openness* of a particular system? The following are some proposed criteria for judging the openness of systems (Ref. 3):

1. The system adheres to a well-defined specification available to the industry. This means that anyone can develop software for the system without threat of a lawsuit.

2. The specification is met by products from several independent companies. This means that more than one company is selling systems that adhere to the specification and that buying a system does not lock one into a single vendor for future purchases. It also means that software developed by one piece of computer hardware can run on computer hardware from another vendor.

3. The specification is not controlled by a small group of companies. Any changes that are made to the specification are generally made to improve the specification and not to serve the special interests of one segment of the industry.

4. The specification is not tied to a specific machine architecture or technology. Vendors can take advantage of new technology and still ship systems that adhere to the specification. This protects users' investments in software and training.

An open systems approach can provide many advantages to the user involved in batch control:

1. The best equipment can be used for the given application without the normal concerns that there will be communications problems with other devices in the system.

2. Access to data is available to anybody on the network who has the appropriate security clearance.

3. Applications can potentially be ported to other hardware platforms with a minimum of effort.

4. Application software products become available from multiple vendors and are more interchangeable.

5. Knowledgeable personnel are easier to find.

6. Product costs are lower.

To achieve these items requires some standardization in four areas: computer communications, database management systems, operating systems, and user interfaces.

Communications
Today, computers supplied by different vendors often have difficulty communicating with each other. Even different models provided by the same vendor sometimes fail to communicate. The result is discontinuity within the end user's automation system. One solution is to "open" the system by providing consistent, rule-driven communications between different computers in order to derive the benefit of efficient data transfer.

Communications Network Requirements Communications networks must provide plant-wide information exchanges with appropriate interactive workstations and permit ready access to plant information by all users of the data. The following requirements must be met (Ref. 4):

1. Connectivity and interoperability between systems of different vendors must be provided for adaptability and ease of expansion.

2. Integrity and security of data in transmission and access to databases must be assured for reliable plant operation.

3. Delay or latency in transmission must be minimized, with highest economic speed for timely analysis and decisions.

4. Internetwork bridges, routers, and gateways must be supplied, where needed, to provide connectivity.

5. Voice, data, and video image transmission must be integrated, where needed, to provide consistency of information.

This is the role that MAP (Manufacturing Automation Protocol) and TOP (Technical & Office Protocol) will play in the batch process industry.

MAP and TOP MAP and TOP are specifications for building manufacturing and office-based communications networks that are based on international standards. They allow currently incompatible computers, or computer-based devices, to communicate with each other (Ref. 5). MAP and TOP are complementary and are designed to work together in separate, but supportive, sectors of a multi-vendor computer network. Both are based on the ISO (International Organization for Standardization)/OSI (Open Systems Interconnection) Reference Model, and both share as many of these standards in common as possible. MAP and TOP meet all four requirements for openness discussed above.

The use of standards for data communications has varied benefits for both the vendor and the user of communications products. The following are some benefits for the vendor (Ref. 6):

1. The use of standards helps to control development costs. Software and hardware development costs have been escalating for the vendor. The communications area has been the most uncontrollable.

2. With a standard interface, the system configurations will be easier to design for all sizes of systems.

3. By adhering to a standard interface and protocol, the vendor will address a larger marketplace and be allowed penetration into different industries.

4. The vendor will be able to make more cost-effective products by using standard semiconductor chips that employ large-scale integration techniques.

There are even more benefits for the user of communications products (Refs. 5 and 6):

1. A multi-vendor plant floor environment. When vendors offer their equipment with a MAP or TOP interface, the choice of computer-based and programmable devices for the plant floor and the office will no longer be restricted by the communications system the user happens to have installed.

2. Lower capital cost for communications equipment. MAP and TOP are sure to reduce the capital cost of setting up a communications infrastructure. First, market growth between suppliers of MAP-compliant and TOP-compliant products will bring prices down. Second, the availability of mass-produced chips will cut the cost of connecting devices to the network.

3. Lower software maintenance costs. Market forces will inevitably reduce the maintenance cost of MAP and TOP software, including upgrades of the specification. This process will be encouraged by the stability of the MAP and TOP specifications and the existence of conformance testing organizations. By using standards, the user's software investment is preserved.

4. Full functionality with room for expansion. MAP and TOP are designed to provide a full range of basic services in Layers 1 through 7 of the OSI model.

5. Standard applications interfaces. By using standard applications interfaces, the user can readily take advantage of new hardware technology while not affecting his applications programs.

6. Fewer point-to-point connections. The need for developing and maintaining many "point-to-point" connections, which require much attention every time there is a change in the hardware or software (operating system), is minimized.

7. Lower manpower costs. Acceptance of MAP and TOP as the standard industrial communications system will eliminate the time and effort many now spend trying to stay up to date with current networks. The entire hardware and software maintenance and support should be simplified. With a minimum of different interfaces to maintain, there will be less training involved and a greater chance to develop in-house expertise. Also, more tools will be available for maintenance and diagnosis.

8. Integration of the office and plant. Integration of the office and plant systems is one of the aims of integrated manufacturing. What MAP does in the plant, TOP does in the office. The two are designed to work together.

MMS (Manufacturing Message Specification) MAP and TOP provide the OSI standard protocols for data transmission between nodes on the network, but the structure and relationships of the control signals and data must be understood by the network so they can effectively help control manufacturing processes. ISO 9506, Manufacturing Message Specification (MMS), provides services at the application interface to facilitate the exchange of data and control signals with remote devices. MMS is a generic message specification that applies to all manufacturing devices for control, monitoring, upload, and download. However, a companion standard is also needed that defines how the control signals or data in the messages affect the behavior of the machines under control. This is because different classes of devices behave differently, and MMS has to be extended to suit the particular behavior of those classes of devices. ISA's SP72.02 committee is now defining the ISO 9506 companion standard for process control systems. Other companion standards are being developed for programmable controllers, robots, and numerical control machines. These companion standards will be registered and balloted in ISO as subsequent parts to ISO 9506 (MMS).

The goal of standard communications products is to provide communications networks that are dealt with as a utility, not as a group of specialized circuits. They allow the user to concentrate on the ends for the network without worrying about the means. Standards allow the user to choose the right equipment for the job rather than whatever equipment connects to the present hardware.

Communications is discussed in more detail in Appendix A.

Database Management Systems   MAP and TOP solve the problem

of interoperability. However, before computer systems can be compatible they also must be able to readily exchange data. Database management systems should be global in nature and must interconnect, interrelate, and integrate all department and area databases of the plant, including corporate, business, and research and marketing strategies as well as plant operations and production control (Ref. 4).

Database Management System Requirements The following are some

requirements that need to be met by these systems (Ref. 4):

1. Industry standard relational database structures and systems must be employed to permit easy integration.

2. Ease of access through a user-friendly, ad hoc query language must be supported to permit timely analysis of plant operations problems.

3. Integrity of temporal data must be maintained via high-speed network access rather than large-scale collection and copying.

4. Security of the data must be maintained while providing access to all users with a need.

5. Support of plant-wide information gathering must be available for formulation of management decisions, with simultaneous access of a single user program or person to multiple databases as the system grows.

SQL (Structured Query Language) and RDA (Remote Database Access)

To meet these needs, many people feel that this can best be accomplished by using a distributed database management system throughout the system that will run on the various hardware/operating systems used. A standard query language, e.g., SQL (Structured Query Language), must be used in conjunction with the database management system. By design, SQL makes it possible for users and vendors to access data, regardless of where it's located, what database or operating system maintains it, or what kind of hardware it's stored on.

SQL has emerged as the standard method for users and applications to access relational databases locally, but there is no standard method to access databases remotely over a network. Remote Database Access (RDA) is the standard that is being developed to facilitate access to databases over OSI networks from intelligent workstations and other database systems. The standard defines the format and meaning of messages to support this application.

Database management systems are discussed in more detail in Appendix B.

Operating Systems
UNIX has emerged as the first practical operating system that allows software to operate across diverse computer hardware. This is especially important in manufacturing, where there has been much pressure to automate in order to remain globally competitive. Manufacturers are faced with trying to protect previous investments while integrating islands of automation into new plant designs that will increase productivity.

UNIX, however, is not totally open. It does fail Rule 3 of the four criteria for testing the openness of systems.

UNIX is the foundation of an open systems approach that will allow total batch automation (CIM) to be actually, and effectively, implemented. With UNIX, the question of protecting past investments doesn't center on computer hardware. It focuses on software, where today's real costs lie. Those investments to develop software applications tailored to specific manufacturing operations have to be made only once when UNIX is used. They will not become worthless when the next generation of hardware is introduced, or if another hardware vendor is chosen.

Users want interoperability and compatibility because they don't want to deal with only one vendor; they prefer to pick and choose and make the best choice for a particular job. However, they also want their software to be portable across different models and brands of machines because software costs are extremely high and show no signs of lowering.

A new version of Berkeley UNIX that supports the full seven-layer OSI model is expected to spur wider user and vendor acceptance of OSI (Ref. 7).

User Interfaces
User-friendly interfaces are extremely important in batch control systems. Today there are far too many different approaches to user interfaces — usually at least one per process control system vendor. X Windows appears to be the emerging standard for networked systems to pass graphic information to each other (Ref. 8). X Windows was developed at the Massachusetts Institute of Technology (MIT) and defines the protocol for displaying and manipulating graphics and text applications simultaneously on one computer screen. It provides a single programming interface for distributed workstations that support bit-mapped graphics on multi-vendor workstations working together in a local area network (Ref. 9). The single screen for single applications concept will be replaced with a single screen with windowed applications using X Windows protocols (Ref. 8). Advantages of X Windows include its graphics capabilities, portability, and flexible architecture.

Total Integration
Many people involved in the batch automation and integrated manufacturing areas are coming to the following general consensus:

1. The ideal of total integration in one system is probably unrealistic. For example, the concept of a single corporate database has given way to distributed databases tied together in a network and sharing only needed information. The basic need is for an information flow system that allows information to be accessed in different forms to meet different requirements. In many cases, this

turns out to be a distributed system in which the constituents are integrated into a single, organization-wide database, accessible on line by every authorized user.

2. The "all or nothing" concept for implementing batch automation/integrated manufacturing, obtaining everything from one vendor, has proven unworkable. Major hardware/software vendors claim that they can supply all the answers, because they would like integration to be primarily a technology issue. But integration is a management issue, not a technology issue. It must be established through methods and standards. Integration is not a magic wire running among various machines. It is a managed infrastructure of what runs on the machines, regardless of the manufacturer.

3. Islands of automation can generate significant short-term savings and pave the way for integration through the eventual linking of these productive units. However, they must not be stand-alone, incompatible units. A plan must be available for integrating stand-alone systems, or their limits will be reached very quickly and the investment will begin to lose value rather than accrue long-term returns.

All components of the total plant system must be able to work with existing systems, data, and machines, plus future systems, data, and machines. A system designed to bring information in, or port out, in a flexible fashion will guarantee upgrade possibilities far into the future.

Information must be shared to be of any long-term use in creating the knowledge base needed to drive manufacturing improvements. Timely access to accurate information within the enterprise is a key factor for productivity and quality improvements. The major cause of all of the islands of information and the resultant lack of information sharing is multi-vendor incompatibility. Several options are available to integrate the islands of information into one shared system:

1. The first option available is to adopt a single vendor. This involves replacing all non-complying existing equipment and losing the dollars invested in that equipment. Another drawback, or limiting factor, is that no one vendor can solve all of the information needs of an entire plant.

2. A second option to achieve plant integration is to employ gateways, or protocol translators. Companies that have tried this approach have found it to be an expensive solution. Efficiency of the information flow suffers using this approach. Also, this option requires the development of special hardware and software. Even if this can be done, it solves only the connectivity problem.

3. The third option is to endorse international standards. An open architecture is attractive for a number of reasons. It allows users to preserve their software investments, even when hardware technology changes.

Before this concept of an open systems architecture becomes reality, users must begin including standards in their specifications. Until vendors know that the users are committed to open systems, there is not enough incentive for them to move in that direction. The users must drive this move towards the use of standards in batch control systems if our industry is to achieve the goal of integrated manufacturing.

EXERCISES

6.1 Why do some vendors continue to push their proprietary products rather than adopt an open systems approach?

6.2 What is the advantage of having a sequence diagraming technique that is simply a subset of the overall batch language?

6.3 Why do the models developed for computer integrated manufacturing in the discrete parts industries not meet the needs of the batch process industries?

REFERENCES

1. Mergen, R. J., "Batch Control Systems Standards: An Update On ISA/SP88," April 23, 1990.

2. Caro, R. H., "The Fifth Generation Process Control Architecture," ISA/88, Paper #88-1487.

3. Pajari, G., "Just What Is an Open System? *UNIX WORLD*, November 1989.

4. Williams, T. J., ed., *A Reference Model for Computer Integrated Manufacturing (CIM)*, Prepared by CIM Reference Model Committee, International Purdue Workshop on Industrial Computer Systems, ISA, 1988.

5. *The Computer Integrated Organization: Some Business and Technical Issues for the OSI-MAP/TOP Solution*, Department of Trade and Industry, U.K., as edited by B. Thacker for the Society of Manufacturing Engineers, Dearborn, MI, 1988.

6. Jones, J. W., "Data Communications Standards—Who Needs Them?" 1988 NPRA Computer Conference, Pittsburgh, October 30–November 2, 1988.

7. Desmond, P., "New Unix Version To Incite User and Vendor Acceptance of OSI," *Network World*, December 19, 1988.

8. Chatha, A., "Systems Integration: New Technologies Simplify the Task," *I&CS*, July 1989.

9. Moore, K., and R. Rio, "Using DECwindows as a Control System Interface," *Control Engineering*, April 1990.

Part III
Batch Control

7

General Control Requirements

Introduction   The problem in selecting a batch control language is that there is no standard: no one has developed the ideal batch control language. A batch control language should allow batch control to be implemented in the same language a process engineer would use to describe batch control operations to another engineer or to an operator (i.e., a natural language). None of the batch control methods available at the time of this writing offers the desired vendor independence or the natural language format desired.

Standardization is going to be difficult because of the variety of batch control implementation methods being used by various vendors of batch control systems. Every system has its own merits and problems. Most users will at least agree that they would like to be able to write batch control programs that run on a variety of vendor systems without the need to reprogram. They would also like to learn only one language for the control of batch processes; that language should be as close to the natural language of batch control as relay ladder programming is to the design of interlock logic.

Many different software packages are available for batch control systems, depending on the hardware selected. Some of this software was designed expressly for batch control; others were just adopted from existing practices, e.g., the use of ladder logic in programmable controllers for batch sequencing.

There is an increased demand in the industry for production flexibility, and development of control software is a significant cost factor. It also represents a bottleneck in meeting schedules for changes in production.

Two of the goals in developing a standard method for implementing batch control programs are reduction in the cost of developing control software and reduction in the time required to develop the program. One way of achieving this is to make the process so easy that shop floor personnel themselves can construct valid control instructions directly from the process instructions (Ref. 1). Achieving this goal must not be allowed to interfere with the security of the control system. This means that pretailored modules must be used and personnel must be trained in their use and interconnection.

Types of Control   Seven different control activities are required to implement batch control (see the control activity model of Figure 5-1):

1. Safety interlocking
2. Discrete control
3. Regulatory control
4. Sequential control
5. Batch management
6. Recipe management
7. Production scheduling

Safety Interlocking

Safety interlocks are designed to prevent unsafe operating conditions in a batch process. For example, a feed valve to a reactor cannot be opened if the level in the reactor is above the setting of the high-level shutdown switch.

Safety interlocks do not include only such devices as temperature switches, level switches, and automatic shutoff valves; they can also incorporate other techniques such as (Ref. 2):

- rate of change alarms,
- calculated or inferred variables, and
- combinations of variables.

Discrete Control

Many applications also require process variable monitoring and exception-handling logic designed to deal with abnormal conditions (Ref. 2). This monitoring logic is different from safety interlocks because it changes as the batch sequence changes and it does not implement a true safety function. For example, some interlock logic may have to verify that sequence actions occur as directed, e.g., the valve really did open. The monitoring logic must also determine if an unexpected change of state has occurred and alarm it if necessary.

Exception logic allows different actions to be taken for certain abnormal situations, for example (Ref. 2):

1. Abnormal situation, but not critical. The control system must alert the operator to the abnormal condition. No corrective action is required by the control system.

2. Critical abnormal situation. This means that the control system must either take automatic corrective action or drive the process to a predefined safe state.

3. Return to normal. Recovery logic that aids in the return to normal operations may be necessary so that an operator does not have to finish a batch by hand.

Regulatory Control

Regulatory loops are needed to control operating parameters such as reactor temperature and pressure. Flow and level controls are also examples of regulatory control.

Sequential Control Sequential control is required to step the batch process through its prescribed sequence. Organizing these batch sequence events is a very important design issue. These events should be grouped into manageable and definable groups such as operations, phases, control steps, etc., and should follow the natural operations of the process.

The sequencing nature of batch process operations results in many potential equipment operational states. These operational states must be identified and functionally defined, e.g., so that the system can handle abnormal conditions during the production of a batch of product. The following operational states are typical of many batch processes (Refs. 3 and 4):

1. Start-up — A batch is ready to start. Any necessary auxiliary equipment is brought to operational condition.

2. Normal (run) — The process is operating according to the prescribed procedure.

3. Hold — This is a partial shutdown because of one or more abnormal conditions. Operating conditions are maintained at a safe level.

4. Normal shutdown — This is a planned shutdown, e.g., at the end of a batch or the end of a campaign. All equipment is emptied out to save as much of the raw materials and product as possible and to minimize safety problems while the equipment is idle.

5. Emergency shutdown — This is an unplanned shutdown that occurs because of a hazardous condition in the process. All equipment is stopped immediately. Usually, no effort is made to empty out the contents unless required for safety considerations.

6. Restart — This is exception logic that enables a safe transfer from a hold condition back to the normal state (the state the process was in prior to going to the hold state).

7. Maintenance (idle) — The equipment has been emptied and cleaned, if necessary, and is ready for the next normal processing.

Control is transferred within these states as a function of process conditions; for example, the actuation of a high-pressure shutdown switch could result in a transfer from the normal to the emergency shutdown state, or an operator might detect some unusual condition, decide to stop normal operation, and transfer to the hold state. The return to normal from other control states should always be initiated by the operator.

The interaction of operational states becomes increasingly complex with increased numbers of process equipment (Ref. 3). Taking a unit to the "hold" state can be a very straightforward operator action in a process with only one unit. However, as the number of units under the control of a common control system increases, more state issues must be considered.

Integration between the safety interlocking, discrete control, regulatory control, and sequential control subsystems is essential to effectively control the batch reactor process.

Batch Management Batch management works in conjunction with the recipe management subsystem and the production scheduling subsystem to allow the operator to select and edit a recipe, schedule and allocate resources to a particular batch, and monitor the execution of the batch.

Recipe Management Most batch processes require the development of multiple recipes. This requires a program to change both the order of operations and phases and the control parameters that are needed to make the specific product. The recipe may be (Ref. 5):

- manually entered by the process operator (normally the operator would only be making changes to the parameters resident in the formula),
- selected from a table of predefined recipes, or
- downloaded from the supervisory computer that is performing the recipe management function.

Production Scheduling The throughput of a batch production system can usually be increased by proper utilization of the major equipment such as reactors and recovery systems. This equipment assignment and scheduling package usually assigns the recipe and products to the production system that provides the lowest possible manufacturing cost.

An equipment assignment and scheduling package is needed for at least two reasons:

1. To select a production system consisting of one or more units that is needed to meet the market demands and can meet those demands in the most economical manner.

2. To schedule and assign the shared equipment, such as weigh tanks, that service multiple reactors. This reduces batch cycle time by minimizing the wait time for a reactor to use the shared equipment.

Requirements for a Batch Control Language The choice of a
batch control language is very important. The batch language can directly affect the amount of time it takes to do the programming, the ease with which program changes can be made, the flexibility of the system, etc. Developing a widely applicable batch process computer control language is a difficult task. Many features must be considered for inclusion into the language.

The following are some of the features a batch control language should provide (Refs. 6 through 12):

1. Ease of use and flexibility. The batch control language should be easy to use by engineers, supervisors, process operators, and instrument personnel. It should be flexible because of the many different types of batch processes in the world today.

2. A systematic way of defining the batch applications. This should allow the orderly definition of process variables, processing sequence, controls, interlocks, alarms, etc.

3. A method of specifying discrete controls, regulatory controls, and sequential controls in an equally convenient manner.

4. Easy-to-use operator and engineer interfaces. The operator interface to the computer through a batch process control language is a very important design feature. Operators should be able to easily acquire information about their processes and be comfortable using the computer to monitor and control them. The batch control system should accept real-time data entries and generate messages from/to the operators' interfaces and various peripherals. It should have an integrated display/logging capability to provide operators with alarm/event/status information.

Engineers and supervisors also require information from batch processes, and they need to modify process operations. They need to be able to easily modify recipes and the process database without becoming computer experts. The batch control language should have features added that make the control system easy to use by engineers and supervisors.

Color graphics can greatly enhance operator and engineer interfaces. Graphic displays of the process equipment and controls can be displayed on a video display unit (VDU). As the batch proceeds, the color graphics system can show valves opening and closing as well as other operations in progress. This feature gives operators a view of the process without going to the process units.

5. The use of a high-level language to generate sequence logic. To generate sequence logic for process operation, a high-level process-oriented language should be provided that has a standard set of instructions and enforces the hierarchy of procedures, operations, phases, and control steps. Instrument and process engineers should be able to learn the language easily so that they can write, compile, debug, and change programs at the customer's site or at the vendor's facility.

The language should support multiple or parallel operations and/or phases on a unit. This is especially necessary when multiple pieces of equipment are being operated with a common set of utilities and where several batch programs will be active at the same time. Because synchronization of the various control tasks is complex, it is necessary to be able to start another task in parallel and to have multiple tasks running at the same time.

Named user subroutines and functions should be available to supplement batch statements. All loop, device, phase, and recipe attributes should be accessible so they can be changed or verified. Operation and phase length, along with the number of operations and phases, should be variable and hardware/memory-limited only. Access to a distributed system database should be transparent.

6. Recipe-handling capability. Recipe building should be high on the design features list. If the batch package is to be flexible in its use, then recipe generation and modification must be easy.

7. A way to collect batch history data, including batch tracking.

8. Logic and interlock capability.

9. Advanced alarm handling.

10. Floating point math.

11. Configuration capabilities for complex algorithms. Even though advanced process control may not be used as often for controlling batch processes as it is for continuous processes, this feature should be included in the batch control language.

12. Report generation. The batch control language needs to provide a powerful report generation facility. Different processes require different batch reporting data with modified formats. Some batch processes require an elaborate reporting scheme with batch summary data saved for years. Other batch processes require little or no batch report information.

13. System redundancy. This should be relatively transparent to the user. It also should not require a significant amount of extra programming to implement.

14. Alphanumeric process parameters and equipment identifiers (minimum 12 digits). Wherever possible, such as in variable naming, the control engineer should be able to use his or her own plant's nomenclature. The adherence to industry standards for process control terminology and symbols should be followed for elements in the environment.

15. Adequate development and debugging tools.

16. Portability. The software should be able to be transferred from one brand of computer to another with the least amount of effort. Although this is not a common capability today, some packages are being written under the UNIX operating system, so this capability is inevitable.

17. Ease of maintenance. Program maintenance is also a primary concern. The batch language should be easily maintained and easily modified to meet the specific needs of each batch process.

Software Modularity
The application of a control system to batch processing can be very complex. Most larger batch applications require the design team to consider many more things than just control loops and batch sequences, as shown in Figure 7-1 (Ref. 2). However, batch production systems can be described hierarchically, and the levels of the hierarchy can be controlled through a correspondingly constructed batch control system. The functions executed by this control system (e.g., opening/closing valves, starting/stopping pumps, ramping set points, etc.) can be specified through a hierarchically constructed system of control technology commands via phases (Ref. 1).

As phases are site-specific and rarely changed, their implementation in either programmable logic controllers or distributed controls makes a lot of sense. However, procedures and recipes must be changed more frequently. Computer-based systems are better suited for providing the flexibility for making those kinds of changes.

If the process changes slightly, the specification of functions, or the logic that actually implements the phases, does not have to be changed. For processes that are adapted to large shifts in market demand, however, frequent changes in the formula and the sequence of phases may be required. Although perhaps only the quantities and process parameters must be changed, frequently the order of basic operations requires changes as well. This means that the order of the phases must be redefined.

The object of software modularity is to structure and describe the phases and their links with the formula in such a manner that the operators, or other personnel, can make use of them and combine them into a functionally operable sequence on a suitable control system. This is done by providing the person who is going to

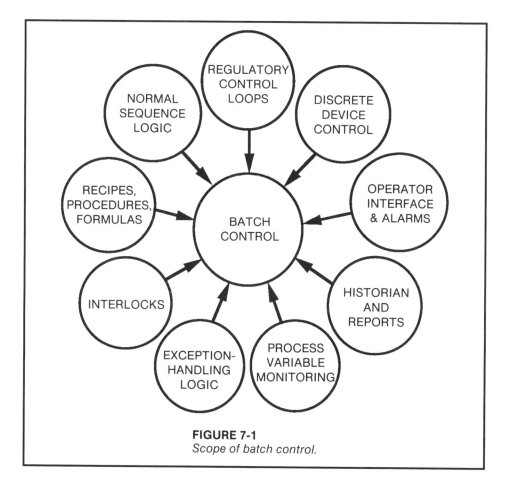

FIGURE 7-1
Scope of batch control.

develop a new recipe with a library of phases from which to draw. Those phases have built-in logic required to execute that phase. Parameters are established that relate directly to each phase, allowing the input of the various formula quantities.

The primary objectives in writing cost-effective application software are normally (Ref. 1):

- reliability (achieved by having the phase logic designed and debugged by an instrument engineer or designer who is intimately familiar with the batch process and batch process control),
- low first cost (achieved through use of high-level tools and libraries of previously written and tested code), and
- long-term maintainability (achieved by making modifications or additions to the current list of batch recipes very easy).

Software modularity addresses all three issues.

Most batch control systems support a predefined set of simple devices such as pumps and valves. However, if the user needs to work with something more complex, e.g., an equipment module, then a user-written program must often be developed. That programming may have to be repeated every time that same function is repeated in another unit.

Batch software implementation and maintenance costs can be substantially reduced using a modular approach to batch configuration. This approach consists of segregating batch functions into discrete control, regulatory control, and sequential control components. Each function is configured using the most effective method available. Logic devices, for example, are usually programmed with traditional relay ladder elements. Regulatory control loops are most often configured using a graphical approach via function blocks that resemble the old analog control functions implemented through pneumatic and electronic equipment. Sequential control is best implemented by utilizing a high-level sequencing language that closely emulates the actions of an operator during the processing of a batch. These various functions can be combined together using the "phase library" to provide a very cost-effective programming environment.

Control programs can be written much faster if program segments can be developed in parallel by separate programmers. The concept of software modularity allows multiple programmers to attack a software development effort and drastically reduce the time it takes to bring a control system on line. To do this, however, utilities must be provided within the programming environment that allow the merging of various program segments. These same utilities must also allow users to reuse program segments anywhere within the batch control system. Program segments may also be stored in an applications library, which is accessible to anybody on the overall communications network, so that they can be used in other projects if they are applicable.

EXERCISES

7.1 How do the various process control vendors define batch management? Is there is any consistency among these definitions?

7.2 What is the difference between an operational state and an operating mode?

7.3 If a recipe was in the *charge* operation and executing the *add ingredient A* phase when an emergency shutdown occurred, to what operation and phase would the system return when the emergency condition was corrected?

7.4 Is it the phase itself or how the phase is executed that is actually site-specific?

REFERENCES

1. NAMUR Recommendations, "Development of Sequence Controls for Charge Processes," July 1985.

2. Bradbury, R. K., M. C. Rominger, and J. D. Verhulst, "Promoting Modularity in Batch Control Software," ISA/88, Paper #88-1404.

3. Roerk, P. E., "Control, Scheduling and Optimization of Batch Processing, Batch Process Automation Difficult but Cost Effective," AIChE National Spring Meeting, March 25–28, 1985, Houston, TX.

4. Gidwani, K. K., "Batch Control Methodology," ISA/82, Paper #82-819.

5. Staples, R. A. C., "Cost Effective Batch Control System Using Programmable Controllers," ISA/87, Paper #87-1129.

6. Gidwani, K. K., "Integration of Batch and Continuous Control," ISA/84, Paper #84-819.

7. Arnold, J. A., D. L. Brandl, and S. A. Jefferys, "The Next Generation of Process Control Programming," ISA/87, Paper #87-1192.

8. Ward, J. C., and M. R. Scalera, "Developing a Batch Process Computer Control Language," ISA/82, Paper #82-821.

9. Bristol, E. H., B. D. Campbell, and A. Gunkler, "A Batch Language Study," ISA/81, Paper #81-797.

10. Dunbar, R. D., "The Use of Programmable Controllers for Batch Process Controls," 16th Annual International Programmable Controllers Conference and Exposition, April 7–9, 1987.

11. Hertanu, H. I., "Understanding and Using Batch Software," ISA New Jersey/New York Section Joint Spring Symposium, April 5–6, 1983.

12. Blaiklock, P., "Programmable Controllers — A Good Choice for Batch Control," *I&CS*, March 1987.

8

Safety Interlocking

Introduction   Safety interlock systems are used to provide for the safe operation of process units. Safe operation means safety of plant personnel, of plant equipment, and of the community surrounding the plant. Magison (Ref. 1) defines safety as "freedom from danger" or as "an acceptably low risk that a system will injure workers, destroy the plant, or function in some other socially, economically, or legally unacceptable way."

Safety, however, cannot be absolute. It is always relative and relies on probability. Because there is always a probability that some activity will put life and property at risk, the following basic concept should be applied in the design of safety interlock systems (Ref. 1):

No single event should lie between the safe situation and a catastrophe.

The safety interlock system is generally the backup system that takes over when an unsafe situation occurs and returns the process to a safe state. The safety interlock system oversees the operating plant and the basic process control system (BPCS) to make sure that a failure in either of those systems does not cause a hazardous situation (see Figure 8-1).

What Is an Interlock?   NFPA Standard 85A (Ref. 2) defines interlock as "a device or group of devices arranged to sense a limit or off-limit condition or improper sequence of events and to shut down the offending or related piece of equipment, or to prevent proceeding in an improper sequence in order to avoid a hazardous condition."

Interlocks are of two types: permissive and failure (or shutdown). An example of a permissive interlock occurs when valve A must be open before valve B can open. In another example, valve A cannot open unless the batch reactor sequence is in Phase 4. A high level shutdown on a vessel is an example of a failure interlock. If there is high level, then something in the system has failed. The high level switch closes feed valve A to prevent the vessel from overflowing.

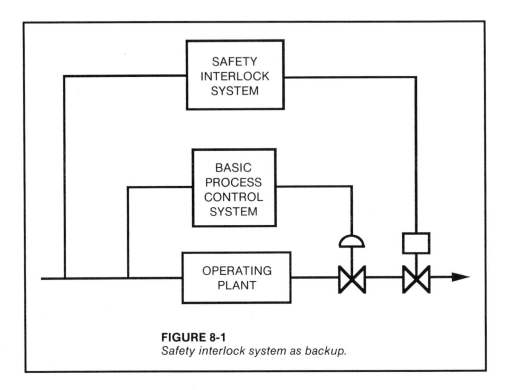

FIGURE 8-1
Safety interlock system as backup.

Design Philosophies   A systematic procedure for designing safety interlock systems is a necessity. Conger (Ref. 3) defines systematic procedure as follows:

> Carefully establish protection priorities and design strategy (or philosophy of design) for a specific installation. Write this in the form of a specification or standard against which all subsequent system design, hardware selection, and maintenance procedures are compared.

Priorities must be established for a given plant (or process), because they have a significant effect on the design of the safety interlock system. Once they are established, they must be strictly adhered to for the remainder of the system design. An example of such a set of priorities is (Ref. 3):

- First Priority — Personnel Safety
- Second Priority — Equipment Protection
- Third Priority — Continuity of Production
- Fourth Priority — System Cost

The protection strategy (design philosophy) will vary from application to application, and it may vary from one piece of equipment to another within a given process. The equipment and processes to be protected must be identified, along with the variables relating to the equipment and/or process that must be monitored. Careful attention must be paid to the design to be sure that it meets the pre-defined system priorities and design philosophy. The following are some examples of design techniques and how they apply to the above philosophies (Ref. 3).

1. The design technique in which instruments used for control purposes are completely separate from the instruments for the safety interlock system emphasizes personnel and equipment protection at the expense of system cost. If the system is well designed, it should have little impact on continuity of production.

2. Designs with both control and safety interlock functions based on one instrument place top priority on system cost.

3. Designs that utilize a normally energized safety interlock system, so that the system is fail-safe, optimize personnel and equipment protection and should have little effect on cost. Designs that utilize a normally de-energized system place continuity of production ahead of personnel and equipment protection.

4. Systems that require two or more devices to operate in order to shut down a process typically place top priority on continuity of production. However, it is possible to design a system that provides an optimum shutdown system in terms of personnel safety, equipment protection, and continuity of operation.

5. Parallel systems in which a shutdown occurs if any of the devices sense an unsafe condition place top priority on personnel and equipment protection.

General Design Framework

It has always been difficult to determine how much reliability should be built into the safety interlock system. What interlocks should be considered as first-level safety devices? Should the interlock system include redundant or fault tolerant components? Should the redundancy or fault tolerance be extended to the field devices? There is no recognized method available to resolve these problems.

It is important that people who are implementing safety interlock systems know what the limitations of some of this equipment are, especially with respect to microprocessor-based systems. This is necessary for the safe design of control systems.

A properly specified and designed safety interlock system is needed so that an acceptable level of safety can be achieved in hazardous installations. A general design framework, consisting of four phases, is shown in Figure 8-2. In the first phase of this design process, the potential hazards in the system must be identified and quantified.

First, the potential hazards existing in the plant as designed must be identified. This is often done with a "hazards and operability" study (HAZOP), which is a rigorous, formal analysis that involves applying a set of routine questions to each item of equipment to examine the effects if the process should go out of tolerance. With this study, the hazards and the problems that prevent efficient operation are identified.

The next step is to assess (analyze and quantify) the hazards that have been identified and decide how far to go in removing them or in protecting people and property. There may be a cheap and obvious way to eliminate the hazard; sometimes past experience or a code of practice provides the solution. When these

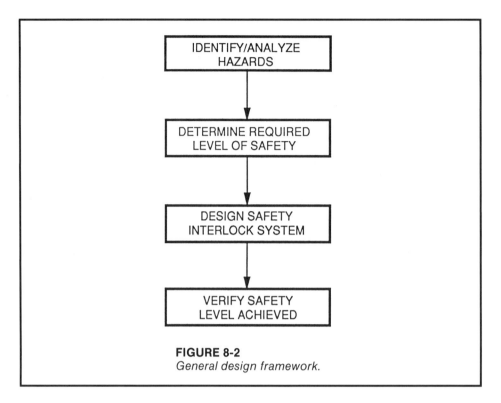

FIGURE 8-2
General design framework.

methods fail, the probability of an accident and the extent of the consequences can be calculated, using statistical methods, and then compared with a target or criterion. This method is known as hazard analysis (HAZAN). Such a study is called hazard analysis rather than risk analysis (Ref. 4), because risk analysis is used to describe methods for estimating economic risks.

When the sources of hazards have been identified, the plant design is reexamined to see if the hazards can be eliminated at the source or reduced to the practical minimum. For example, can the inventory requirements for hazardous materials be reduced? Can a different raw material be used that is less hazardous?

In the second phase of the design, an analysis must be made of the potential hazards existing in the plant and the acceptable risk so that the desired level of safety can be incorporated. Where the plant is a remote, unmanned production platform, economic factors are likely to be the chief concern. However, when the risk will be shared by people working in the plant and those living in its immediate neighborhood, the acceptable hazard rate must be determined by more subjective means.

Wilkinson (Ref. 5) recommends a top-down approach to safety interlock system design for this stage. This method, a structured development program, first considers the requirements needed by the installation without looking at how the design will eventually be implemented. Maggioli (Ref. 6) introduced the "Safety Matrix" concept, which can be used at this phase of the design process. Both of these techniques are discussed later in this chapter.

The third phase of the design process is the actual design of the safety interlock system. Many choices are now available to the instrument engineer to implement the safety interlock system: pneumatic logic, relay logic, hard-wired solid-state logic, and programmable microprocessor-based equipment. Once the system technology has been defined, a preliminary design can be prepared.

In the final phase, the preliminary design is then subjected to a rigorous analysis, which identifies the effects each component will have on the system upon failure. The design is then improved in an iterative manner until the desired level of safety is achieved.

Fail-Safe Systems

The design specification should state whether the safety interlock system is to be designed to be fail-safe, have high availability, or both.

Bryant provides a definition of a fail-safe control system (Ref. 7):

> A fail-safe control system is one whose outputs are de-energized (or neutralized) when a component or circuit failure occurs in the control loops associated with a particular output.

This means that when there is a failure, the system will go into a safe state.

A system designed to operate in the "normally energized" mode will inherently fail safe on loss of both electrical power and instrument air.

Normally Energized Mode With the "normally energized" mode of operation, inputs are energized under normal operation and de-energized under shutdown conditions. This means that a shutdown is initiated when the input contact opens, if the wiring breaks, a connection comes loose, etc. Output devices are also energized under nomal operating conditions. They are de-energized to go to the shutdown condition.

Normally De-energized Mode This mode of operation is just the opposite of the normally energized mode. Here, inputs are energized to initiate a shutdown. Output devices are also energized to go to the shutdown condition. This mode of operation is normally used when continuous operation of the equipment is important and unwanted shutdowns must be minimized.

Availability

A useful definition of system availability is:

A = Uptime/Total Time

where A = availability.

Availability is the probability that the system is working throughout the total mission time. If it is always working, the availability is 1.0. Multiplying the availability by 100 percent permits expression of availability as a percentage; a perfect system has 100 percent availability.

Before looking further at availability, it is important to look at the two types of faults that are present in batch control systems: fail-to-safe and fail-to-danger.

Fail-to-safe (FTS) faults result in an immediate system shutdown; they signal their presence. They are called "revealed" faults or "overt" faults. These types of shutdowns can be dramatically reduced by using redundant elements within the system, because control is maintained if one element becomes faulty.

Fail-to-danger (FTD) faults are the most dangerous. They prevent the system from responding to hazard warnings, thus allowing hazards to develop. They are called "unrevealed" faults or "covert" faults, because they can remain undetected until revealed by testing; otherwise, the system would not be available when a demand arose. With testing, very high degrees of protection can be achieved, and the shorter the time interval between tests, the smaller will be the probability of two faults existing in different elements of the system.

Availability should be determined based on both FTS and FTD faults. Availability based on FTD faults is most important in safety interlock systems because it determines whether the safety interlock will be operative whenever a demand is placed on the system.

A distinction must be made between "availability" and "fail-safe." Availability is calculated based on any failures that require the system to shut down. However, no distinction is made between failures that cause the system to go to a safe state and failures that cause the system to go to a dangerous state. Availability is only a measure of how often a system fails. A fail-safe system fails in a known, predetermined manner to a safe state.

High availability is important because the system is less likely to fail, to a safe state or a dangerous state. Fail-safe is important so that failures that do occur don't become disasters. Some systems that maintain availability do so by sacrificing their ability to operate safely. The desire in most safety interlock systems is to have a system that is both fail-safe and has high availability. This means that the safety interlock system is extremely reliable to protect the environment, personnel, and equipment. It also avoids false trips and the resulting economic penalties.

Redundant and Fault Tolerant Systems

Redundant and fault tolerant systems can be used to make systems more fail-safe and to increase availability. However, some people use the terms "redundancy" and "fault tolerant" interchangeably. A distinction can and should be made (Ref. 8):

> Redundant systems have individually specified duplicate components and manual or automated means for detecting failures and switching to backup devices.

> Packaged fault tolerant modules have internally redundant parallel components and integral logic for identifying and bypassing faults without affecting the output.

Redundant and fault tolerant systems will be discussed in more detail in Chapter 17, Reliability/Availability.

Regulatory Controls vs. Safety Interlock Systems

Regulatory controllers normally include built-in facilities for transferring from automatic to manual (and vice versa) so that the operator can take over operation at any time. Therefore, the operator has the ultimate responsibility for safety. The normal operation of regulatory controls is dynamic, and the system is continuously active for long periods. Faults in these systems tend to be self-revealing. Since the operator has frequent interaction with the system and has the capability to take over on manual control, these systems are relatively less critical than safety interlock systems (Ref. 9). The inputs and outputs in regulatory controls are generally analog.

Contrast that to the safety interlock system that typically sits there dormant, waiting for a demand on the system. The safety interlock system may be used relatively infrequently (perhaps never), except when the system is tested. The operator has limited interaction with the safety interlock system. Because this system should never be off line when the basic process control system is operating, and since not all faults in safety interlock systems are self-revealing, the design of safety interlock systems is more critical (Ref. 9). The inputs and outputs in safety interlock systems are primarily digital.

EXAMPLE 8-1

Problem: What does this difference between regulatory controls and safety interlock systems mean with respect to the design of these systems?

Solution: This means that different criteria should be applied to regulatory controls and safety interlock systems when availability is considered. Safety interlock systems need comprehensive testing and diagnostic features to maintain high integrity. The system availability can be improved by frequent testing, and for large systems this is practical only by automatic means.

Fail-Safe Considerations with Programmable Electronic Systems

The equipment used in the safety interlock system should fail in a safe direction. If the safety interlock system uses a standard, off-the-shelf programmable electronic system (PES), e.g., a programmable controller, it is inherently unsafe. This is because of the potential for internal PES failures and failures in triacs or SCRs that are used in output modules to energize field equipment.

A PES failure can cause a complete control system shutdown. PESs can also fail in an undeterminable mode. Programmable electronic systems are also prone to internal failures that can affect the scan cycle. It is very important that a PES failure be detected and that the proper shutdown sequence be performed.

Triacs and SCRs are inherently NOT fail-safe. They do not fail in a predictable mode; they can fail in the ON condition. This can cause output devices to become energized even though the output is supposed to be in the OFF condition. Special precautions must be taken when using such devices.

Cures have been developed that some feel get around the inherently unsafe characteristics of solid-state logic devices:

1. Use feedback monitoring loops from the field devices. This feedback principle relies on a detection or comparison circuit to either alarm or shut down the system when there is a discrepancy. And the detection circuit itself can fail unless it is fail-safe. But feedback monitoring circuits are usually composed of more solid-state devices, which can make the system more complex and less reliable, and it does not solve the fail-safe problem. This does not mean that output feedback should not be used. It is a very desirable feature on most safety interlock systems. It simply means that feedback in itself does not improve the fail-safe features of the solid-state device.

2. Use electromechanical relays for the output switching device. This also does not make the system fail-safe. When relays are used as output switches with solid-state systems, they are usually driven by a solid-state driver, such as a triac. These solid-state devices can fail so the relay becomes energized.

PES Logic System Most programmable electronic systems manufacturers build fault-diagnostic systems into their PESs. This is especially true of the newer microprocessor-based systems. The following are some incorporated methods (Ref. 10):

1. Watchdog timer. This is basically a device that checks to make sure that the PES is going through its normal scan. It is usually located at the end of the program. If it is not serviced during each scan, the PES can be shut down according to a pre-defined program.

2. Parity checks. Parity bits are added to each word and are constantly checked to see if a memory location fails or if an error has occurred in the program.

3. Checksum. With this technique, the corresponding bits in a word are added from column to column digitally without carry. This forms a word that uniquely represents that particular word. A bit change in any word will change the checksum. The PES constantly computes the checksum and compares it with the base checksum (usually determined on system power up) to check for errors. Checksum systems are more efficient than parity checking.

EXAMPLE 8-2

Problem: Are these types of diagnostics sufficient for critical safety interlock systems?

Solution: Even with these checking features, a problem can arise if they are built into the software. They may then be subject to similar types of errors. A recent article (Ref. 11) states that these types of self-tests will detect only 70% to 80% of all faults.

EXAMPLE 8-3

Problem: Is there an easy way to improve the diagnostics of PES-based safety interlock systems?

Solution: One solution is to build an external watchdog timer circuit. This watchdog timer monitors an output or a number of selected outputs to make sure they are constantly being scanned. If not, then that same watchdog timer can be used to effect an orderly shutdown of the system. An example circuit, shown in Figure 8-3, uses a motion detector to monitor a programmable controller. A PLC output is programmed to cycle ON and OFF periodically. A time delay is preset into the motion detector. The motion detector output is energized as long as this output toggles ON and OFF within the preset time. If the PLC output remains in the ON or OFF state and does not cycle, the motion detector output de-energizes. This output can be used to turn off power to critical outputs and/or sound an alarm.

This watchdog circuit should be set up so that it checks to make sure that input devices are working, the PLC scan is working, logic is actually being solved within the PLC, and the output devices are working. In systems where inputs and outputs are located in racks, it may be necessary to utilize inputs and outputs from each rack in the watchdog circuit to prove communication between the central processing unit and the I/O devices. In PLCs where memory is added by adding additional memory cards, it may also be necessary to make sure that the watchdog circuit is solved in all parts of the memory.

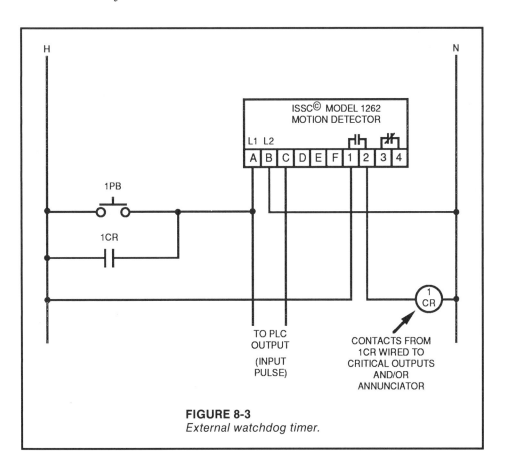

FIGURE 8-3
External watchdog timer.

Output Devices Many output interface devices use triacs to switch the load. Triacs are very sensitive to overvoltage damage. Surge suppressors should be installed across the triac in any case where a mechanical switch is installed in series with the load or in parallel with the output module (see Figure 8-4).

Triacs also have a minimum load requirement for the triac to turn ON. Some loads are not high enough to supply this minimum load, and an artificial load must be supplied. This problem can occur when a PES output is directly driving a solid-state input device on another PES, e.g., a computer.

For extremely hazardous situations, critical shutdown devices should be hardwired externally to the PES. For example, an extremely critical high-pressure switch might be wired directly to a reactor feed valve. This switch is hardwired in this manner and wired into the logic system for alarm and lockout purposes using an interposing relay (see Figure 8-5). Lockout means that once the switch has tripped and closed the valve, the valve will not reopen until the switch has reset and a RESET button has been pushed. It is good practice to hardwire a manually operated on-off selector switch between the output interface device and the final output device so the final output device can be returned to a safe position if the PES fails.

Look at all the outputs to see what happens to them when a fault is detected in the PES. Very often the outputs are turned OFF when a fault is detected. But not all outputs are safe when turned OFF. It may be desirable for the PES to maintain the "last state" on a fault.

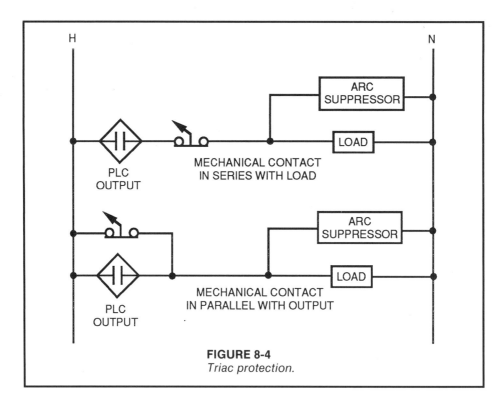

FIGURE 8-4
Triac protection.

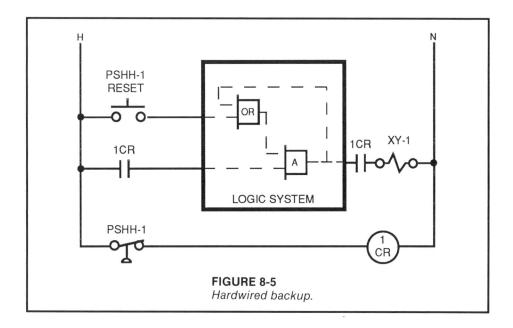

FIGURE 8-5
Hardwired backup.

Input Devices A major problem can occur with input interface devices. An input voltage of 60 to 70 volts is enough to turn ON many 115-V ac input devices. A field signal wire to an input can easily pick up this much induced voltage in long runs of wiring when it is installed in conduit or tray cable with other I/O. Induced current is not normally a problem with electromechanical relays, since the current flow required to pick up the coil is usually more than the current that can be supported by the induced voltage. With some of the high impedance input devices used on some PLCs, the current draw of an input can be as low as 9 or 10 mA. The result is that inputs can get turned ON by the induced voltage even when the field contact is open. One solution is to install a resistor between the input and ground that is sized to achieve the required current flow.

Remember that input switches (e.g., limit switches, pressure switches, level switches, etc.) are not all normally open devices. Use normally open (NO) or normally closed (NC) as needed for the greatest safety; decide which switches cover the most unsafe conditions and make them normally closed. The most common failures are either a broken wire or a contact that fails to close. If a wire or switch fails, the PES will sense an unsafe condition. In particular, STOP circuits must be wired using normally closed push buttons.

Program Design Problems can occur when changes are made to a program while the machine is running, e.g., changing the preset of a timer. On-line programming is especially dangerous, although it is a very desirable feature during checkout. Some type of keylock device should be installed to prevent on-line program changes by maintenance and operating personnel.

The ease of programming also makes it possible for unauthorized personnel to change programs. Allowing maintenance and operating personnel access to a

PES can cause problems; even though skilled in their particular job area, they may lack the knowledge to program a PES safely. Even if they know how to program the PLC, they may not know the procedures followed in a particular plant. The use of PROM or EPROM memory for program storage offers the only effective protection against unauthorized tampering.

Many PESs allow inputs and outputs to be forced ON or OFF. This means that an input and output can be turned ON or OFF manually, regardless of process conditions. Forcing is a very desirable feature during checkout and maintenance of a system, but it is very easy to forget and leave inputs and outputs in a forced condition. Also, forcing I/O in one section of a program can cause disastrous results in another section of the program. I/O forcing should not be used while the system is operating.

Safety can be increased by the coding of the program itself. One of the biggest problems is in the use of latched outputs, i.e., outputs that stay ON once they have been turned ON, even after a power interruption. Although latches work well for storing error codes or for batch stepping (sequencing), some problems can arise when latched coils are used to control real-world outputs. A latched output that comes back ON when the PES is powered up can cause a serious or dangerous machine motion to occur immediately. Outputs that cause any machine movement should be programmed with non-retentive outputs. If these circuits must be locked in, use a holding circuit and seal-in contacts, as is done with relays.

Top Down Design Approach

Figure 8-6 is an example of the top down approach recommended by Wilkinson (Ref. 5). An estimate of the acceptable hazard rate is needed so that the target availability can be calculated. Kletz's articles (Refs. 4 and 12) are a good place to look for some guidance in this area. An estimate of the rate at which hazards may occur must then be made. From these values, the requirements for the safety interlock system to respond to a hazard situation can be determined and, thereby, its reliability and integrity. Once these requirements are known, the system design implementation can be considered in terms of the technology employed and its configuration.

All items of plant hardware are subject to failure at characteristic rates, and any failure may result in a hazard. The safety interlock system must act to protect the plant if the potential hazard occurs; this is known as a shutdown demand. A dangerous situation will arise only if the system fails to respond to the demand. The demand rate is simply the sum of the individual failure rates for each component in the plant. Failure rates are obtained from manufacturers' data or from historical data; they are usually specified as the Mean Time Between Failures (MTBF).

System availability indicates the probability of a safety interlock system being able to respond to a hazardous situation during a given period. A target value is determined for each installation from the demand rate and the acceptable hazard rate as follows:

Target Availability = [1 – (Hazard Rate/Demand Rate)] × 100

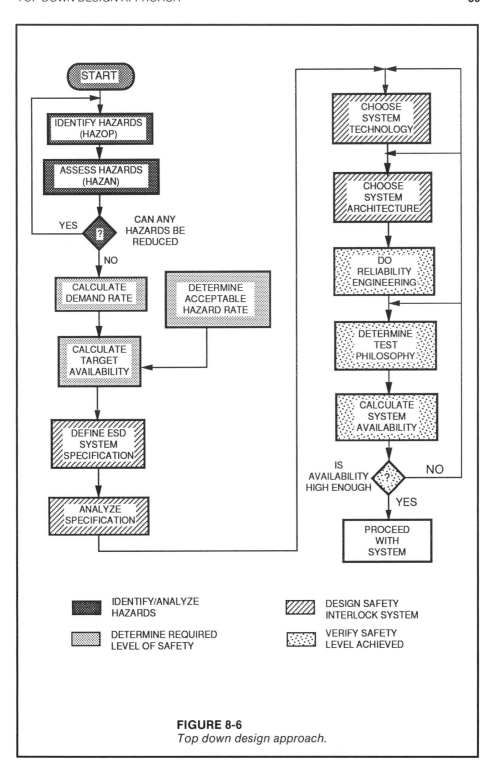

FIGURE 8-6
Top down design approach.

The hazard rate is the rate (occasions/year) at which hazards occur. The demand rate is the rate (occasions/year) at which a safety interlock system is called upon to act. If the safety interlock system never fails to operate when required, then the hazard rate is 0. If there is no safety interlock system, the hazard rate is equal to the demand rate. Usually, the safety interlock system is inoperative or dead for a (small) fraction of the time. A hazard results when a demand occurs during a dead period. Therefore (Ref. 4),

Hazard Rate = Demand Rate * Fractional Deadtime

Fractional deadtime is that fraction of time the safety interlock system is inactive.

For a safety interlock system to be adequate, its system availability must exceed the target availability. For a given system configuration, the system availability can be calculated from the time taken to test the system (when it is locked out), the frequency of testing, and the time taken to maintain and service the equipment, along with the MTBF data for the various components.

Safety Matrix Approach

In this technique, the required level of safety is based on what the safety interlock system is designed to protect, e.g., the community, plant personnel, plant equipment, etc. These can typically be divided into classes, as shown below in order of decreasing severity (Refs. 6, 13 and 14):

- Class I — Environmental Risks (these can affect the community and plant personnel)
- Class II — Employee Safety Risks (such as from an explosion)
- Class III — Major Equipment and Production Cost Risks (these typically can cause costly business interruptions)
- Class IV — Minor Equipment and Production Cost Risks
- Class V — Product Quality and Product-Handling Risks (an example might be mixing two different products together)

Based on the above classifications, safety interlocks can be rated according to their relative importance to the business. The criteria used in the design of the interlock system vary according to the risk classification and the type of equipment selected for interlocking. This forms the basis for the matrix shown in Table 8-1, where these classifications are compared with various system architectures in a matrix.

The objective of the matrix is to provide guidelines that can be used when designing or accessing a safety interlock system. It is a method of assuring that the desired level of safety is achieved when implementing a safety interlock system. These guidelines are not meant to replace standard methods of safety analysis already in place. In fact, they should not be used without first addressing and implementing those analysis tools.

This matrix is defined by individual companies based on the potential impact of an event upon the business. In the operation of chemical processes, a business cannot afford to have any occurrence that could impact upon the safety or health of any employees or local off-site citizens. Furthermore, any event that

TABLE 8-1
Safety Matrix

Interlock System Architecture	Classifications				
	Class I Environmental	Class II Employee Safety	Class III Major Equipment and Production	Class IV Minor Equipment and Production	Class V Product Quality
Single relay	Not Suitable	Not Suitable	Not Suitable	Suitable	Suitable
Single programmable controller with external watchdog timer	Not Suitable	Not Suitable	Not Suitable	Suitable	Suitable
Redundant programmable controller with external watchdog timer, on-line updating and switchover, and non-redundant I/O	Not Suitable	Not Suitable	Not Suitable	Suitable	Suitable
Redundant programmable controller with external watchdog timer, dual sensors and final control elements (outputs wired in series in a 1 out of 2 arrangement)	Suitable	Suitable	Suitable	Suitable	Suitable
Fault tolerant programmable controller with dual sensors and final control elements (2 out of 3 voting)	Suitable	Suitable	Suitable	Suitable	Suitable

might result in a long-term shutdown of the process or the destruction of major equipment is also undesirable. Controls are typically put in place to prevent such occurrences. Therefore, the incentive behind the matrix is to provide for safe and reliable operation of the process.

Design Guidelines

When emergency shutdown systems are implemented, Class I, II, and III risks are often grouped into a category called "First-Level Safety." When the emergency shutdown system must be fail-safe and have high availability, then fault tolerant systems appear to be the best choice. When the system must be fail-safe but availability is not so important, a redundant system (with redundant I/O) may be a good choice. Each of the programmable devices in this redundant configuration should be equipped with external watchdog timers. Fail-safe outputs should also be used.

Single programmable devices, even if they are equipped with external watchdog timers and fail-safe outputs, are not suitable for first-level safety interlock systems, because normal fault detection techniques, even using external watchdog timers, are not 100% effective at detecting faults (Ref. 11).

Many users prefer to implement the safety interlocks in separate unit controllers, in separate programmable controllers, in separate hardwired relay logic systems, or in separate hardwired discrete solid-state logic systems. This provides the safety interlocks as an independent function so that the program is protected from inadvertent changes, e.g., while an operator or engineer is making revisions to the batch sequencing program. Then all outputs from the discrete controls, regulatory controls, and sequential controls are processed through the safety interlock system as a watchdog on proper operation.

In line with the guidelines from Chapter 5, A Control Model for Batch Systems, all inputs and outputs needed in the safety interlock system must be directly connected to the equipment used to provide the safety interlock logic. Inputs and outputs must not be routed through higher-level control activities. They especially should not come from another device, even if it is at the same level, via a data highway. Data highways are not secure enough to be used for these critical inputs and outputs.

Class IV and V risks can be grouped into a category called "Second-Level Safety." It is difficult to justify either the cost of fault tolerant systems or completely redundant systems for this level of risk. A single programmable device with an external watchdog timer and fail-safe outputs may be suitable for these applications. Where redundant programmable devices are used, usually only the processor (CPU) is redundant.

Documentation

Good safety interlock system documentation is just as important as the design of the logic system itself. If adequate documentation is not available, operating and maintenance personnel will not properly understand the system, maintenance will be difficult, and design changes will be next to impossible to achieve.

ISA Binary Logic Diagrams   For many companies, the ISA binary logic diagrams are the working drawings that show all the interface connections for inputs and outputs and the internal logic that describes the operation of the safety interlock system. Binary logic diagrams are not tied to any particular brand of hardware or software; they are generic.

Logic symbols used in these drawings should conform to ISA Standard S5.2 (Ref. 15). Before a system is finalized, the logic sequences should be reviewed by both production and safety personnel. The ISA binary logic diagram will become the basis for design of the final logic system, since it is easily converted into schematic wiring diagrams for relay logic, binary logic diagrams for solid-state logic systems, and ladder logic for programmable controllers. The production and safety personnel need not know how the final logic will be executed; consequently, they only need to learn how to read one type of logic drawing — the ISA binary logic diagram. They do not have to be concerned with how the various manufacturers implement different types of logic functions. The ISA binary logic diagram becomes a part of the permanent documentation for the particular process.

Written Description   Regardless of the type of logic used to represent the actual logic, the documentation is not complete if it doesn't include a written description of how the logic system is supposed to function (sometimes called a sequence of operations). A written description, in conjunction with the binary logic diagrams, can prove invaluable to operations, maintenance, process, and safety personnel.

Programming Languages   When safety interlocks are implemented in PES-based systems, the particular device that is used is usually a programmable controller (PLC). The programming language of PLCs has always been a controversial aspect of this technology. Ladder logic, which has its roots in relay logic, is undoubtedly the most familiar of all the programming languages for PLCs. This is mainly because of its simplicity and the fact that maintenance electricians are comfortable with it.

When programmable controllers were first developed, they were used as relay logic replacers. This meant that there was a need for a programming language that an electrician or a person with an electrical background could easily understand. Electrical people had been working for years with ladder diagrams, which are drawn to emphasize logic flow. So electricians and maintenance people found that, when programming and troubleshooting programmable controllers that used ladder logic, they were only doing things they had done before — designing and interpreting electrical diagrams.

The system designer doesn't always have a choice in programming languages and has to work within the constraints and influences of his surroundings. These include the application itself, historical precedents, the personnel who interface to the system, and the internal support system of the organization.

The preferences of plant instrument and electrical technicians are often used as the reason for the continued use of ladder logic. They can usually understand the logic diagrams and their relationship to real-world devices. However, the system designer today may not be familiar with ladder logic. Most college graduates entering industry today are more apt to be familiar with a computer language than they are with ladder logic, since few institutions teach ladder logic.

As manufacturers introduced successive generations of programmable controllers, new languages also emerged. But now that the technology is maturing, there is increasing pressure from users for formal language standards. Users have found that switching from one PLC model to another is costly and inefficient in terms of retraining, re-engineering, and the purchasing of programming devices. And with the increasingly computer-like capabilities of the new PLCs, users have found that some of the existing programming languages are cumbersome and somewhat inflexible.

Standard for Programming Languages

A standard for programming languages is being prepared by Working Group 6 of Subcommittee 65A (System Considerations) of the International Electrotechnical Commission's Technical Committee 65 (Industrial and Process Measurement and Control); IEC, SC65A/WG6, for short (Ref. 16). The group working on this standard includes experts from all major industrial nations who must reconcile differences between proposed and existing national standards in a very complex field.

This draft is out for final balloting. What is proposed is a hierarchy of languages, with the primary language called Sequential Function Chart (SFC) and the four secondary languages named Ladder Diagram (LD), Function Block (FB), Instruction List (IL) and Structured Text (ST), respectively.

Sequential Function Chart The Sequential Function Chart language is a graphically expressed language that allows the programmer to represent his process or program as steps or transitions in a function chart. Sequential Function Chart can be combined with any of the four secondary languages. It is intended for sequential applications; it will be discussed in more detail in Chapter 10. The secondary languages are the ones that would typically be used for safety interlocks.

Secondary Languages Figure 8-7 (Ref. 16) shows the same PLC function programmed in each of the four secondary languages. The ladder diagram is practically identical to that used by most U.S. programmable controllers today. The function block is a carryover from the old solid-state control symbology. Although it will be unfamiliar to most U.S. engineers, it is reportedly much favored by Europeans. This function block language should not be confused with the "function blocks" that are part of the ladder diagram language used by many U.S. manufacturers. The instruction list language is very similar to the language used by some small programmable controllers. It is also very similar to assembly language used in computers. The structured text language was derived from higher-level computer languages. The draft standard permits any of these four to be used to represent actions or transition conditions in a sequential function chart.

Each of the four has its advantages and limitations. This allows the user the option to choose the one best suited to express his particular logic or the one that most closely matches his skills and background.

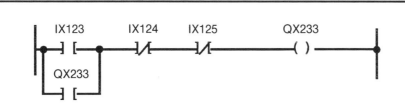

LADDER DIAGRAM LANGUAGE

FUNCTION BLOCK LANGUAGE

LD IX123

OR QX233

ANDN IX124

ANDN IX125

-    QX233

INSTRUCTION LIST LANGUAGE

QX233 - (IX123 OR QX233) AND NOT IX124 AND NOT IX125

STRUCTURED TEXT LANGUAGE

FIGURE 8-7
Secondary PLC languages (Ref. 16).

Although this IEC standard is apparently not complete at this time, all of the programming languages are available in some form.

EXERCISES

8.1 Why are some companies trying to move away from on-off input devices for safety interlock systems and moving toward the use of analog transmitters as input devices?

8.2 When would a PES-based safety interlock system want to maintain its outputs in the last state on a failure of the system?

REFERENCES

1. Magison, E. C., "Make Sure Your System Is Safe," *Instruments & Control Systems*, December 1979.

2. NFPA 85A-1982, "Standard for Prevention of Furnace Explosions in Fuel Oil- and Natural Gas-Fired Single-Burner Boiler Furnaces," National Fire Protection Association, 1982.

3. Conger, N. L., "Designing Safety Shutdown Systems — A Systematic Approach," ISA/73, Paper #73-756.

4. Kletz, T. A., "Eliminating Potential Process Hazards," *Chemical Engineering*, April 1, 1985.

5. Wilkinson, J., "A Top Down Approach to Safety Systems," *C&I*, November 1986.

6. Maggioli, V. J., "The Safety Matrix," Presented at the Fifth Process Computer Users Forum of the Chemical Manufacturers Association, May 1986.

7. Bryant, J. A., "Design of Fail-Safe Control Systems," *Power*, January 1976.

8. Krigman, A., "Reliability Enhancement Techniques: Can You Afford To Use Them? Can You Afford Not To?" *InTech*, July 1985.

9. Balls, B. W., "Safe Operation of Process Plants, Part 2," *In Control*, September-October 1988.

10. Benedetto, J. A., "Preventing Operational Errors in Programmable Controllers," *Control Engineering*, July 1981.

11. Humphrey, J. A., "Applying Fault Tolerant System Architectures," *I&CS*, October 1987.

12. Kletz, T. A., "Practical Applications of Hazard Analysis," *CEP*, October 1978.

13. Johnson, W. H., C. L. Lowrie, R. McCall, R. A. Oldach, and W. S. Opong, "Interlocking with Microprocessor-Based Equipment," ISA/87, Paper #87-1016.

14. "Instrument and Electrical Design and Test Guidelines for Process Interlocks," Monsanto, November 3, 1986.

15. ISA-S5.2, Binary Logic Diagrams for Process Operations, Instrument Society of America, 1976.

16. Hollo, R. F., "Proposed Language Standards for Programmable Controllers," *Control Engineering*, September 1985.

9

Discrete and Regulatory Controls for Batch Processes

Introduction   Regulatory controls and discrete controls for batch processes are very similar to those for continuous processes. Similar contact inputs and outputs are needed for motors, agitators, on/off valves, etc. Analog inputs representing flows, temperatures, pressures, etc., are also needed. The same analog outputs that are used to drive final control elements in control systems for continuous processes are also used in control systems for batch processes. However, batch processes tend to require more discrete devices than are required for continuous processes.

Discrete Control   By the very nature of batch processing, many different processing steps are carried out on the batch in the same process equipment (Ref. 1). This requires the manipulation of different types of operating equipment such as valves, pumps, agitators, and so on. If this equipment is to be manipulated by an automatic control system, there must be some way to interface with it. This is done through the use of discrete control devices. Typically, these devices are switches, relays, indicating lights, limit switches, solenoids, etc., usually operating on 120-volt ac or 24-volt dc power. All of these devices are controlled by simple on/off electrical contacts. Many complex discrete control devices are similar to analog control loops: they may have a set point, a process variable, and an implied output position (Ref. 2).

Discrete Device Monitoring Logic Some discrete devices involve only a single electrical contact. However, most involve several contacts, such as pumps, valves, and agitators. The positions of these devices can be defined in a position table. These tables show the status of each discrete input and output contact for every device position, using binary zeros to represent open contacts and binary ones to represent closed contacts.

   An example is a solenoid actuated on/off valve. It takes one discrete signal to control it, one input to indicate that it is open, and one input to indicate that it is closed. When the solenoid is actuated (powered), the valve opens; when the solenoid is deactuated (power turned off), the valve closes. There are two limit switches: the open limit switch actuates (contact closes) when the valve is open; the closed limit switch actuates (contact closes) when the valve is closed. Table 9-1 shows the state of these discrete signals for the on/off valve.

At the lowest level of control, manual discrete control requires access to the individual electrical contacts that interface the control system to the process equipment. Under manual control, discrete inputs to the control system may be read and discrete outputs may be manually changed. Manual discrete control is similar to the manual loading of a regulatory control device.

If an operator manipulates a device manually, he must verify that his actions have resulted in the desired response. When a device is automatically operated, its position should always be verified automatically. Using Table 9-1 for an on/off valve, the logic may be stated as follows:

> If the solenoid is not energized AND the closed limit switch is not closed AND the open limit switch is not open OR if the solenoid is energized AND the open limit switch is not closed AND the closed limit switch is not open, then activate an alarm (and take some action if necessary) after sufficient time to allow for valve travel.

This logic is shown graphically in Figure 9-1, using ISA binary logic symbols (Ref. 3). It is good practice to use both limit switches to verify valve travel, as shown in Figure 9-1.

Such monitoring logic was traditionally implemented using hard-wired relays. The wiring diagrams for such logic are referred to as relay ladder logic. The relay ladder in Figure 9-2 shows the logic for the on/off valve of Table 9-1.

Many batch control systems offer built-in software routines or function blocks that allow discrete control device monitoring to be implemented very easily. For the standard modules, the user basically has to connect the inputs and outputs using software wiring (in some systems this may be as simple as listing the addresses of the input and output signals). Figure 9-3 shows a possible implementation for the on/off valve discussed above. This implementation has three inputs: valve open limit switch, valve closed limit switch, and the desired valve position (from other logic within the control system). It has an output signal to control the position of the valve and two outputs that can be used for alarm

---

TABLE 9-1
A Discrete Device Example

Valve Position	Solenoid	Closed Limit Switch	Open Limit Switch
Closed	0	1	0
Open	1	0	1

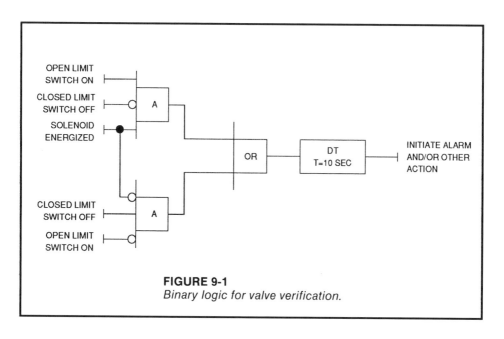

FIGURE 9-1
Binary logic for valve verification.

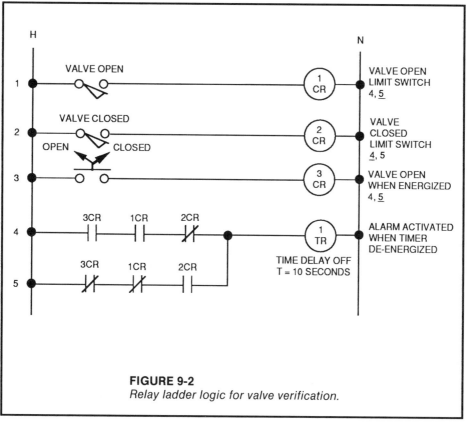

FIGURE 9-2
Relay ladder logic for valve verification.

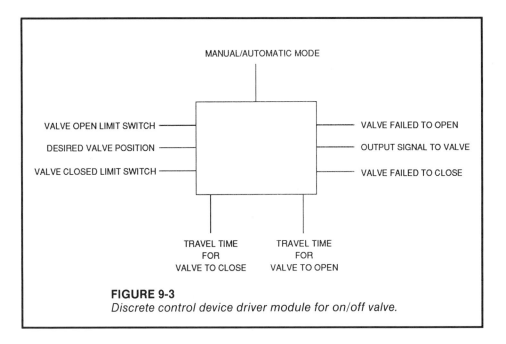

FIGURE 9-3
Discrete control device driver module for on/off valve.

purposes: valve failed to open and valve failed to close (assumes the valve is in the automatic operating mode). Three parameters need to be set within this discrete control device driver module: travel time for valve to open, travel time for valve to close, and manual/automatic mode.

Provision is usually made to allow non-standard modules to be implemented within the control system. In this case, the user must provide the logic that relates the inputs and outputs of the module. Once the operation of this new module is verified, it should then be possible to put the new module into the discrete control device driver library so that it can be reused as necessary.

EXAMPLE 9-1

Problem: The discrete control device driver module in Figure 9-3 is actually more sophisticated than the logic drawings of Figures 9-1 and 9-2. What are the differences?

Solution: There are three differences: (1) the discrete control device driver module provides separate travel times for the open and closed travel directions, (2) it provides a manual/automatic operating mode selection, and (3) it provides separate alarm outputs for the open and closed positions.

EXAMPLE 9-2

Problem: Figure 9-4 shows a pneumatic conveying system that is capable of supplying solids material to three different reactors through the four on/off valves shown in the figure. Describe a custom discrete control device driver module for this device that consists of these four valves.

Solution: Inputs will be required for the following: desired device output (destination selection) from other logic within the control system (e.g., R-501, R-502, R-503, and possibly no selection, i.e., all valves are closed) and two limit switches for each valve. Outputs would include status signals to show that the valves are lined up properly to the three destinations (i.e., one for each destination). Alarm output signals are needed, but the user must decide how many and what type. For example, one alarm output signal could be provided that simply shows that the valves within the device are or are not lined up in agreement with the destination select input signal. It may be desirable, depending on the application, to have one alarm output signal for each destination. Parameters would probably include a manual override to allow the destination to be manually selected, regardless of the destination called for by the control system logic. Valve travel times must also be specified. There are several options, such as one travel time parameter for the device, separate travel time parameters for each valve, or separate travel time parameters for each travel direction for each valve. Since this is a custom module, the user must make all these choices.

Interlocks Interlocks are needed for a variety of reasons that include human safety and equipment protection. As discussed in Chapter 8, there are two basic types of interlocks: failure interlocks and permissive interlocks.

Failure interlocks are continuous and are usually associated with equipment shutdown. A high-level switch in a tank may be interlocked with the fill valve. This causes the valve to close when the level switch sees liquid in order to prevent a tank overflow. If the failure interlocks are safety-related, they should be implemented in the safety interlock system. If not, they can be implemented as part of the process interlock system that resides at the regulatory/discrete control level.

A permissive interlock is used when a specific condition must exist before some other action may be taken. For example, a reactor should not be charged with ingredient A unless the vent valve is open, or pressure will build up in the reactor; therefore, ingredient charge valve XV-1 is interlocked with the limit switches on vent valve XV-2 so that XV-1 is "permitted" to open only when XV-2 is opened. Once charging is complete, this interlock may no longer be necessary. Another example of a permissive interlock occurs when the reactor sequence must be in the "ADD INGREDIENT A" phase before valve A can be opened.

Regulatory Controls

Regulatory control of a batch process is basically the same as regulatory control for a continuous process. It involves the monitoring and manipulation of process variables in the same manner. The batch process, however, is discontinuous. This adds a new dimension to regulatory control because of frequent start-ups and shutdowns. During these transient states, control parameters such as controller gain adjustments may have to be changed for optimum dynamic response.

By the very nature of batch processing, it is inevitable that process equipment will have idle time between batches. During the idle time, control considerations such as reset windup must be considered. There are also frequently changes in recipes, in product grades, and in the process itself. All of these things put increased demands on the regulatory control loops in a batch process.

The basic regulatory control loops are flow, level, pressure, temperature, and composition. However, problems often arise in measuring system parameters that must be taken into consideration when preparing a regulatory control strategy. Extreme process conditions, e.g., high pressure or high temperature, may

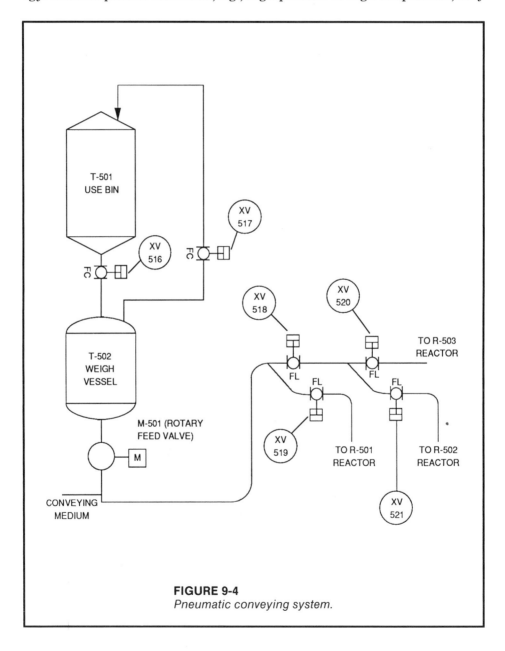

FIGURE 9-4
Pneumatic conveying system.

cause measurement errors in a composition measurement (Ref. 2). Time lags in temperature measurement in batch reactor systems is a frequent problem. Although most systems have continuous direct measurement of temperature, pressure, and flow, composition is often very difficult to measure. Control may have to rely on periodic lab analyses.

Different control strategies are often necessary for the same piece of equipment. This could involve changing to a different controller or changing the control algorithm. The choice of which controller or control algorithm to use may be product-dependent and specified in the recipe.

Since batch reactors are very common batch processes, this discusssion of regulatory control systems will use examples based on batch reactors, but these same concepts apply to any batch control system.

Batch chemical reactors offer some of the most difficult challenges to control engineers (Ref. 4). Because of the inherently dynamic or time-varying nature of a batch process, process variables can change greatly during the course of a batch cycle. No normal steady-state operating condition exists at which controllers can be tuned for good dynamic response.

Probably the most challenging control problem presented by batch reactors is the open-loop instability caused by reactions that produce heat. A small increase in temperature can make a reaction proceed more rapidly, which generates more heat and raises the temperature even higher. Runaway reactions can occur if temperatures are not controlled properly.

Other control problems include batch-to-batch variations in the chemical reaction caused by catalyst activity or reactant purity, reset windup in conventional controllers, and large changes in process gains and time constants.

Most control loops can be successfully handled with single-loop feedback control based on the conventional PID (proportional-integral-derivative) algorithm. This control loop can provide tight set point tracking and fairly good response to disturbances and set point changes for many applications. As just discussed, batch control systems offer additional demands on control systems because of the need for alternative control strategies, different controller settings depending on the state of the process, etc. This often means that more sophisticated control strategies are required, such as feedforward control, cascade control, and override control. Advanced control schemes can be designed to detect changes in process conditions and counteract them by adjusting controller tuning constants, by adjusting the controller output directly, by switching to different control algorithms, and so on.

Single-Loop Feedback Control   A typical single-loop temperature control system is shown in Figure 9-5. This control system consists of the process, a transmitter, a controller, and two final control elements (control valves) to provide both heating and cooling capability. This is an example of split-ranging final control elements. In this case, the water control valve fails open to full cooling; the steam control valve fails closed to no heating. The water control valve would be fully open at 0% controller output and fully closed at 50% controller output. The steam control valve would be fully closed at 50% controller output and

fully open at 100% controller output. When control valves are split-ranged in this manner, valve positioners should be used on each control valve to ensure that the valves sequence at the proper values of controller output.

Many batch reactors still use a steam/cooling water system for temperature control. In this system, either steam or cooling water (only one at a time) flows through the jacket or coils. If the reactor is currently heating with steam on the jacket, the steam flow must be stopped and the pressure released before the cooling water can be applied. A similar problem occurs in going from cooling to heating.

Beatty points out three problems with this type of heating/cooling system (Ref. 5):

1. Switching from heating to cooling requires a significant amount of logic.

2. These one-pass cooling systems provide poor heat transfer coefficients and result in large temperature differences between the inlet and outlet.

3. Significant deadtime in the reactor results in poor control.

The circulating system in Figure 9-5 gets around those problems. The high flow rate through the jacket improves heat transfer in the jacket and eliminates hot and cold spots in the jacket. The deadtime in the system is also reduced. Having the ability to switch from heating to cooling and vice versa with no logic makes the control system much simpler.

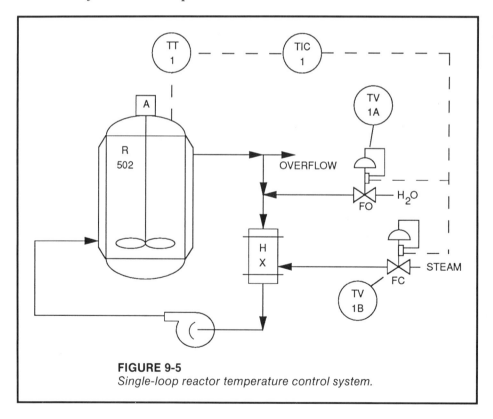

FIGURE 9-5
Single-loop reactor temperature control system.

EXAMPLE 9-3

Problem: What kind of problems might be encountered with the single-loop feedback temperature control system of Figure 9-5?

Solution: The following are some limitations to this control system:

1. Perfect control is not obtainable with feedback control alone, since a measurable error must exist before a control effect can take place. The controlled variable is corrected based on a past event such as the measured variable drifting away from the set point. Feedback control solves the control problem by trial and error. This is a crude method of problem solving and is characteristic of the oscillatory response of a feedback loop. Therefore, each time an upset occurs, there can be cycling and poor control while the controller compensates for the disturbance. Each feedback loop has a characteristic natural period. It normally takes several periods to recover from an upset. If upsets occur at intervals less than this, no steady state will ever be reached.

2. A proportional-integral-derivative (PID) controller would normally be used for this temperature controller. A controller that has the integral (reset) mode will continue to change its output as long as there is a deviation from set point. If the deviation is sustained for a long enough period of time, the controller output will saturate either at the high end or the low end, depending on the direction of the deviation. As a result, when the process finally reaches the set point, some overshoot beyond the set point is inevitable. This type of sustained deviation from set point is very common in the start-up of batch reactors.

3. This temperature control loop is very sensitive to supply pressure changes in both the cooling water and the steam.

The PID Controller in Microprocessor-Based Systems

The PID algorithm is often implemented in microprocessor-based controllers. The most common way to configure control loops in these systems is with function blocks. In general, users would prefer configuring their PID loops and other regulatory control functions with standard function blocks rather than programming the control scheme (Ref. 6).

However, not all function blocks, even if they are intended to perform the same function, work the same way. Figure 9-6 shows two implementations of a PID controller. Figure 9-6(a) is the function block in a commercially available, stand-alone, microprocessor-based process controller. The "TRACK" signal is a logical input, i.e., value equals either 0 or 1. "RESET" is an analog variable. When the TRACK signal is 0, the module functions as a normal PID controller, and the RESET input is ignored. When the TRACK signal is 1, integral action is suspended, and the controller OUTPUT equals the value applied at the RESET input.

Figure 9-6(b) is the function block in a commercially available, single-station, microprocessor-based digital controller. The TRACK input works the same as the TRACK command in the controller in Figure 9-6(a), except that the TRACK input can be an analog variable for this controller. When it exceeds a certain value, the TRACK signal is considered ON, and reset action is suspended. The controller OUTPUT then equals the FEEDBACK signal. When this variable is below a certain value, the TRACK signal is considered OFF, and the block functions as a normal PID controller. However, the FEEDBACK signal is not ignored. The FEEDBACK signal is the input to the integral (reset) section of the controller. As such, it must be connected to some input signal. For normal control use, the OUTPUT of the controller block would be connected to the FEEDBACK input (this is the same as a standard pneumatic or electronic analog controller). There are definite advantages to having this separate FEEDBACK signal, particularly when advanced control loops are configured or when reset windup is a problem.

The blocks previously discussed are simply function blocks that implement a PID controller function. They are not a complete control station that performs an input and output function, auto/manual transfer, set point tracking, etc. The user has to add those functions onto the PID controller block using other function blocks available in the controller. Figure 9-7 shows the PID controller block of Figure 9-6(b) modified to show the input and output blocks, auto/manual transfer, and set point tracking. In a controller equipped with set point tracking, the controller set point will track the controller input signal when the controller is in the MANUAL mode. When the MANUAL input is turned ON, e.g., by a switch on the controller or on a CRT, the TRACK input to the controller turns ON (controller OUTPUT tracks the FEEDBACK signal), the track/hold module input is turned ON (causes the OUTPUT of the track/hold module to follow the INPUT signal), and the auto/manual block is switched to the MANUAL mode (allows the manual valve signal to go to the output block).

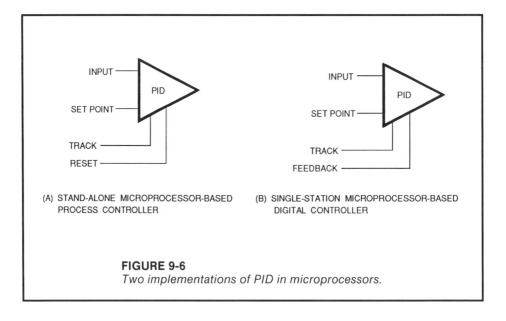

(A) STAND-ALONE MICROPROCESSOR-BASED
PROCESS CONTROLLER

(B) SINGLE-STATION MICROPROCESSOR-BASED
DIGITAL CONTROLLER

FIGURE 9-6
Two implementations of PID in microprocessors.

This type of configuration, although extremely flexible, can be very time consuming. Fortunately, some manufacturers supply these microprocessor-based controllers pre-configured to include some of these functions, such as the set point tracking controller in Figure 9-7. This extra work is usually not necessary with distributed control systems. Although most of the distributed control systems use function blocks, the controller is configured via a menu format, as shown in Table 9-2 (Ref. 7).

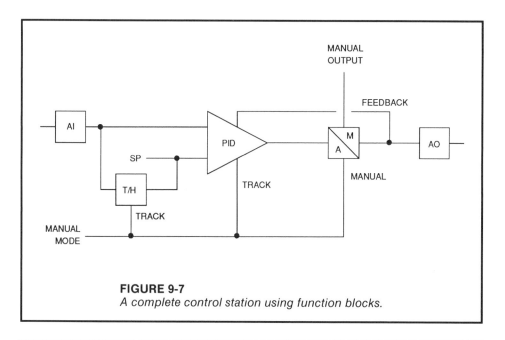

FIGURE 9-7
A complete control station using function blocks.

TABLE 9-2
PID Controller Configuration Using a Menu Format

PID LOOP	TITLE:
PID ALGORITHM:	
LOOP FLAG ADDRESS:	
PROCESS VARIABLE ADDRESS:	
SQUARE ROOT OF PV:	
PV RANGE:	
HIGH	
LOW	
SAMPLE RATE (SECS):	
DERIVATIVE GAIN LIMITING	
COEFFICIENT:	
LOOP OUTPUT ADDRESS:	
REVERSE ACTING:	
LOOP GAIN:	
RESET (INTEGRAL TIME):	
RATE (DERIVATIVE TIME):	

This greatly lessens the burden to do the controller configuration, although the overall system may not be quite as flexible. This example shows only a partial listing of the menu items that need to be addressed in some systems.

Menu-driven programming formats such as these are used by many vendors to supply PID and other analog control techniques. The entries that the control engineer chooses from the menu should be ones he/she is familiar with. The user should make control choices from given options or "fill in the blanks" with the desired control variables. The actual algorithm, which takes these choices and variables and converts them to machine code, is transparent to the user.

Set Point Ramping

Batch processes have optimum conditions that will yield the maximum product with minimum time and cost. This often involves a profile of process variable (usually temperature) versus time (common with batch reactors), and the control strategy must conform to and be tuned for this profile. This could cause problems when product grades are changed and different ingredients are used and could cause changes in reaction rates that would affect the controller tuning. It could also require a different profile, which means that the control system must be capable of generating the new profile.

Since a different set point ramping profile may be needed for each different product or product grade, it may be necessary to have a menu of these profiles that the operator can select from or, ideally, this profile is made a part of the recipe that is used for making the product. Once the correct profile is selected, some type of set point-generating algorithm is needed. This algorithm continuously calculates the set point, usually as a function of time, and sends it to the controller that is being used to control the particular process variable. These profiles may be based directly on calculations, generated as straight-line segments, specified as the rate of change of the process variable with time (e.g., 2°F/minute), or programmed as discontinuous functions.

EXAMPLE 9-4

Problem: The temperature in a batch reactor system must be ramped from 250°F to 400°F based on the percentage of ingredient A that has been charged. Determine what algorithm is needed to generate the required temperature set point.

Solution: Convert both the temperature and flow variables into percentages.

For flow, that percentage is F_{TOT}/F_{REQD}, where F_{TOT} is the amount of ingredient A that has been charged and F_{REQD} is the total amount of A that must be charged.

For temperature, the relationship is a little more complicated since the starting point is not zero. The percentage is

$$(T_{SP}-250)/(400-250)$$

The next step is to equate these two percentages and solve for T_{SP}. The set point for the reactor temperature controller is then

$$T_{SP} = 150 F_{TOT}/F_{REQD} + 250$$

Reset Windup Problems

Reset windup is common to many control loops, both single-loop and multiple-loop. But, with the emphasis today on improved control, improved product quality, and energy conservation, it is no longer possible, in most cases, to live with the offset inherent with straight proportional control. Adding derivative, although it can reduce the offset in some cases, does not eliminate offset. When the process must be controlled right at set point, reset (integral) must normally be added to the controller. However, when reset is present in a controller, any sustained deviation of the process from set point will cause the controller to saturate. This means that the controller output will go to its maximum or minimum value, depending on the direction of the deviation.

Reset windup leads to the process variable overshooting the set point. In many batch processes, controlling overshoot is critical to product quality. This problem may occur during the extended heating interval often required for starting exothermic reactions. As the reactor temperature slowly rises to initiate the reaction, the integral term winds up. Once the reaction begins, the integral term may not decrease fast enough to prevent temperature overshoot.

The equation for a proportional-plus-reset controller is:

$$O = (100/PB)(e + 1/R \int e \, dt) \tag{9-1}$$

where: O = controller output signal
PB = proportional band, percent
e = error, $r-m$
r = controller set point
m = measured variable
R = reset in units of time

The reset (or integral) mode moves the controller output as a function of the time integral of the error. As long as an error (i.e., a deviation between the set point and the measured variable) exists, the output will continue to change. When the controller output stops moving (e.g., it reaches either its maximum or minimum possible output) and an error still exists, this equation can no longer be satisfied. The equation below describes this proportional + reset controller in this limited state (Ref. 8):

$$O = (100/PB)(e) + C \tag{9-2}$$

This is basically a proportional controller with manual reset, where the manual reset is the constant of integration, C. In the above equation, C could be maximum output or minimum output depending on the sign of the deviation. On a sustained deviation, the output O will increase to its maximum value or decrease to its minimum value. Sustained deviations are common in the start-up of batch systems.

Consider start-up of the reactor control system of Figure 9-5. If this system is started up automatically, the controller set point will be set at the desired operating temperature. Assume the reactor contents are at 100°F and the reactor temperature set point is at 300°F. Then there is a large deviation between the set point and the process. Since it will take some time for the reactor contents to reach the operating temperature, there will be a sustained deviation. For this reactor, the heat input increases as the temperature controller output increases.

Because of the sustained deviation, the integrating action of reset will force the controller output to its maximum value (this maximum value is above the value that corresponds to 100% controller output). This has the effect of moving the PB completely above the set point (see Figure 9-8). When the process variable reaches set point (error = 0), the controller output O will be equal to C. Since C will be at its maximum value, the controller output will be beyond the signal range of the final control element (e.g., the maximum output of a pneumatic controller can be as high as 18 psig with a 20 psig supply pressure, while the final control element operating range is normally considered to be 3–15 psig). Not only does the measured variable have to cross the set point before the output will start to decrease, it must cross it far enough for the output to drop to 100% before the control valve will start to throttle (see Figure 9-8). Therefore, overshoot is inevitable.

A number of different techniques can be used to minimize or eliminate the effects of reset windup.

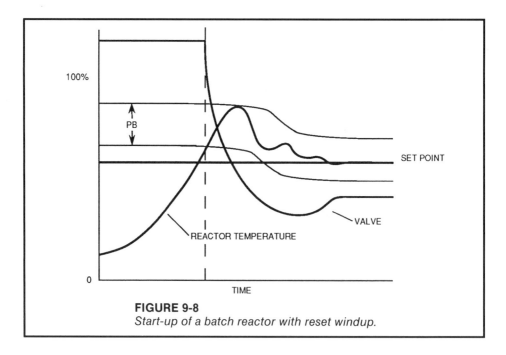

FIGURE 9-8
Start-up of a batch reactor with reset windup.

Set Point Ramping Reset windup can often be prevented by ramping or gradually increasing the set point. This prevents the error from becoming large enough to allow the integral term to wind up. This technique works only as long as the control system is capable of following the ramp. If not, the controller will still wind up.

Use the Derivative Mode Since the reactor temperature controller normally has derivative, it can help to minimize overshoot. But some of the old style three-mode controllers have the derivative acting on the output of the controller (also true for some PID algorithms in programmable controllers). This type of derivative is almost totally ineffective in this case, because the derivative doesn't come into play until the controller output starts to change. This doesn't happen until the batch temperature overshoots the set point.

Derivative is effective in minimizing the effects of reset windup only if it acts on the measurement signal. The effect of derivative on the measurement signal makes the controller think that the measurement has crossed the set point before it actually does (see Figure 9-9). Derivative should be the first choice for the solution to a reset windup problem of this type because it requires no external connections, it is effective on either high or low windup problems, and it helps control under non-windup conditions.

In some cases, however, the derivative time required to prevent overshoot is too high to allow optimum tuning under non-windup conditions, and another technique must be used.

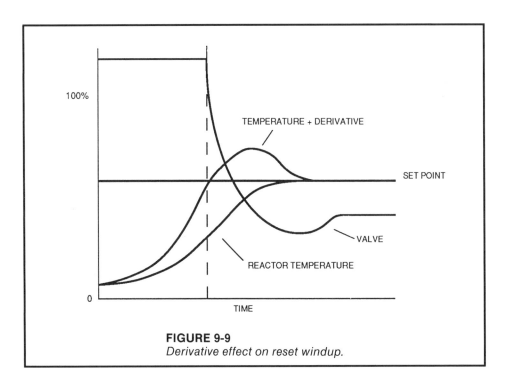

FIGURE 9-9
Derivative effect on reset windup.

Use Adaptive Gain Techniques Some of the newer microprocessor-based controllers allow the proportional band, reset, and derivative settings to be changed on line. This means that the system could be started up under one set of tuning parameters and then switched to another set of parameters when the measured variable is near set point, which would make this controller effective for the start-up of batch systems. Note that it would be desirable if all three settings could be adjustable on-line; proportional band changes alone are not enough.

Use a Batch Switch For those applications where the above techniques will not solve the windup problem, a batch switch (anti-windup relay) should be considered. A batch switch prevents reset windup by artificially loading the constant of integration in Equation 9-2 to some level (it does not change the tuning adjustment). This type of system requires the controller to have external reset feedback. This was true of most analog PID controllers (both pneumatic and electronic). It is also applicable to digital PID controllers that are mathematical images of pneumatic or electronic analog controllers (e.g., the PID function block of Figure 9-6(b)). This then forces the controller to act like a proportional-only controller as long as the batch switch is active. The batch switch is tied to the controller output and artificially changes the reset value (value in the reset module) to limit the controller output to 100% (high batch) or 0% (low batch) (see Figure 9-10). The preload setting limits the maximum or minimum value of the constant of integration to allow the temperature to reach set point more rapidly. When there is a large deviation or the controller has high gain (low proportional band), the batch switch may not be able to limit the controller output to 100% or 0%, even if the reset value is raised to its maximum level or lowered to its minimum level. Although Figure 9-10 shows a batch switch implementation in a micro-processor-based controller, batch switches can be used with both pneumatic and electronic analog controllers.

On a high batch application, such as the reactor temperature control system in Figure 9-5, the batch switch reduces the constant of integration in Equation 9-2 to try to prevent the controller output from going above 100%. The preload setting on a high batch switch acts to limit the minimum setting of the constant of integration value.

Figure 9-11 shows the effect of the preload setting on the proportional band range on a controller equipped with a batch switch. Figure 9-12 shows response curves for start-up using various preload settings. Any curve between the "0% Preload" and "100% Preload" curves can be achieved by varying the setting of the preload. A controller with "0% Preload" effectively drops the proportional band range below the set point, which means that the controller will start throttling sooner. This results in a slow approach to the set point, which might result in too much off-specification product.

With 100% preload setting, the controller would start to throttle as soon as the measurement crossed the set point, but there would still be overshoot. A controller that suspended integral action and limited the output signal to 0% or 100% would function like the "100% Preload." Under normal operating conditions, when the output is within the limits of 0 and 100%, the controller functions like a

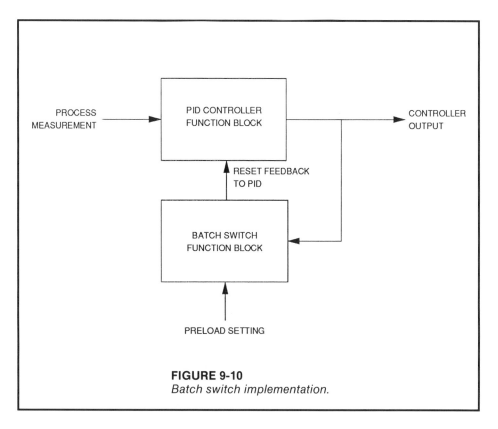

FIGURE 9-10
Batch switch implementation.

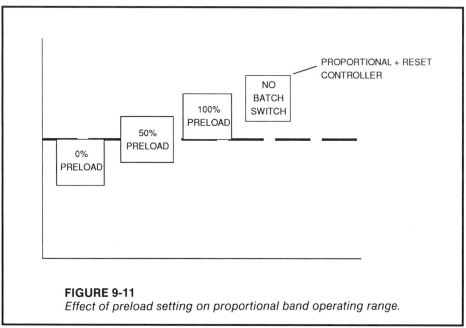

FIGURE 9-11
Effect of preload setting on proportional band operating range.

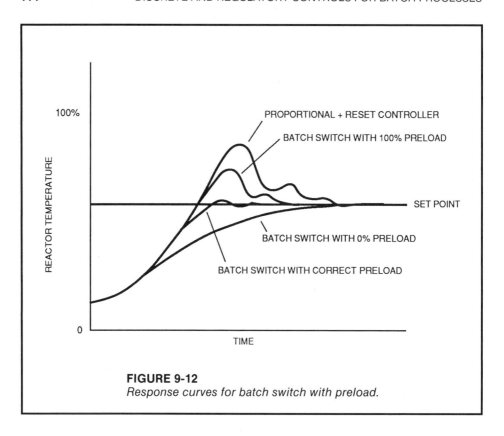

FIGURE 9-12
Response curves for batch switch with preload.

normal controller with no batch switch. For a high-batch application, Shinskey (Ref. 9) recommends that the preload setting be adjusted slightly lower than the steady-state controller output once the controller reaches the set point.

Cascade Control Systems   A cascade control system is one in which the output of one controller (primary or master) adjusts the set point of a second controller (secondary or slave) (see Figure 9-13). The purpose of the secondary controller is to correct for as many outside disturbances as possible before they can affect the primary controller.

The following are some advantages of cascade control over single-loop control:

1. Disturbances appearing within the secondary loop can be corrected before they affect the primary loop. This can reduce the peak height of deviations in the primary loop by at least 1/2 and possibly by factors of ten.

2. The speed of response of the primary loop is improved. For disturbances entering the primary loop, the peak height of deviations in the primary loop can be reduced by 1/2. Since the speed of response of the primary loop is faster, the natural period is shorter. This means that the primary variable will line out faster after a disturbance.

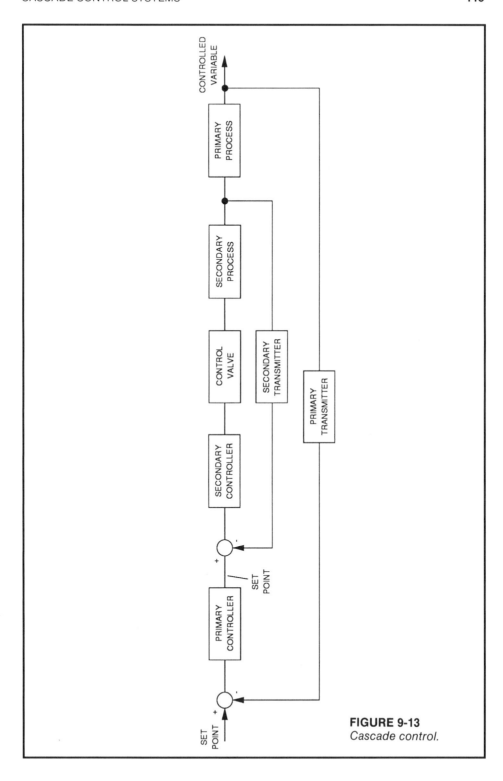

FIGURE 9-13
Cascade control.

3. The value of the secondary variable can be accurately limited. This is accomplished by adding high and/or low limits on the output of the primary controller, which limits the secondary controller's set point to some desired value.

The following are some rules of thumb for designing cascade control systems:

1. Make the secondary loop include the input point of the most serious disturbances.

2. Make the secondary loop fast by including only minor lags of the complete control system. One should normally try to close the secondary loop around the second largest lag in the system. The ratio of the time constant of the primary process to the time constant of the secondary process should be at least 3 to 1 and preferably 5 or 10 to 1. The higher the ratio, the more the cascade system will reduce deviations that result from disturbances entering the secondary loop.

3. Use a secondary variable with set point values that are definitely and usefully related to values of the primary variable. Preferably, this relationship should be a straight line.

4. If the secondary loop can be kept relatively fast, make it include as many of the disturbance inputs as possible.

5. Choose the secondary variable that will provide stable performance with the narrowest proportional band.

Although many types of variables can be used in the secondary loop of a cascade system, the most common are valve position, flow, and temperature. A valve positioner is a proportional controller with a narrow proportional band that is used to close the loop around the valve actuator (see Figure 9-14). It minimizes the effect of hysteresis and valve unbalance forces on the valve stem. Valve positioners should not be used in flow control loops, most liquid pressure control loops, and some gas pressure control systems. The secondary loop should never be closed around the longest lag in the control loop. In the above processes, the valve actuator is usually the slowest element in the control loop.

Cascade flow loops are used to provide consistent delivery of material to or from a process as controlled by the primary controller. The flow loop overcomes variable pressure drop, valve friction, and nonlinear valve characteristics. An example is the batch reactor system shown in Figure 9-15 (Ref. 9). Reactant A is charged to the reactor at ambient temperature. Full cooling is applied to the reactor jacket and the external heat exchanger as Reactant B is being charged to the reactor. The reaction is exothermic and proceeds very rapidly, thus allowing the control of heat input to the reactor to be controlled by controlling the rate of addition of Reactant B. The temperature controller adjusts the flow of Reactant B in a cascade arrangement.

The most common example of a secondary temperature loop is the exothermic reactor where composition is very sensitive to temperature (see Figure 9-16). Cascade control is more effective with the secondary measurement at the jacket exit because it includes the jacket dynamics in the secondary loop. The valves are split-ranged using positioners. Also shown is a high temperature limit on the primary controller outlet to limit the maximum jacket temperature. Liptak cites

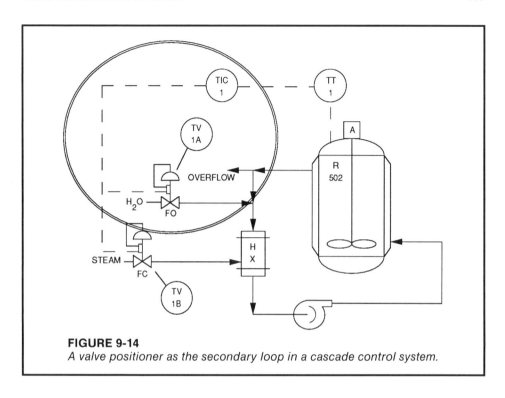

FIGURE 9-14
A valve positioner as the secondary loop in a cascade control system.

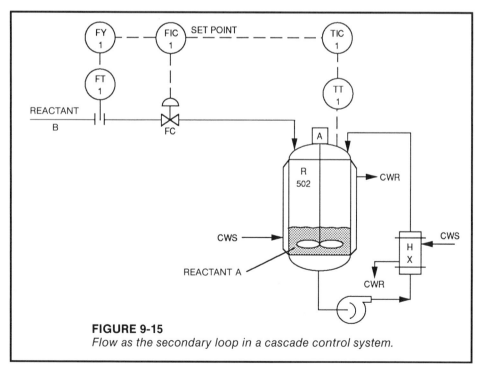

FIGURE 9-15
Flow as the secondary loop in a cascade control system.

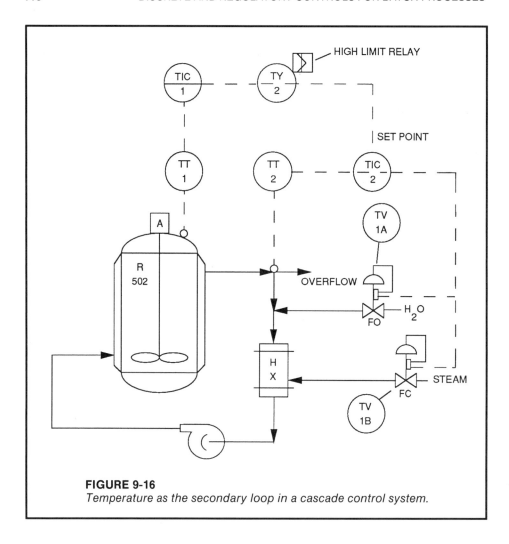

FIGURE 9-16
Temperature as the secondary loop in a cascade control system.

the following as potential improvements in control loop performance over single-loop feedback control as a result of implementing this temperature/temperature cascade system (Ref. 10):

1. The period of oscillation of the primary loop is usually cut in half, which might mean, for example, a reduction from 40 minutes to 20 minutes in the period. This could mean a corresponding reduction in the proportional band from 30 to 15% and a reduction in the derivative and integral settings of an interacting controller from about 10 to 5 minutes. Overall, this represents a fourfold improvement in control loop performance.

2. It removes the principal nonlinearity of the system from the primary loop, because reaction temperature is linear with jacket outlet temperature. The nonlinearity is the relationship between jacket outlet temperature and the flow rate of the heat transfer medium. This nonlinearity is now within the secondary

where it can be compensated for by an equal percentage valve. The secondary controller should operate properly with proportional control only, with a proportional band of 10 to 20%.

Some care must be used in selecting the controller modes of the secondary control loop. Reset should be avoided unless absolutely necessary because it slows down the response of the secondary loop. Valve positioners are proportional-only controllers, so reset is not a problem. However, flow controllers must be proportional-plus-reset controllers. Reset is not needed in the secondary controller if the proportional band is reasonably low (25% or less). This is normally true with the jacket temperature controller on a batch reactor. The minor amount of offset in the secondary loop will be corrected by the primary controller. The primary controller must have reset. Derivative can be used on the secondary controller if it acts on the measurement signal. Derivative that acts on the controller output cannot be used in the secondary because it responds to set point changes.

EXAMPLE 9-5

Problem: Is reset windup a problem in cascade control systems?

Solution: In cascade control systems where there is no reset in the secondary controller, the primary controller can still wind up. In those cases, the primary controller should be equipped with a batch switch or one of the other techniques previously discussed to prevent reset windup. When the secondary loop has reset, then both controllers can wind up. If a batch switch is used on the secondary controller to prevent reset windup, a batch switch cannot be used on the primary controller.

There is a simple way of getting around the reset windup problem in the primary controller in many applications for controllers such as the one in Figure 9-6(b), where the controller output is used as the external feedback signal to the reset section. In processes where cascade control loops are employed and the secondary controller has reset, the effects of reset windup may be eliminated simply by using the secondary process measurement as the reset feedback signal to the primary controller. This is illustrated in Figure 9-17 using the temperature/flow cascade control system of Figure 9-15. If the secondary controller is controlling at set point, the secondary measurement is the same as the set point, which is the primary controller output. Feeding back the secondary signal in this way will eliminate reset windup in the primary controller. When those two signals are not the same, such as when the final control element has reached its limit, the positive feedback loop in the primary controller (the reset or integral mode) is broken, and reset action stops. The primary controller then acts like a proportional controller whose constant of integration is the secondary measurement. The secondary windup problem can be solved by any of the methods previously discussed. In some cases, as with most secondary flow controllers, the secondary loop recovers rapidly enough to minimize the overshoot problem, even under windup conditions. If the flow overshoot will not harm the process during this short period, reset windup protection is not necessary.

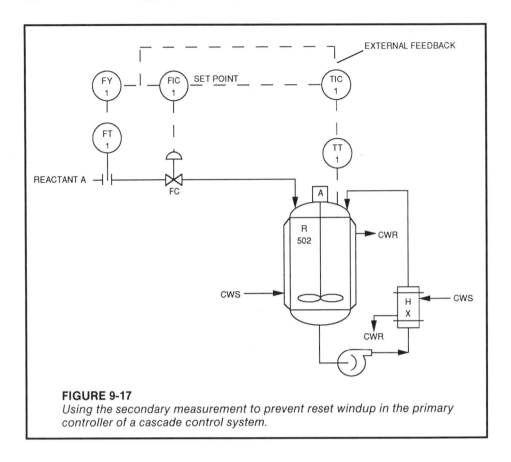

FIGURE 9-17
Using the secondary measurement to prevent reset windup in the primary controller of a cascade control system.

Shinskey (Ref. 8) points out that this scheme is not intended for batch reactor control, because it is designed to follow a smoothly changing load through the limit of the final control element. Automatic start-up of a batch reactor involves a massive set point change. However, this control scheme has been shown to be very effective for the start-up of a batch reactor system when the primary controller has derivative that acts on the measurement signal (Ref. 1).

Reset windup is also a problem with microprocessor-based controllers used in cascade. One method of solving this (through software) is to place the primary station in MANUAL whenever the secondary station is not in the CASCADE mode.

EXAMPLE 9-6

Problem: Consider the steam-heated heat exchanger of Figure 9-18 that is being used to control the feed temperature of an ingredient charge to a reactor. If the major disturbance in the control system for this heat exchanger is step changes in flow rate of ingredient A, is either single-loop feedback control or cascade control capable of providing adequate control of the heat exchanger outlet temperature?

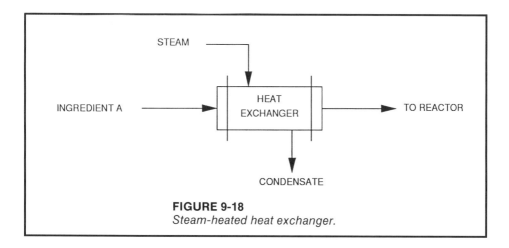

FIGURE 9-18
Steam-heated heat exchanger.

Solution: If ingredient A feed temperature requires tight temperature control, neither of these control systems can adequately solve the problem. Both of these control systems are feedback control loops. As previously discussed, no control action is applied in a feedback control loop until there is a deviation between the set point and the measured variable. In this example, that control action is too late.

EXAMPLE 9-7

Problem: If the major disturbance in the control system for the heat exchanger of Figure 9-18 were a change in steam supply pressure, what type of control system would be recommended?

Solution: A cascade control system would adequately solve this problem. Possibilities for the secondary controller are either steam pressure or steam flow rate.

Feedforward Control
Feedforward control is theoretically capable of perfect control, because it measures the inputs to a process and computes the amount of control agent required (see Figure 9-19). The feedforward control system is really a model of the process, and it does not use trial-and-error techniques. It is an open-loop control system; pure feedforward control does not use the measurement of the desired controlled variable in its model.

Feedforward control will adequately solve the problem of temperature control of the heat exchanger in Figure 9-18, where the major disturbance is a change in the flow rate of the ingredient A. Figure 9-20 shows a simple diagram of a feedforward control system for a heat exchanger of this type. It is not practical to measure all the disturbances in such a control system; the specific heat of ingredient A and the heat of vaporization of the steam are examples. Therefore, they are assumed to be constant. If they actually do vary, there will be an error in the feedforward model.

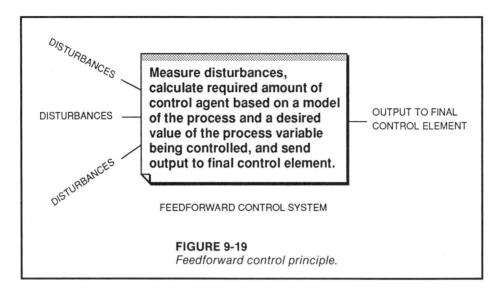

FEEDFORWARD CONTROL SYSTEM

FIGURE 9-19
Feedforward control principle.

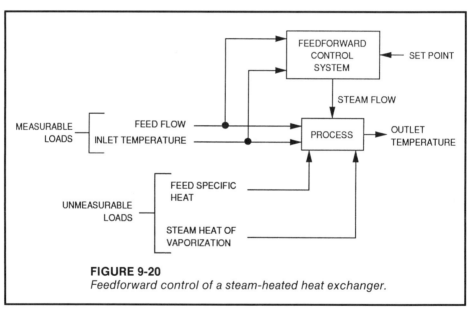

FIGURE 9-20
Feedforward control of a steam-heated heat exchanger.

A model of the heater can be made from a steady-state energy balance around the heater:

$$W_p C_p (T_{out} - T_{in}) = W_s H_s \qquad (9\text{-}3)$$

where: W_p = process flow rate, lb/hr
 C_p = specific heat of the process fluid, Btu/lb/°F
 T_{out} = temperature of process fluid exiting the exchanger, °F

T_{in} = temperature of process fluid entering the exchanger, °F
W_s = steam flow rate, lb/hr
H_s = heat of vaporization of steam, Btu/lb

This equation can be rearranged to solve for the steam flow rate:

$$W_s = W_p C_p (T_{out} - T_{in}) / H_s \qquad (9\text{-}4)$$

Equation 9-4 is the feedforward model; it can be implemented as shown in Figure 9-21. Note that the output of the feedforward control system sets the set point of a steam flow controller. This makes sure that the steam flow is what is called for by the feedforward system. More detail of the implementation of the feedforward model is shown in Figure 9-22.

The feedforward control system of Figure 9-21 is based on the steady-state energy balance. When a process fluid flow change occurs, the control system will adjust the steam flow by the proper amount so that in the steady state the outlet temperature will not change.

Feedforward control will give perfect control in the steady state as long as the model is absolutely correct, all the disturbances are included in the model, and the instruments used to make up the feedforward control system are 100% accurate. Obviously, this is not possible. For this reason, feedforward control is normally used with feedback trim (see Figure 9-23). The feedback trim signal in this case comes from a single-loop feedback controller whose measurement variable is the heat exchanger outlet temperature; it replaces the set point signal in the feedforward model. The feedback trim signal will normally replace the set point signal, although there may be reasons for introducing the feedback trim signal at some other point.

The steady-state feedforward implementation provides a significant improvement in response of the heat exchanger outlet temperature to a step change in ingredient A flow rate versus the single-loop feedback controller (Ref. 8). The response of the feedforward loop can be greatly improved by adding dynamic compensation (lead-lag unit). The lead-lag unit could be added between the output of the ingredient A flow transmitter and the feedforward model (Ref. 8).

Ratio Control

Ratio control means maintaining one variable, the controlled variable, in a preset ratio to a second variable, the wild variable. The wild flow is not necessarily uncontrolled; it is wild only insofar as the ratio control system is concerned. Ratio systems are not limited to two components. One wild flow can adjust several controlled flows, each with its own ratio controller. Note that with all ratio control systems the wild flow and the controlled flow transmitters must be of the same type. If the wild flow transmitter is linear, the controlled flow transmitter must be linear. If one of the transmitters is square root, then the other transmitter must also be square root.

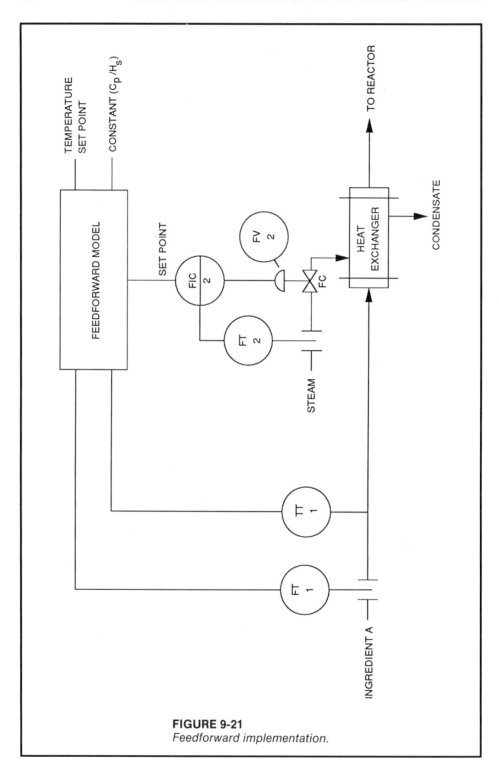

FIGURE 9-21
Feedforward implementation.

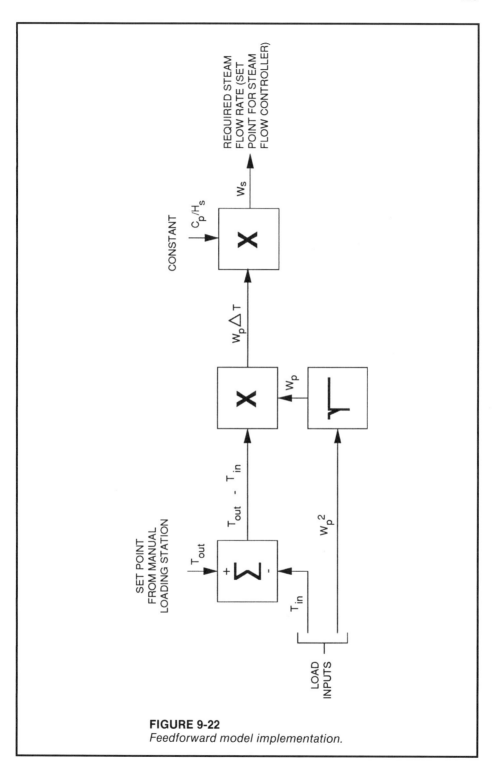

FIGURE 9-22
Feedforward model implementation.

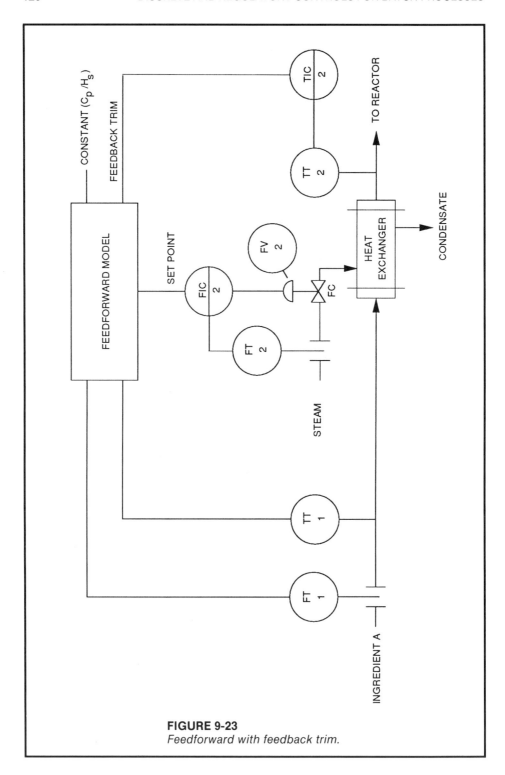

FIGURE 9-23
Feedforward with feedback trim.

In most ratio control systems, it is desirable and/or necessary to be able to easily change the ratio of wild to controlled flow. This can be done using a multiplying relay (see Figure 9-24). A manual loading station supplies the ratio signal for the multiplying relay. The advantage of this system is that the ratio can be remotely set by some other signal instead of by a manual loading station. This capability is necessary when feedback trim is applied, as will be shown later. Note that many other forms of ratio control are possible.

The ratio control system in Figure 9-24 uses analog flow transmitters. But transmitters with direct pulse outputs, such as turbine meters and positive displacement meters, can be considerably more accurate than analog flowmeters, such as orifices, rotameters, etc. This accuracy is usually necessary for charging materials to batch systems. To use the pulse-producing flowmeters with analog ratio control systems means that the pulse signal must be converted to an analog signal, at some sacrifice in accuracy. To take full advantage of the turbine meter or positive displacement meter, a digital ratio controller should be used. This controller takes in the pulse inputs directly and provides an analog output signal to the final control element. This can be accomplished quite easily with microprocessor-based controllers as long as they can accommodate the pulse input signals.

Ratio control is a simple form of feedforward control. Like other feedforward control systems, ratio control systems work well as long as the system functions as designed. For example, if the composition of one of the feed streams should change slightly, the resulting blend will be in error, since the ratio control system

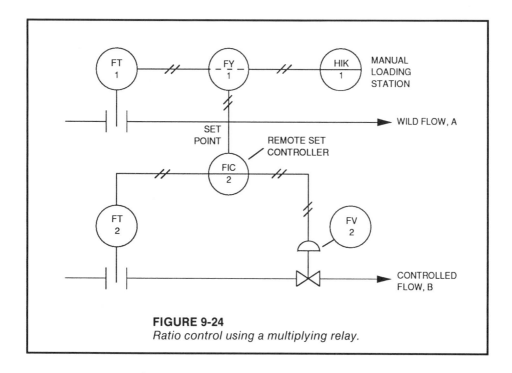

FIGURE 9-24
Ratio control using a multiplying relay.

cannot recognize this change in the system. This could be extremely important in the feeds to a batch reactor, since the correct combination of reactants is necessary to produce the desired product. The obvious solution is to use a measurement of the resulting blend ratio as a feedback control signal to adjust the ratio in the ratio control system (see Figure 9-25). In this system, the output of the analyzer controller (AIC-1) sets the ratio through the multiplying relay. If the ratio starts to drift off specification, the analyzer controller will adjust the ratio to bring the blend back into specification.

Dual Mode Reactor Control
Although the batch switch is effective in eliminating overshoot, it can be slow at bringing the process to the set point. Liptak (Ref. 10) says that the batch switch is a good choice if the proportional band of the controller is less than 50%. When the proportional band is greater than 50% and where the start-up time must be reduced to the minimum without overshoot, a dual-mode system may be used (Refs. 9 and 11). Dual-mode systems are well suited for exothermic reactors where the batch has to be heated to reaction temperature in the minimum amount of time, then cooling applied to remove the heat of reaction. Figure 9-26 (Ref. 9) shows the operating principle of a dual-mode system; it is called dual-mode because there are two distinct modes of operation. There are two controllers in this system: (1) TC-1, an on/off controller, and (2) TIC-1, a three-mode (PID) controller. For this system to work as shown, TIC-1 must function the same as the PID controller of Figure 9-6(b), where the controller output is fed back to the reset section.

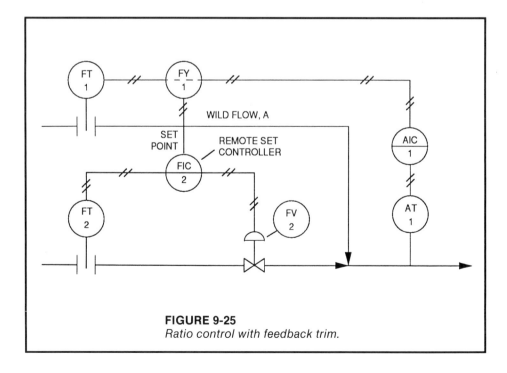

FIGURE 9-25
Ratio control with feedback trim.

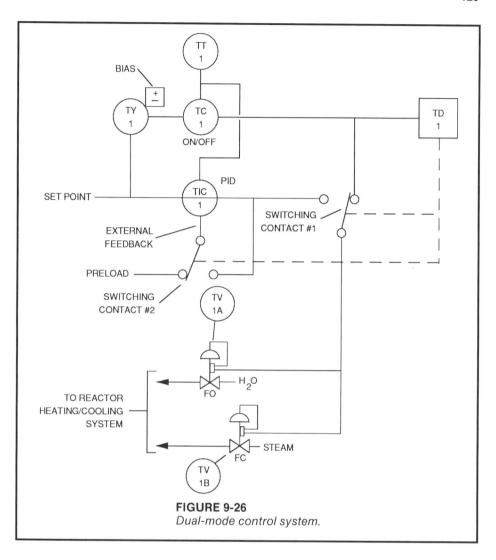

FIGURE 9-26
Dual-mode control system.

Mode 1 — During the heat-up, the system acts like an on/off controller. With the measurement below set point, the output of the on/off controller (TC-1) is at its maximum value, which actuates the two SPDT (single-pole, double-throw) switches and allows this signal to go to the heating and cooling valves (TV-1A and TV-1B). Full heating is applied. The preload signal is also switched to the PID controller's (TIC-1) reset section, which disables the automatic integral action in this controller. When the measurement reaches the set point of TC-1, which is lower than the set point of TIC-1 by the amount of the bias, the output goes to 0. The control valves switch to full cooling immediately, but the switching contacts delay for a preset time. Full cooling is applied only long enough to dissipate the energy stored in the jacket.

Mode 2 — After the time delay, switching contacts #1 and #2 change, and TIC-1's output is directed to the control valves and to the reset section. TIC-1 is now in control and functioning as a normal three-mode controller.

Liptak (Ref. 10) suggests using different time delays. These time delays would be activated when the on/off controller switches from full heating to full cooling. The first time delay would change switching contact #1 at the end of the full cooling period (same as the time delay in the above example). The second time delay would be slightly longer to allow both the error in TIC-1 and the rate of change of the measurement to be zero before changing switching contact #2 to let TIC-1 function as a normal three-mode controller.

Figure 9-27 (Ref. 9) illustrates the closed-loop response capable with a dual-mode system. If the switching parameters are properly adjusted, the process will be driven to within 1 or 2% of the set point as rapidly as possible, the "brakes" then applied, and the set point reached with zero velocity.

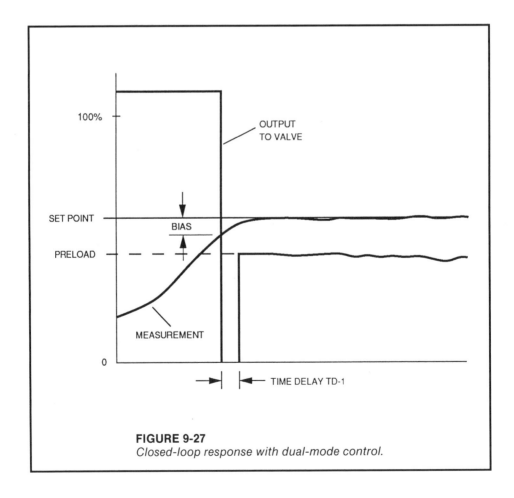

FIGURE 9-27
Closed-loop response with dual-mode control.

Override Control Systems

Two ways to protect a process from a severe disturbance that could endanger personnel, process equipment, or product quality are interlocks and override controls. Interlocks shut down systems to prevent damage to equipment or injury to personnel. Because interlocks cause an actual shutdown, significant and costly downtime can result if an operator does not respond rapidly to the situation. Override controls provide a soft constraint and allow the system to continue running but at a reduced rate.

An example of an override control system for a batch reactor is shown in Figure 9-28. This is a batch reactor that adds a second material (a gas) to a previously charged amount of liquid ingredient. The reaction is exothermic. The reactor is operated with the vent closed. As long as the reaction is proceeding normally, the gas is absorbed in the liquid, and the pressure in the reactor will be low. If something stops the reaction or the gas feed is greater than can be absorbed, the pressure will start to rise, and the pressure controller will reduce the gas feed.

The intention is to run this reactor at the maximum feed rate of the gas to minimize the time cycle, but the reactor is also cooling-limited. Therefore, if the

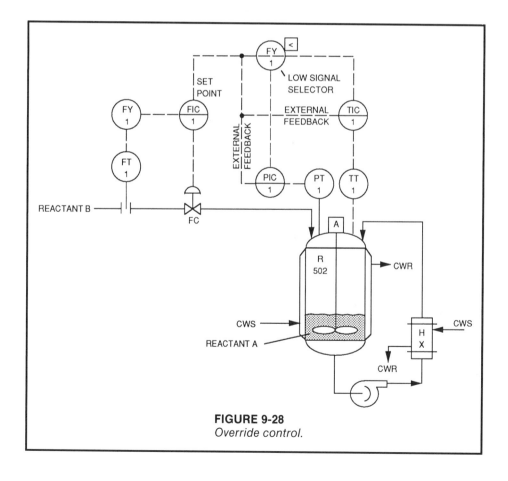

FIGURE 9-28
Override control.

pressure controller calls for a gas flow that exceeds the cooling capability of the reactor, the temperature will start to rise. The reaction temperature is not critical, but it must not exceed some maximum temperature. The temperature controller will then take over control of the feed valve and reduce the feed rate. The output of the selector relay sets the set point of a flow controller. The flow controller minimizes the effects of supply pressure changes on the gas flow rate. So this is a cascade control system, with the primary controller being an override control system.

In an override control system, one of the controllers is always in a standby condition, which will cause that controller to saturate. Reset windup can be prevented by feeding back the selector relay output to the reset section of each controller (see Figure 9-28). Since the reset sections of both controllers have the same feedback signal, control will transfer when both controllers have no error (see Figure 9-29). Then the outputs of both controllers will be equal to the signal in the reset sections. Since neither controller has any error, the outputs of both controllers will be the same. Particular attention must be paid to make sure that at least one controller in an override control system will always be in control. If not, then one or more of the controllers can wind up, and reset windup protection is necessary.

Override control systems are easier to implement in microprocessor-based controllers if the controllers have external feedback capability, such as the controller shown in Figure 9-6(b).

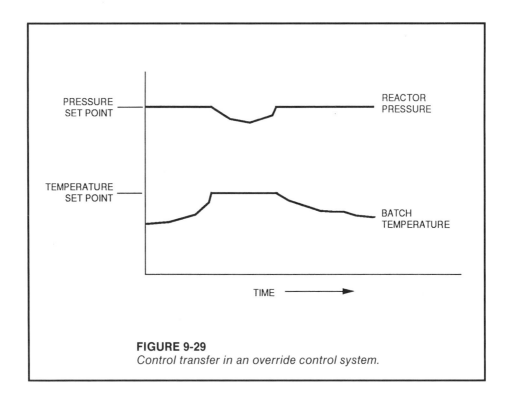

FIGURE 9-29
Control transfer in an override control system.

Metering/Weighing/Blending Requirements   Weighing and metering are common in batch processes, because materials must be accurately charged to ensure consistent product quality. Blending also requires highly accurate metering and weighing systems. Batch blending is common in many industries, especially for low volume products.

Metering   Because of the importance of metering in a batch system, it is desirable to have two independent means to measure quantities of materials. In manual operations, these measurements may be simply tank level indicator readings on the feed or storage tank and the vessel receiving the material. Automatic batch operations most often utilize at least one flowmeter. The second measurement may be another flowmeter, a tank level, or a weight. High-accuracy, pulse-producing meters (such as turbine meters and positive displacement meters) have been found to give the best results for batch operations where flowmeters are used.

Since formulations depend on weight, not volume of constituents, liquid volumetric measurements may have to be compensated for density variations. For single-component ingredients, temperature is often a good indication of density and may be used to compensate for density changes. Where the ingredient is a mixture of compounds, it may be necessary to use a density meter for compensation. True mass flowmeters are now available with sufficient accuracy for batch charging. For single-component gas flowmeters, both temperature and pressure compensation may be necessary to compensate for density variations. Again, true mass flowmeters are available for gas flows.

An important consideration with batching stations is the capability of two-stage shutoff. This means that at some point before the final set point is reached a switch is actuated that reduces the feed flow rate. For the last part of the charging, the meter will be fed at a lower flow rate. Because the final control element cannot close immediately, some material will pass through the meter between the time the switch actuates at the final set point and the time the final control element actually stops the flow. Feeding at a lower flow rate during the final stage of charging will minimize this overcharge. The batching station should continue to record the material that is fed through the meter after the final set point is reached so that the actual amount of material that was charged is known. Some batching stations provide an additional adjustment that shuts off the feed at a predetermined amount less than the final preset to account for the material that is fed while the final control element is stopping the flow.

The two-stage shutoff has an additional advantage in liquid flow applications. Any time a liquid flow stream is abruptly stopped, there is potential for water hammer. The lower flow rate during the final stage of charging will minimize the pressure surge experienced by water hammer.

Weighing   Weighing is generally implemented through the use of load cells on a weigh vessel (e.g., the weigh vessel may be the batch reactor) to control the addition of materials. This type of weighing system is applicable to both liquid and solid charging.

Weigh vessels can be supported by either tension or compression load cells; the number of load cells is generally determined by the physical configuration of the weigh vessel. In multiple load cell installations, consideration must be given to the number of support points, the load shared by each point, and the structural design of the weigh vessel (Ref. 12). It is important to minimize the weight of the weigh vessel where possible because the usable weight of a load cell is reduced by the force applied to the load cell by the tare weight of the weigh vessel. Any force that is applied to the weigh vessel will affect the weighing accuracy. Therefore, electrical connections are typically made using flexible cable, while piping connections usually are provided with expansion joints.

Figure 9-4 shows a typical application utilizing a pneumatic conveying system, where material is fed to a batch system from a weigh vessel. The weigh vessel is normally filled from an in-process use bin or from a storage silo. The weighing system for the weigh vessel can be either a net-weighing system or a loss-in-weight system.

With a net-weighing system, the weigh tank is emptied when the material is charged to the batch system. This means that the weigh tank must be charged with the exact amount of material required by the batch system. Consequently, absolute accuracy of the load cells is extremely important in a net-weighing system.

In a loss-in-weight system, the weigh tank is charged with more material than is needed by the batch system; then only as much material is fed from the weigh tank to the batch system as is needed, based on the difference between the initial weight and the final weight (i.e., the loss in weight) of the weigh vessel. The weigh tank is never emptied. Therefore, the absolute accuracy of the charge to the weigh tank is not critical, as long as more material has been charged than is needed by the batch system. Since drift in the load cell measurement could eventually result in the tank either having too little material in it or overflowing, separate level alarms should be installed on the weigh vessel to indicate these extremes in material level.

When material is being fed into a weigh vessel, the weight reading will lag behind the actual weight of material that has been charged. This is because it takes some time for the material to fall from the feed system to the weigh vessel (free fall) and because there is some finite response time for the weighing system. There is also a time delay between the time the charging set point is reached and a stop feed signal is given and when the feed actually stops. These all contribute to inaccuracies in the weight measurement. These inaccuracies can be minimized by keeping the free-fall distance as short as possible and by choosing weighing systems with fast update times. In general, the faster the feed rate, the lower the accuracy (Ref. 13).

Two functions used in controlling solids feeding in batching systems are "dribble" and "free-fall compensation" (Ref. 14). The dribble function indicates the point at which the batching controller switches from the high feed rate to the low feed rate. For example, if the set point were 1,000 lbs and the dribble set point were set at 100 lbs, the batching system would switch from high feed rate to low feed rate when 900 lbs of material had been charged. Feeding the final material at a low feed rate increases the accuracy because it minimizes the amount of material that is still charged to the system once the weigh feeder has been shut off.

Free fall compensation indicates the weight short of the set point at which the dribble feed is cut off. This compensates for material that has left the feeder but has not yet been measured by the weighing system. If, in the above example, the free fall compensation were set to 25 lbs, the feeder would be shut off when 975 lbs of material had been charged. The amount of free fall adjustment needed varies from batch to batch and depends on the feed rate, how full the weigh vessel is, etc. As a result, the actual free fall adjustment typically is fine tuned over a number of batches to zero out the average error.

Blending Blending systems are used when it is necessary to combine two or more components proportionally to obtain a desired mixture. In continuous flow operations, blending requires precise flow control on each of the components. Results are instantaneous, and there is little room for error. In batch blending, on the other hand, components may be added simultaneously or sequentially. Components can be blended batchwise by ratioing the components together into a vessel to some desired weight or volume. Here, the rate is not important; it is the total quantity that is important. The batch is then mixed and can be sampled for results. This makes the process much more forgiving, because adjustments can be made to bring the blend into specification.

Although the components can be fed under ratio control to a batch blender using the ratio control systems previously discussed, digital blending systems offer some definite advantages:

1. They will handle pulse input signals directly with no conversion required.
2. They are easily modified for feedback trim.
3. They are easily adaptable to temperature or density compensation of the flow rate signal.
4. With built-in scaling, the system can be set up so that the actual percentage of the component in the total blend is always being set.
5. Overall system accuracy can be better than with an analog system.
6. They are available with "pacing" and "memory" features.

In a batch blending system, it is the total blend ratio that is important. If, during the blending operation, one of the components is not able to keep up with the total blend rate, the final blend is going to be in error. A digital blending system with the "memory" feature stores this error until the component again becomes available and then adjusts its flow rate to bring the total error back to zero. This controller then acts to reduce the total blend ratio error to zero, even if there are instantaneous errors during the blending operation.

However, this memory feature would not be desirable on a continuous blending system, such as a semibatch reactor where two or more feeds are being fed at the same time in a constant ratio. Trying to recover the error in a continuous system means there are going to be alternating slugs of material that are either rich or lean in the particular component. For example, assume that component A becomes temporarily unavailable. This means that the blend being fed into the reactor will be temporarily lean in component A. When it again becomes available, the memory feature is going to correct for the error, and a blend will be fed into the reactor that is now rich in component A. This type of operation will occur every time one of the components is temporarily unavailable. This is highly undesirable. A standard ratio system would be a better choice for this application.

The best choice, however, is probably a digital blending system with the "pacing" feature. With the pacing feature, if a particular component is not able to keep up with the demand flow ratio, its control station will send a signal back to the master pacing unit. This feedback signal reduces the output of the master pacing unit (total demand flow rate) until this component can keep up with the demand flow rate. In this way, the blend ratio is held, even though the total blend flow rate is reduced.

EXERCISES

9.1 Modify the override control loop of Figure 9-28 so that the reactor temperature can be accurately controlled and not merely limited. This will require the addition of a control valve on the cooling water flow.

9.2 Show how the override control loop of Figure 9-28 could be modified to replace the temperature control loop with a dual-mode control system to provide for automatic start-up.

9.3 Figure 9-30 shows a batch reactor system consisting of three reactors along with some auxiliary equipment. Six raw materials are used in this reactor system (A, B, C, D, E, and F) that have the following characteristics:

- Ingredient A is a viscous material that is stored in storage tank T-501 and fed to all three reactors using a positive displacement pump.
- Ingredient B is a nonviscous material that is supplied to all three reactors from a header that is distributed throughout the plant.
- Ingredient C is a granular solid that is fed to all three reactors via the pneumatic conveying system shown in Figure 9-4.
- Ingredient D is a corrosive catalyst that is fed to reactors R-502 and R-503 from weigh tank T-502.
- Ingredient E is a gas that is fed to all three reactors from a header that is distributed throughout the plant.
- Ingredient F is a nonviscous liquid that is used only in the scrubber system.

   Four different products are made in this unit, as shown in Table 9-3. Only products W and X are made in reactor R-501. All four products are made in reactors R-502 and R-503.

   Whenever solid ingredient C is fed to the reactors, gaseous products are generated. A recoverable gas makes up a portion of the gaseous stream; it is absorbed in the scrubber system using ingredient F. The composition of the gaseous stream varies depending on the degree of the reaction. This is a once-through scrubbing system; the liquid that is taken off the bottom of the scrubber is pumped directly to storage. From there it is sold to outside customers. Therefore, it is extremely important that the scrubbing system be on control at the correct composition at all times.

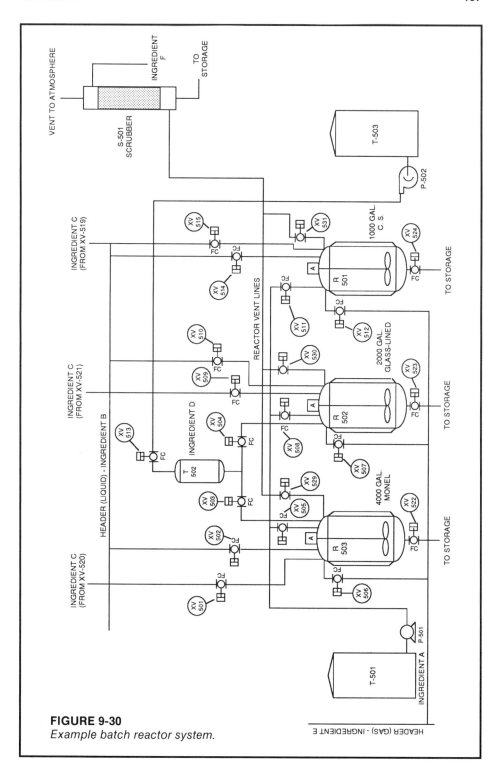

FIGURE 9-30
Example batch reactor system.

TABLE 9-3
Product Sequences

Product A	Product B	Product C	Product D
1. Initialize	1. Initialize	1. Initialize	1. Initialize
2. Charge A	2. Charge A	2. Charge A	2. Charge A
3. When enough A has been charged to cover the agitator, turn on the agitator, start charging B. Ratio B to A so that they complete charging at the same time.	3. When enough A has been charged to cover the agitator, turn on the agitator, start charging B. Ratio B to A so that they complete charging at the same time.	3. When enough A has been charged to cover the agitator, turn on the agitator, start charging B. Ratio B to A so that they complete charging at the same time.	3. When enough A has been charged to cover the agitator, turn on the agitator, start charging B. Ratio B to A so that they complete charging at the same time.
4. Heat to 200° F	4. Heat to 200° F	4. Heat to 200° F	4. Heat to 200° F
5. When temperature is at 200° F, start the pneumatic conveying system and feed C.	5. When temperature is at 200° F, start the pneumatic conveying system and feed C.	5. When temperature is at 200° F, start the pneumatic conveying system and feed C.	5. When temperature is at 200° F, start the pneumatic conveying system and feed C.
NOTE: C will feed over a several hour period based on the preset quantity and the capacity of M-501 rotary feed valve.	NOTE: C will feed over a several hour period based on the preset quantity and the capacity of M-501 rotary feed valve.	NOTE: C will feed over a several hour period based on the preset quantity and the capacity of M-501 rotary feed valve.	NOTE: C will feed over a several hour period based on the preset quantity and the capacity of M-501 rotary feed valve.
6. Raise temperature to 300° F as rapidly as possible while feeding C. Minimize overshoot to reduce amount of off-spec product.	6. Raise temperature to 300° F as rapidly as possible while feeding C. Minimize overshoot to reduce amount of off-spec product.	6. Raise temperature to 300° F as rapidly as possible while feeding C. Minimize overshoot to reduce amount of off-spec product.	6. Raise temperature to 300° F as rapidly as possible while feeding C. Minimize overshoot to reduce amount of off-spec product.
7. Hold at 300 ° F for one hour.	7. Hold at 300 ° F for one hour.	7. Hold at 300 ° F for one hour.	7. Hold at 300 ° F for one hour.

(continued)

TABLE 9-3
Product Sequences (continued)

Product A	Product B	Product C	Product D
8. Sample to laboratory.	8. Sample to laboratory.	8. Sample to laboratory.	8. Sample to laboratory.
9. When sample is OK, cool to 100° F and pump to storage.	9. Determine amount of E to be charged based on lab analysis.	9. Charge preset amount of catalyst D.	9. Charge preset amount of cata lyst D.
	10. Feed E at 1000 lb/hr with vent valve closed while holding the temperature at 300° F.	10. Determine amount of E to be charged based on lab analysis.	10. Determine amount of E to be charged based on lab analysis.
	11. Sample to lab and cool to 100° F as rapidly as possible to stop the reaction.	11. Feed E at the maximum possible feed rate to minimize cycle time as long as pressure and temperature do not exceed their respective set points. Vent valve must be closed during E feed. Hold temperature at 400° F during E feed.	11. Feed E at the maximum possible feed rate to minimize cycle time as long as pressure and temperature do not exceed their respective set points. Vent valve must be closed during E feed. Raise temperature to 450° F during E feed based on % of total E fed.
	12. When lab sample is OK, and temperature is at 100° F, pump to storage.	12. Sample to lab and cool to 100° F as rapidly as possible to stop the reaction.	12. Sample to lab.
		13. When lab sample is OK and temperature is at 100° F, pump to storage.	13. When sample is OK, cool to 100° F and pump to storage.

(a) Identify the exclusive-use and shared-use resources in Figures 9-4 and 9-30. Since no instruments have been shown in these figures, their selection could affect this answer.

(b) Show how ingredient A system could be set up as either an exclusive-use or shared-use resource. What are the advantages and disadvantages of each approach (e.g., equipment sizes, equipment costs, scheduling difficulties, etc.).

(c) Partition this batch process into the appropriate loops/devices, equipment modules, and units. Identify the reasons for your choices.

(d) Identify loops and/or devices where there are opportunities to apply advanced control techniques (e.g., cascade control, feedforward control, override control, etc.).

(e) What should be the failure positions of vent valves XV-529, XV-530, and XV-531?

(f) Why are the on/off valves in the pneumatic conveying system of Figure 9-4 specified as fail in the last position (FL) while the on/off valves in the lines feeding the reactors from that system are specified as fail closed (FC)?

9.4 Figure 9-31 shows glass-lined reactor R-502 with its heating/cooling system. This system uses a supply of hot oil (heat transfer fluid) as its source of heat; cooling is supplied via the heat exchanger in the circulating loop. It is extremely important to limit the temperature differential between the reactor and the jacket to prevent the glass from cracking because of the uneven expansion characteristics of the glass and the carbon steel. Show how a cascade control system could be installed on R-502 that will limit the temperature differential across the glass in this reactor (in both directions, i.e., when the reactor is either being heated or cooled). Should the temperature sensor for the secondary controller be installed on the inlet or the outlet of the jacket? Determine the operating ranges for each of the three temperature control valves in this system using the following assumptions: (1) when the secondary controller output is at 0%, full cooling will be applied; (2) as the secondary controller output is modulated from 0% to 50%, the amount of cooling will be modulated from full cooling to zero cooling (there is no cooling above 50% controller output); (3) at 50% controller output, there will be neither heating nor cooling, and the jacket contents will circulate continuously; (4) as the controller output is modulated from 50% to 100%, the amount of heating is modulated from zero heating to full heating (there is no heating below 50% controller output); and (5) as the control valves are modulated over the controller output range of 0 to 100%, there should be no significant change in the circulation rate through the jacket.

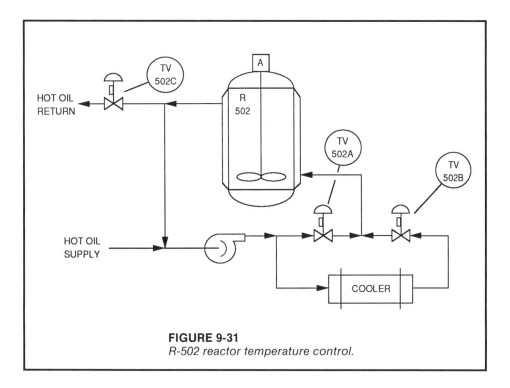

FIGURE 9-31
R-502 reactor temperature control.

REFERENCES

1. Mergen, R. J., "Introduction to Batch Control," ISA Cleveland Section Symposium on Batch Control Systems, May 1982.

2. "Introduction to Batch Processing," Fisher Controls, PS Sheet Application Note AP4:020 (A), August 23, 1982.

3. ANSI/ISA-S5.2, Binary Logic Diagrams for Process Operations, Instrument Society of America, 1981.

4. Luyben, W. L., "Batch Reactor Control," *Instrumentation Technology*, August 1975.

5. Beatty, B. D., "Techniques for Improving Control of Batch Reactors," *CONTROL*, October 1988.

6. Staples, R. A. C., "Cost Effective Batch Control System Using Programmable Controllers," ISA/87, Paper #87-1129.

7. Dunbar, R. D., "The Use of Programmable Controllers for Batch Process Control," 16th Annual International Programmable Controllers Conference and Exposition, Detroit, April 7-9, 1987.

8. Shinskey, F. G., "Effective Control for Automatic Start-up and Plant Protection," *Canadian Controls & Instrumentation*, April 1973.

9. Shinskey, F. G., "Batch Reactor Control System," *Instruments and Control Systems*, January 1972.

10. Liptak, B. G., "Controlling and Optimizing Chemical Reactors," *Chemical Engineering*, May 26, 1986.

11. Shinskey, F. G., and J. L. Weinstein, "A Dual-Mode Control System for a Batch Exothermic Reactor," 20th Annual ISA Conference, Los Angeles, CA, October 4-7, 1965.

12. Anderson, C. E., "Automated Minor Ingredient Weighing," *Weighing & Measurement*, February 1990.

13. Sheperdson, R., "Batching - The Outer Limits," *Weighing & Measurement*, February 1990.

14. Morris, H. M., "Stand-Alone Controllers Offer Flexible Choices for Batch Control," *Control Engineering*, May 1983.

10

Sequential Control of Batch Processes

Introduction   Batch control strategies involve more than minimizing the set point deviations caused by steady-state disturbances. Often, alternate sets of control actions are needed to respond to events such as major ambient upsets, equipment failures, or major process load changes. Other strategies are needed because of the frequent start-ups and shutdowns that occur. Strategies that involve changing control actions based on events generally fall into the classification of sequential control strategies.

Whether a sequential control strategy applies to the simple start-up and shutdown of a motor or to a sophisticated batch process, the control actions and status of the process equipment change with time. Time and event sequencing, whether fixed or variable, is the underlying consideration in designing a batch control strategy.

Events that initiate changes in the state of the batch process are called trigger events. Trigger events are usually based on either the control actions themselves (e.g., such as the reaching of a temperature end point) or by the completion of a certain time period (e.g., a 1-hour hold). Several events may have to occur simultaneously to trigger a change in the sequence.

Operation/Phase/Control Step Hierarchy   As part of the top down design approach (see Chapter 15), the format of the recipes must be established. This allows the designer to put the procedures into a format that enforces the operation/phase/control step hierarchy. However, it is not unusual for the procedure to be specified in the same manner as shown in Table 9-3 when it is issued by a research laboratory or a pilot plant facility.

EXAMPLE 10-1

Problem: Put the batch sequence for Product A of Table 9-3 into the operation/phase/control step format.

Solution: The sequence for Product A is reproduced as Table 10.1.

TABLE 10-1
Batch Sequence for Product A

1. Initialize.
2. Charge A.
3. When enough A has been charged to cover the agitator, turn on the agitator, start charging B. Ratio B to A so that they complete charging at the same time.
4. Heat to 200° F.
5. When temperature is at 200° F, start the pneumatic conveying system and feed C.

   NOTE: C will feed over a several hour period based on the preset quantity and the capacity of M-501 rotary feed valve.
6. Raise temperature to 300° F as rapidly as possible while feeding C. Mimimize overshoot to reduce amount of off-specification product.
7. Hold at 300° F for one hour.
8. Sample to laboratory.
9. When sample is OK, cool to 100° F and pump to storage.

Operations need to be established first; then the phases within those operations can be defined. At this stage of the project, which is before flowmeters, control valves, and other instrumentation have been established on the Process & Instrument Diagrams (P&IDs), it is not possible to specify the control steps in any detail (e.g., with tag numbers for instruments). A possible breakdown of operations, phases, and control steps (assumes that A & B are charged by flowmeter and that C is charged by a weighing system) based on the batch sequence in Table 10-1 is:

OPERATIONS	PHASES	CONTROL STEPS
Initialize.	Initialize.	Put ingredient B ratio controller in MANUAL mode and set output to zero.
		Start jacket circulation pump and set reactor temperature controller to SECONDARY AUTOMATIC mode with a set point of 200°F.
Charge.	Add ingredient A.	Initialize. (Reset ingredient A flow totalizer to zero).

		Open ingredient A charge valve and verify that it has opened.
		Start ingredient A storage tank pump.
		When enough A has been charged to cover the reactor agitator, start the agitator.
		When amount of A charged equals 95% of preset, close ingredient A charge valve to the dribble position.
		When amount of A charged equals preset, close ingredient A charge valve and stop ingredient A storage tank pump.
	Add ingredient B.	Initialize. (Put ingredient B ratio controller in RATIO mode [Note: The ratio controller set point is based on a calculation] and reset ingredient B totalizer to zero.)
		Open ingredient B charge valve.
		When amount of B charged equals preset, close ingredient B charge valve, put ingredient B ratio controller in MANUAL mode, set output to zero.
React.	Heat 1.	Initialize. (Put reactor temperature controller in CASCADE mode with a set point of 200°F.)
	Add ingredient C.	Initialize. (Set weighing system for feed out of weigh tank.)
		Open ingredient C charge valves, start pneumatic conveying system, and start rotary feed valve at desired speed.
		Monitor amount of C charged.
		When amount of C charged equals 95% of preset, set rotary feed valve to dribble speed rate.
		When amount of C charged equals preset, stop rotary feed valve.

		Let pneumatic conveying system run until transfer line to reactor is clear (Note: May be based on time), then stop pneumatic conveying system and close ingredient C charge valves.
	Heat 2.	Initialize. (Set reactor temperature controller set point to 300° F [Note: The reactor temperature controller will stay in CASCADE mode for this phase.].)
	Hold.	Initialize. (Maintain the reactor temperature at 300° F for 1 hour [Note: The reactor temperature controller will stay in CASCADE mode for this phase.].)
		Start timer.
	Sample for laboratory approval.	
Pumpout.	Cool.	Initialize. (Set reactor temperature controller set point to 100° F [Note: reactor temperature controller stays in CASCADE mode.].)
	Transfer.	Initialize. (Set reactor discharge valves for correct storage tank destination.)
		Start reactor discharge pump.
		Set reactor temperature controller to MANUAL mode with output at zero (full cooling).
		Before reactor level gets so low that the agitator blades will be uncovered, stop reactor agitator.
		When reactor is empty, close reactor discharge valves, stop reactor discharge pump, stop jacket circulation pump.

Sequence Diagrams

Before the batch sequence is actually coded into the batch control language, the sequences must be diagramed. These diagrams describe how the batch sequences actually operate; define the interface between sequential control, regulatory control, and discrete control; define the interface between sequential control and operator actions and responses; and provide for coordination between sequential control and the safety interlock system.

Some form of sequence diagraming is essential in batch control because of variable sequences, changing recipes, and resource contentions. They are invaluable when there is a high degree of interaction between the discrete control, regulatory control, and sequential control subsystems. These diagrams should be reviewed and approved by all members of the project team (see Chapter 15 for a discussion on the team approach) before the functional specification can be completed (see Chapter 19 for a discussion on the functional specification). This means that the sequence diagrams must be in a form that is understandable by people who are not computer programmers or who have no control systems background.

The following are some requirements for the sequence diagraming method:

1. Clearly show the overall sequence while maintaining the operation/phase/control step hierarchy.

2. Represent both combinational logic and sequential logic.

3. Able to represent discrete variables, describe alarm status, compare analog variables, and switch control instrument modes.

4. Capable of presenting sequence specifications briefly, intuitively, and accurately.

5. Describe the sequence specification in a form that can be used "as is" to generate the control sequences.

6. Easy for process engineers and people who are not computer programmers to use.

7. Easy to maintain and, as much as possible, self-documenting.

8. Adaptable to generation on an engineering workstation, e.g., a personal computer.

9. Ideally, if the sequence diagram can be generated on an engineering workstation, it should then be directly convertible into the batch sequencing language without having to redo the diagram in a different format.

Several types of sequence diagrams can be used. This list is not meant to be all-inclusive.

- Flowcharts
- State charts
- Decision tables
- Timing diagrams
- Sequence matrix
- Structured English diagraming
- State transition diagrams
- Petri nets
- Sequential function charts

Flowcharts Figure 10-1 shows an example of a typical flowchart for a portion of the "Add Ingredient A" phase. The flowchart is probably the most common means of documenting sequential processes. Rosenof and Ghosh list some drawbacks of flowcharts (Ref. 1):

1. They are undisciplined, and different individuals will often choose varying levels of detail for their representations unless comprehensive standards
exist.

2. They are inefficient in their use of paper.

3. Many people find them difficult to read because the normal progression
of steps may be difficult to determine if a chart contains many branches.

4. They are inefficient to use as checkout tools.

5. They must be carefully maintained over time to retain any real value.

6. Concurrent, dependent processes are difficult to document with flowcharts.

If the complete sequence for Product A were drawn using the example in
Figure 10-1, either a very large drawing or a drawing with a large number of
sheets would result. The resulting drawing would be difficult to follow and use.
Rosenof and Ghosh recommend using a hierarchical set of flowcharts that shows
the entire control sequence at an overview level, with each overview function
broken down into successively finer levels of detail (Ref. 2). This can actually be
carried a step further by making the overview show the operations, with the next
level of detail showing the phases, and the final level of detail showing the control
steps. This philosophy is followed in the flowcharts shown in Figures 10-2, 10-3,
and 10-4, which are drawn according to ISO Standard 5807 (Ref. 3). Figure 10-2
shows the overall operations for Product A from Table 10-1, Figure 10-3 shows the
phases for the CHARGE operation, and Figure 10-4 shows the control steps for
the ADD INGREDIENT A phase. The ISO standard has provided a way to
handle concurrent processes, as shown in Figure 10-3. Software programs are
readily available for developing flowcharts on an engineering workstation. However, the conversion from the flowchart to the batch sequence language is not that
straightforward. Although the normal flowchart does not do a good job of enforcing the operation/phase/control step hierarchy, Figures 10-2, 10-3, and 10-4 show
that it is possible to accomplish this hierarchy by structuring the presentation of
the flowcharts.

State Charts State charts (see Figure 10-5) are most frequently used to document sequential processes that use only contact inputs and outputs. More than
one state chart is needed to define a sequential process. Figure 10-5 shows the
relationship between the control steps and the outputs from the system for the
ADD INGREDIENT A phase. An output is on whenever an X is shown at the
intersection of the control step and the output. An additional state chart is needed
to show what combinations of inputs and outputs are required to step the
sequence from one control step to the next. For example, if the system is in control
step 2, a signal verifying that A charge valve is open would be part of the
requirements to advance to control step 3. Likewise, a signal indicating that
enough A had been charged to cover the agitator blades would be part of the
requirements for advancing from control step 3 to control step 4.

The normal state chart does not provide a means of enforcing the operation/
phase/control step hierarchy. In fact, for this example it would be difficult to
generate a phase state chart because of the difficulty in showing concurrent,

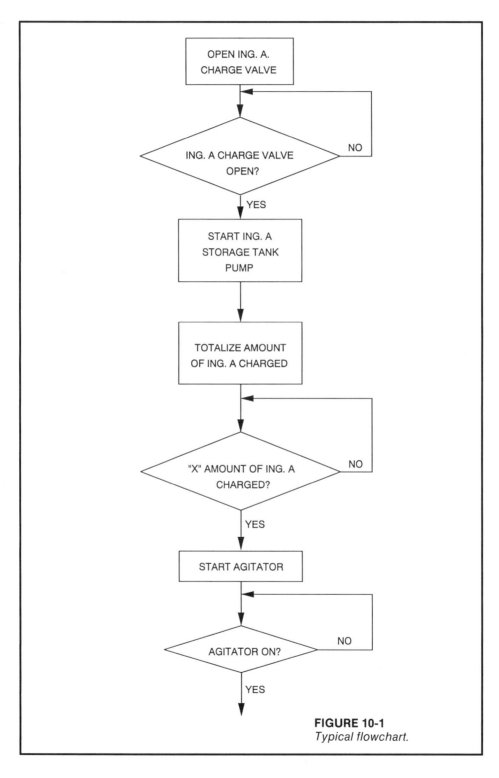

FIGURE 10-1
Typical flowchart.

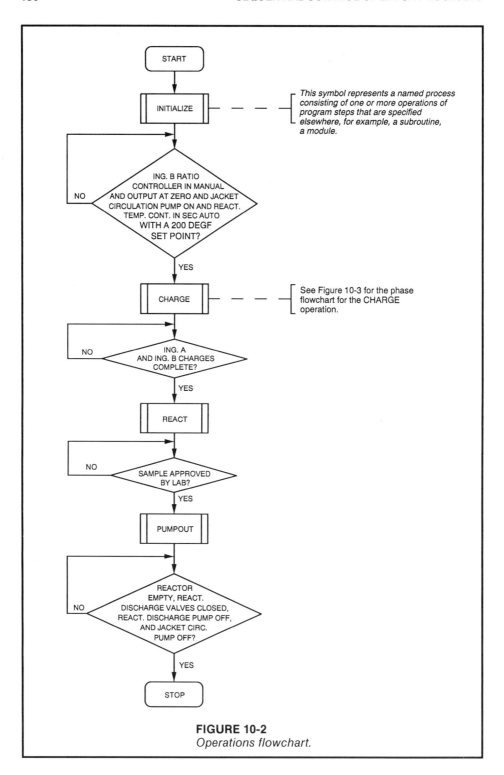

FIGURE 10-2
Operations flowchart.

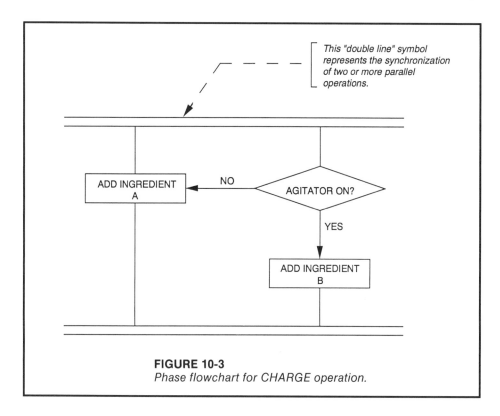

FIGURE 10-3
Phase flowchart for CHARGE operation.

dependent actions. For example, if a phase state chart were generated where the outputs from the state chart were the control steps, how would the state chart show the dependency on A charge valve being verified in the open position so that the storage tank pump could start? It would also be necessary to redefine the phases to allow A and B to be fed simultaneously. State charts also do not do a good job with analog variables unless they are constant value analog variables.

State charts don't have much to offer as a sequence diagraming tool except for very simple sequential processes where the inputs and outputs are primarily digital.

EXAMPLE 10-2

Problem: In the state chart of Figure 10-5, why are Xs shown in control steps 2 through 4 for charge valve A but only in control step 3 for the storage tank pump, even though the valve must be open and the pump must be on until control step 6?

Solution: This is shown in this manner because of the way these devices usually operate. For example, an automatic block valve, such as charge valve A, would probably open when the solenoid valve was energized and close when the solenoid valve was deenergized. Therefore, an output must be provided in each control step in which the valve must be open. On the other

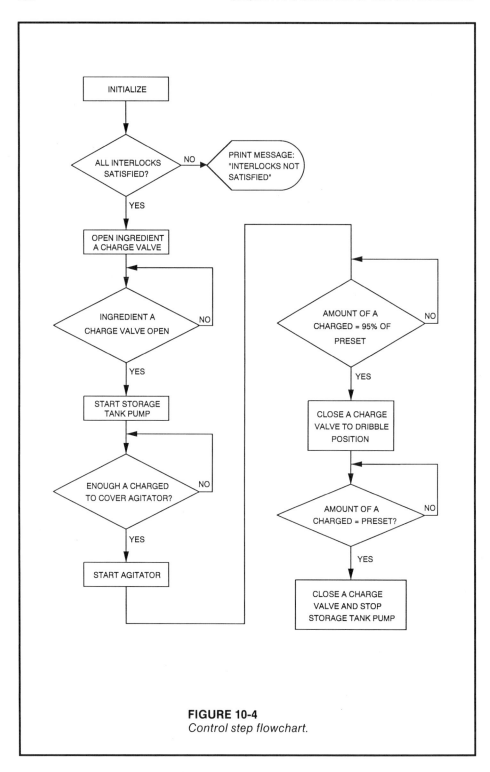

FIGURE 10-4
Control step flowchart.

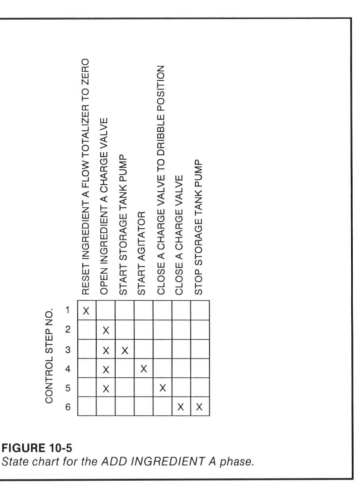

FIGURE 10-5
State chart for the ADD INGREDIENT A phase.

hand, pumps and agitators are normally started by momentary contacts (e.g., by pushing the start push button momentarily) and closed by a momentary contact (e.g., by pushing the stop push button momentarily). Once the pump or agitator has been started, it will continue to run until it receives a stop signal, so it needs an X in the control step only where it must be initially turned on. If the valves, pumps, and agitators operate differently from those in this problem, the state chart must be adjusted accordingly.

Decision Tables Decision tables are a concise way of describing systems that have multiple conditions (inputs) and multiple actions (outputs). A basic decision table, as shown in Figure 10-6 (Ref. 4), consists of a condition stub that is used to describe conditions that require decisions; an action stub that is used to describe execution details; and an area for condition and action entries (i.e., an area to enter sets of actions and the corresponding sets of conditions that determine whether or not the actions are performed). Each column in the table of Figure 10-6 is called a "rule"; it relates the conditions to the resulting actions. The normal

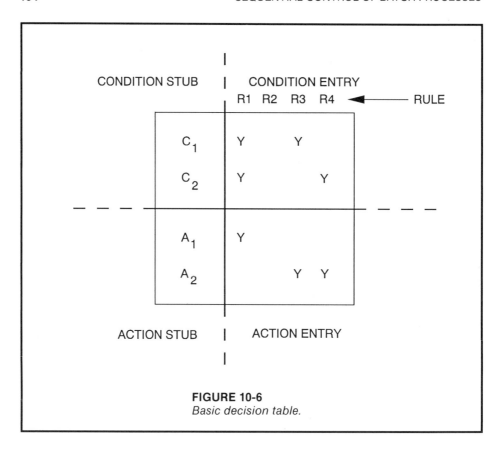

FIGURE 10-6
Basic decision table.

decision table handles only "Yes," "No," and "Don't Care" entries, which is fine for systems that handle only discrete inputs and outputs. They also do a good job of defining combinational logic (logic that depends only on present inputs and requires no memory elements). For batch sequencing, however, a more enhanced decision table is needed, e.g., the ability to have the equivalent of logical and relational expressions, where the expression part is in the condition stub and the value it is compared with is in the condition entry part of the table.

The following are some of the enhancements needed to make the decision table applicable to batch sequencing (Ref. 4):

1. Allow the status of control instruments and timers to be tested and arithmetic expressions evaluated. This also means that the decision table can check the status of a batch, use the parameters from the batch controller program as conditions, and then issue start/stop, restart, and other commands to the batch controllers.

2. Extend combinational logic by grouping rules into STEPs and adding THEN/ELSE columns to indicate the next step, thereby allowing the decision table to represent steps in a time sequence (see Figure 10-7 for a decision table for the CHARGE operation for Product A).

PHASE	ADD INGREDIENT A (PHASE 1)							ADD INGREDIENTS A AND B (PHASE 2)						
RULES	1	2	3	4	5	6	7	1	2	3	4	5	6	7
ING. A FLOW TOTALIZER RESET TO ZERO	Y													
ING. A CHARGE VALVE OPEN			Y											
ENOUGH A CHARGED TO COVER AGITATOR BLADES				Y										
ING. A FLOW TOTAL EQUAL TO OR GREATER THAN 95% OF PRESET					Y									
ING. A FLOW TOTAL EQUAL TO OR GREATER THAN PRESET						Y								
ING. B RATIO CONT. IN RATIO									Y					
ING. B FLOW TOTALIZER RESET TO ZERO									Y					
ING. B FLOW TOTAL EQUAL TO OR GREATER THAN PRESET										Y				
AGITATOR ON							Y							
RESET ING. A FLOW TOTALIZER TO ZERO	Y					N								
OPEN ING. A CHARGE VALVE		Y				N								
START ING. A STORAGE TANK PUMP			Y			N								
START AGITATOR				Y										
CLOSE ING. A CHARGE VALVE TO DRIBBLE POSITION					Y									
PUT ING. B RATIO CONT. IN RATIO MODE								Y		N				
RESET ING. B FLOW TOTALIZER TO ZERO								Y		N				
OPEN ING. B CHARGE VALVE									Y	N				
PUT ING. B RATIO CONT. IN MANUAL WITH ZERO OUTPUT								N		Y				
THEN							2							
ELSE														

FIGURE 10-7
Decision table for CHARGE operation.

3. Extend the tables so that they reference rules in other decision tables as conditions or start execution of other decision tables as actions. This allows decision tables to be used as subroutines; it also means that a hierarchy of decision tables can be set up to enforce the hierarchy of operations, phases, and control steps.

4. Use the action part of decision tables to display messages to the operator, alarm messages on the CRT, record events, etc.

5. Allow the rules (conditions and action entries) to be called like subroutines, with only the input and output signals (condition and action stubs) differing. This simplifies programming for parallel units that have the same logic but different inputs and outputs (see Chapter 12 for a discussion on generic recipes and aliasing).

Decision tables enhanced in this manner can be used to handle relatively complex batch processes. However, implementing decision tables doesn't appear to be completely straightforward. Having the capability to implement any type of function in a batch process doesn't mean that it is a desirable approach. This method may get very cumbersome as the complexity of the batch process increases. Handling concurrent activities may require the phases to be redefined (see Figure 10-7). They also do not work well on batch processes where the procedures are changed; they are more suitable for batch processes where formula parameters are the major changes in recipes. Decision tables are like many of the other sequence diagraming techniques; when the process is small and not too complex, they work well, but when the batch process is complex, a better sequence diagraming technique is needed.

Timing Diagrams If neither flowcharts nor state charts satisfy the sequence diagraming needs of batch processes, a different diagraming technique is needed. Rosenof recognized this need and modified the state chart by rotating it 90 degrees so that the relationship between inputs and outputs could more readily be seen, which allowed both inputs and outputs to be shown as a horizontal channel (Ref. 5).

These types of diagrams are typically called "timing diagrams." Two implementations of timing diagrams have been discussed in the literature (as applied to batch sequencing), although many self-developed versions are used. They are "Process Timing Diagrams" (Refs. 1 and 5) and "Time Sequence Diagrams" (Ref. 6). These two types of timing diagrams are very similar in their presentation; time sequence diagrams will be discussed here.

Time Sequence Diagrams
The purpose of the time sequence diagram is to combine change, status, and decision flow into a concise and consistent format without regard to the actual hardware implementation. It is a structured approach to the development of a control strategy and was designed to allow freedom in the use of the symbology, while maintaining a recognizable format to aid in the important task of develop-

ing and reviewing a control strategy during the design stage (Ref. 6).

The symbols for time sequence diagrams include standard flowchart and logic symbols as well as special symbols for time sequence diagraming. Among these special symbols are the continuous task symbols used to represent the monitoring and manipulating of regulatory control elements.

The time sequence diagram shows the sequential changes in control actions as well as the relative positions of equipment at any point in time. Often, more than one trigger event must occur before a sequence is changed. The diamond symbol is used to indicate a trigger event, and the dotted time line indicates the time coincidence of trigger events and control task changes. When two or more diamonds are connected by a time coincidence line, an AND logic condition is assumed. The time coincidence line can be drawn in the horizontal direction to relate control tasks that cannot be shown on the same vertical line.

In a time sequence diagram, sequences and relative time proceed from left to right (see Figure 10-8). Whenever direction is obscure, arrows may be used to designate the direction of the time sequence flow.

An example of a time sequence diagram is shown in Figure 10-8. This diagram defines the CHARGE operation for Product A. The bars in the upper portion of the diagram are the discrete monitor symbols that represent the monitoring and manipulating of discrete control elements. This symbol can represent single-contact discrete devices such as indicator lamps; discrete control devices such as pumps, on/off valves, and agitators; and groups of discrete control devices such as headers.

Although this time sequence diagram is simplified and doesn't show abnormal event logic, failure conditions must be identified and the failure actions specified. Each process failure condition should be reviewed relative to the time sequence diagrams. Appropriate failure conditions should be added to the diagrams, and special attention should be paid to retry points in order to preserve the batch but avoid jeopardizing personnel, equipment, or product quality. Failure shutdown sequences are shown on separate time sequence diagrams. These sequences are referenced by the system when failure conditions occur.

Time sequence diagrams have the advantage of showing all of the loops and devices needed to accomplish an operation on one drawing. So all the parameters of interest during that particular operation are shown at all times. They are an effective tool to allow engineers and operating personnel, engineers and contractor personnel, etc., to communicate. Concurrency is easy to show because the timing relationships between all the various elements are shown explicitly. However, as shown in Figure 10-8, this may mean redefining phases (e.g., ADD A & B, instead of ADD B).

However, a lot of drawing is involved to generate time sequence diagrams (and process timing diagrams), and, at the time of this writing, software is not available to allow the user to generate these drawings on an engineering workstation. The conversion of time sequence diagrams to the actual batch language is not necessarily straightforward. Changes to the drawings are extremely difficult, so they work better for simple batch processes and for batch processes where the procedures are not changed very often.

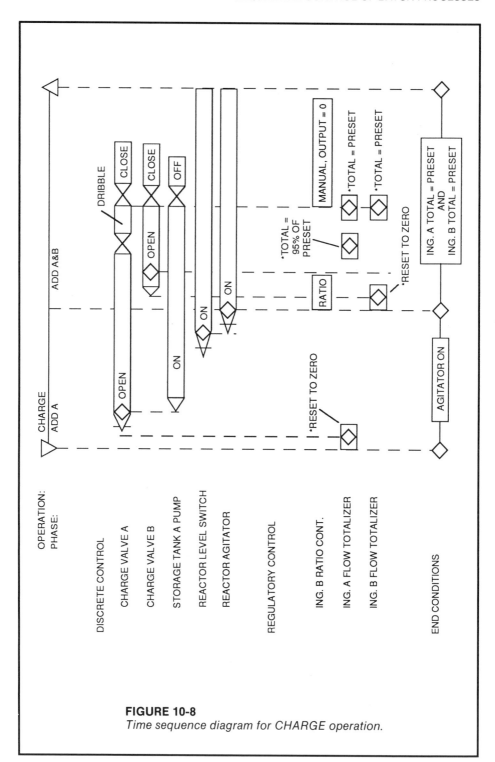

FIGURE 10-8
Time sequence diagram for CHARGE operation.

Sequence Matrix The sequence matrix is a variation of the timing diagram. It uses the same basic format as process timing diagrams and time sequence diagrams, but it replaces the graphic representations of the control steps with text in a spreadsheet format (Ref. 7). It can include operator messages, batch reporting variables, recipe variables, and failure conditions and actions.

An example of the sequence matrix is shown in Figure 10-9 for the CHARGE operation of Product A.

Aside from the fact that the sequence matrix can be generated with an engineering workstation using either a spreadsheet or word processing software package, this sequence diagraming technique has basically the same advantages and disadvantages as timing diagrams (see "Time Sequence Diagrams" earlier in this section). Additional disadvantages are: (1) it tries to say in text what timing diagrams display graphically, and it can sometimes take a lot of text to duplicate a small graphic drawing, and (2) it does not show concurrent actions as well as timing diagrams do.

Structured English Diagraming With structured English (Refs. 1 and 2), the logic is described in plain language but with certain rules and conventions. This type of logic can be developed with a word processor, so changes to the logic are easily made.

Statements preceded by five hyphens are comment statements. Statements preceded by a single hyphen are continuations of the line above it. This may be the continuation of either a comment line or a logic function.

An example of a comment, with continuation on the next line is:

-----THIS IS THE LOGIC THAT IS USED TO ACCOMPLISH THE
-CHARGE OPERATION

An example of a logic function continued to the next line is:

SET INGREDIENT A FLOW TOTALIZER DRIBBLE SET POINT AT 95%
-OF THE PRESET

Subroutines are identified by the double asterisk, e.g., **ADD INGREDIENT A. This is used as the label for the entry point to the subroutine.

Conditional branching in the logic uses the IF, THEN, ELSE format. Multiple levels of branching are allowed, but indentation should be used as shown below:

IF INITIAL CONDITIONS ARE SATISFIED
  THEN GO TO: **ADD INGREDIENT A
  ELSE PRINT-"INITIAL CONDITIONS ARE NOT SATISFIED"

Operator messages are shown in quotation marks, as shown by the ELSE statement in the above example.

AND and OR functions can be used in the logic, but logic functions such as NOR and NAND should be avoided, because they are not as readily understood. For example:

IF INGREDIENT A FLOW TOTAL EQUALS PRESET AND
-INGREDIENT B FLOW TOTAL EQUALS PRESET
    THEN GO TO: **HEAT 1

An example of structured English diagraming, as applied to the CHARGE operation for Product A is shown in Table 10-2.

Structured English logic has some advantages when used for sequence diagraming of batch processes: it is easy to understand since it is written in plain English, it is structured since rules and conventions can be established, subroutines can be used to simplify the main body of the logic, and the operation/phase/control step hierarchy can be enforced. However, concurrency is not easy to show and the conversion from the structured English logic to certain batch languages may not be very straightforward. It does have some definite advantages when used in conjunction with one of the sequence diagraming techniques based on state diagrams (see "Sequential Function Charts" later in this section).

State Transition Diagrams State transition diagrams are just one form of state diagrams. They are constructed from the following classes of elements (Ref. 8):

- States, which correspond to particular stages of a sequence, e.g., ADD INGREDIENT A;
- Transitions, which indicate changes from one state to another, e.g., from Heat 1 to HOLD;
- Conditions, which represent combinations of numerical, logical, or other values that can be examined as permissives for action, e.g., enough A has been charged to cover the agitator blades; and
- Actions, which are the things that are implemented during a transition from one state to another, e.g., starting the agitator.

An example of a state transition diagram for the CHARGE operation of Product A is shown in Figure 10-10. States are shown as circles that contain an associated number and have a name displayed above it (either horizontally or vertically). Transitions are shown as arrows in the appropriate direction between states. If there are multiple transitions to or from the same state, circles are repeated and connected vertically by broken lines (Ref. 8). Using this representation means that the states are not affected by the transitions leading to them. One or more transitions are listed above the transition arrow; one or more actions are listed below the transition arrow.

A strict interpretation of a state transition diagram has only one state operating at a time (Ref. 9), so when two or more states must proceed simultaneously, a new state must be defined that is a combination of one or more states (e.g., redefining the ADD INGREDIENT B phase to the ADD INGREDIENTS A AND B phase as has been done in previous examples).

State transition diagrams can be set up as a hierarchical structure where a master diagram can be further broken down into different levels of detail. Normally, this would provide the ability to enforce the operation/phase/control step

| OPERATIONS | CHARGE | |
PHASES	ADD INGREDIENT A	ADD INGREDIENTS A AND B
DISCRETE CONTROL DEVICES		
CHARGE VALVE A	OPEN WHEN ING. A FLOW TOTALIZER RESET TO ZERO	CLOSE TO DRIBBLE POSITION WHEN ING. A FLOW TOTAL = 95% OF PRESET, CLOSE WHEN ING. A FLOW TOTAL = PRESET
ING. A STORAGE TANK PUMP	START WHEN VALVE A OPEN	STOP WHEN ING. A FLOW TOTAL = PRESET
REACTOR AGITATOR	START WHEN ENOUGH A HAS BEEN CHARGED TO COVER AGITATOR BLADES	
CHARGE VALVE B		OPEN WHEN ING. B RATIO CONT. IN RATIO MODE AND ING. B FLOW TOTAL = ZERO, CLOSE WHEN ING. B FLOW TOTAL = PRESET
ANALOG DEVICES		
ING. A FLOW TOTALIZER	RESET TOTAL TO ZERO	RESET TOTAL TO ZERO
ING. B FLOW TOTALIZER		
ING. B RATIO CONT.		PUT IN RATIO MODE
END OF PHASE CONDITIONS	AGITATOR ON	ING. A FLOW TOTAL EQUAL TO OR GREATER THAN PRESET AND ING. B FLOW TOTAL EQUAL TO OR GREATER THAN PRESET

NORMAL SEQUENCE

FIGURE 10-9
Sequence matrix for CHARGE operation.

TABLE 10-2
Structured English Diagraming of the CHARGE Operation

**CHARGE OPERATION
-----CHARGE OPERATION MAIN LOGIC
  -THIS OPERATION CHARGES INGREDIENTS A AND B TO THE REACTOR
  -THE AMOUNT OF EACH COMPONENT TO BE CHARGED IS A RECIPE
  -VARIABLE

**ADD INGREDIENT A PHASE

RESET INGREDIENT A FLOW TOTALIZER TO ZERO

OPEN INGREDIENT A CHARGE VALVE

IF INGREDIENT A CHARGE VALVE OPENS WITHIN 10 SECONDS
  THEN START INGREDIENT A STORAGE TANK PUMP
  ELSE PRINT - "INGREDIENT A CHARGE VALVE DID NOT OPEN"

IF REACTOR LEVEL SWITCH IS ACTUATED
  THEN START THE AGITATOR

IF INGREDIENT A FLOW TOTAL EQUAL TO OR GREATER THAN 95% OF
-PRESET
  THEN CLOSE A CHARGE VALVE TO THE DRIBBLE POSITION

IF INGREDIENT A FLOW TOTAL EQUAL TO OR GREATER THAN PRESET
  THEN CLOSE INGREDIENT A CHARGE VALVE AND STOP STORAGE
  -TANK A PUMP

**ADD INGREDIENT B PHASE

PUT INGREDIENT B RATIO CONTROLLER IN RATIO OPERATING MODE

-----INGREDIENT B RATIO CONTROLLER SET POINT IS BASED ON A
-CALCULATION

RESET INGREDIENT B FLOW TOTALIZER TO ZERO

IF REACTOR AGITATOR IS ON
  THEN OPEN INGREDIENT B CHARGE VALVE

IF INGREDIENT B FLOW TOTAL EQUAL TO OR GREATER THAN PRESET
  THEN CLOSE INGREDIENT B CHARGE VALVE AND PUT INGREDIENT B
  -RATIO CONTROLLER IN MANUAL OPERATING MODE AND SET
  -INGREDIENT B RATIO CONTROLLER OUTPUT TO ZERO

IF INGREDIENT A FLOW TOTAL EQUAL TO OR GREATER THAN PRESET
  -AND INGREDIENT B FLOW TOTAL EQUAL TO OR GREATER
  -THAN PRESET
    THEN GO TO **REACT OPERATION

---

hierarchy. However, as Figure 10-10 shows, the states that are defined in a state transition diagram don't directly relate to the states in previous diagraming methods. For example, in Figure 10-10 the actions associated with the transitions are really the control steps. The states themselves don't always relate directly to the phases defined for Product A. Given this and the fact that concurrency is difficult to show with state transition diagrams, it doesn't appear that they have much to offer as a sequence diagraming tool.

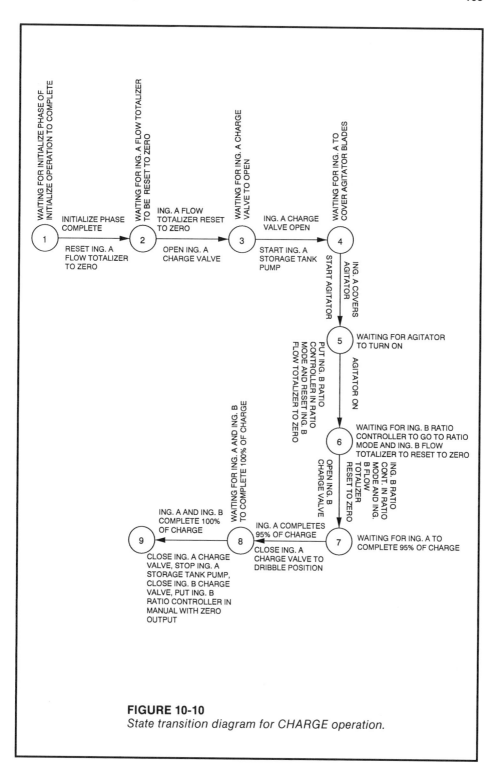

FIGURE 10-10
State transition diagram for CHARGE operation.

Petri Nets Petri nets were developed by Carl Adam Petri as a graphical approach for displaying concurrent or parallel activities. They show the possible states that a system can be in, the inputs and outputs to the system, and the state of the system at any given time (Ref. 10). The three basic components in a Petri net are:

- places, which show the states that a system can occupy;
- transitions, which show the events that can occur within a system; and
- arcs, which connect places to transitions and transitions to places.

Places are represented by circles, transitions by horizontal bars, and arcs by directed lines. Another symbol, the "token," is used to show the present states of the system. Tokens are shown as black dots inside places. As the system functions, tokens move around the net, so the net is capable of giving a dynamic representation of the state of the system.

An event can occur only if tokens are present in each of the input places associated with a transition. After the event occurs (the transition fires), one token is removed from each of the input places to the transition, and a token is added to each of the output places linked with that transition. The number of tokens does not have to remain constant.

The Petri net allows more than one active state at any given time; tokens may split into independent paths that function independently until the paths recombine (Ref. 10). A Petri net for the INITIALIZE and CHARGE operations of Product A is shown in Figure 10-11; Petri nets for the ADD INGREDIENT A and ADD INGREDIENT B phases are shown in Figures 10-12 and 10-13, respectively.

Petri nets appear to have several advantages as a sequence diagraming tool. They are relatively easy to draw and should be readily adaptable to generation on an engineering workstation. They handle concurrent activities very well, and they should be readily changed so that they would be adaptable to batch processes that need the flexibility to have complete recipe parameter changes from product to product. In addition, the conversion from Petri nets to various batch languages should be relatively straightforward.

Sequential Function Charts A better method of diagraming batch sequences uses sequential function charts in conjunction with structured English logic. Not only can the sequential function chart be used to rigidly enforce the operation/phase/step hierarchy, the logic can be directly converted into the batch language, especially if the batch language also happens to be an implementation of sequential function chart programming.

Sequential function charts are a graphically expressed sequence diagraming technique that allows the designer to represent the process or program as steps or transitions in a function chart. The sequential operation of the control system is indicated by the progression of the active steps of the function chart shown in Figure 10-14, which is a sequential function chart of the control steps for the ADD INGREDIENT A phase for Product A. Every step must be followed by a transition, and every transition must be followed by a step. When a step is active, the actions associated with it are performed. A step becomes active when its

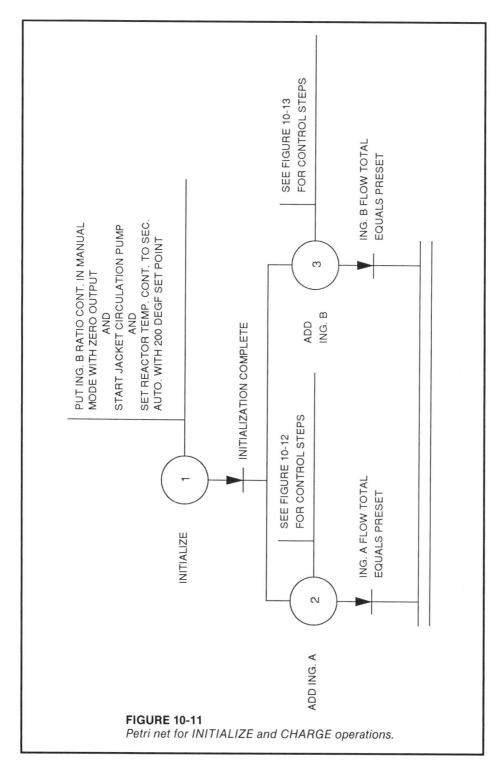

FIGURE 10-11
Petri net for INITIALIZE and CHARGE operations.

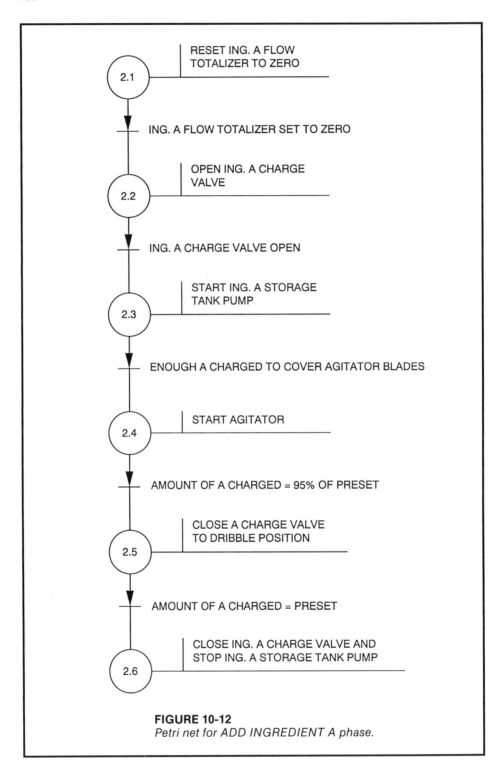

FIGURE 10-12
Petri net for ADD INGREDIENT A phase.

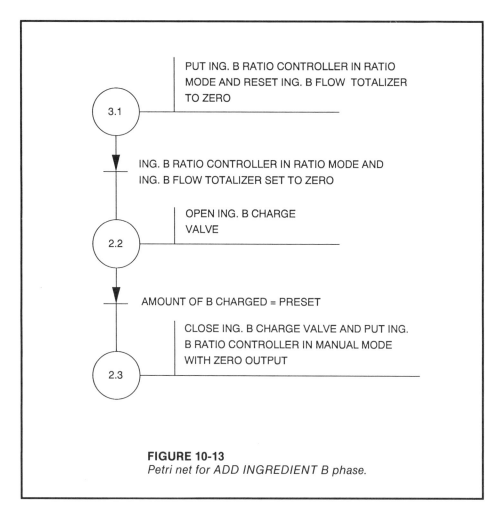

FIGURE 10-13
Petri net for ADD INGREDIENT B phase.

predecessor step is active and the transition conditions between them are satisfied.

The Sequential Function Chart language was specifically designed for describing sequential control systems.

There are only three basic elements in a sequential function chart: steps, transitions, and directed links (see Figure 10-15). Each step in the function chart represents a command or action that is either active or inactive. Control passes from one step to the next based on the condition of the transition (true or false). If the transition condition is true, control passes to the next step, which becomes active. The previous step becomes inactive. Directed links tie steps and transitions together to form complete charts.

A single function chart might represent a specific sequence in the process. More than one of these charts can be interconnected in the required sequence by directed links that show the flow of control, thereby forming a complete sequential function chart.

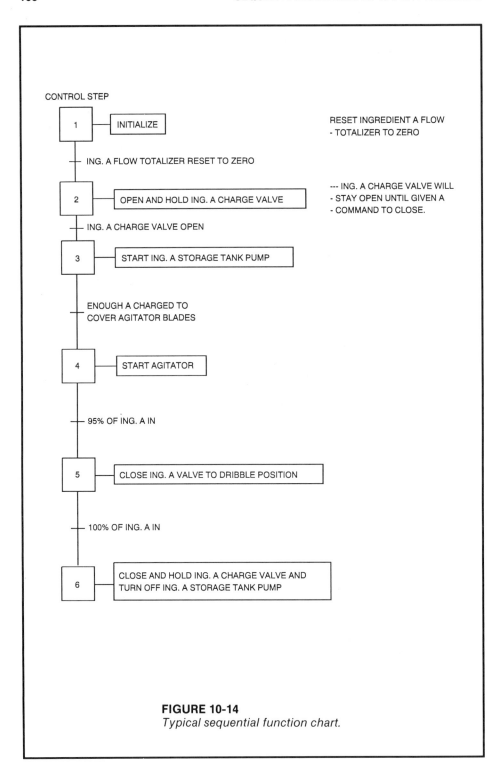

FIGURE 10-14
Typical sequential function chart.

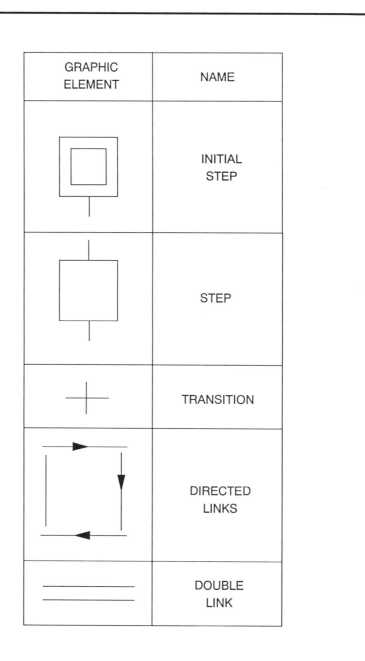

GRAPHIC ELEMENT	NAME
	INITIAL STEP
	STEP
	TRANSITION
	DIRECTED LINKS
	DOUBLE LINK

FIGURE 10-15
Elements of a sequential function chart.

The following are the small number of symbols and conventions used to construct sequential function charts (see Figure 10-15):

1. Initial Step. The initial conditions are represented by a square drawn with double lines.

2. Steps. The individual sequential steps are represented by labelled squares (they can be numbered and/or the squares can contain mnemonics that indicate the principal function for each step).

3. Actions. The actions associated with the steps are shown inside one or more rectangles to the right of each step.

4. Transitions. The transitions from one step to the next are represented by short horizontal lines.

5. Directed Links. The links indicate the flow of control. This is from top to bottom unless otherwise indicated.

6. Double Flow Line. These are used when two or more steps within a program must be synchronized.

7. Conditions. The conditions associated with the transitions can be written to the right.

An example of sequential function chart programming logic applied to the CHARGE operation of Product A is shown in Figure 10-16. This sequential function chart is drawn in accordance with IEC Standard 848 with the following exceptions: (1) the operation symbol is distinguished from phases and control steps by having a double line drawn horizontally through the center of the symbol, (2) the phase symbol is distinguished from operations and control steps by having a single line drawn horizontally through the center of the symbol, and (3) the number in the lower right-hand corner of the operation and phase symbols represents the unit where this particular activity is implemented (the unit number would not be entered at the sequence diagraming stage). Sequential function charts also provide for alternative paths, where one path is selected over another based on when the transition condition goes true (see Figure 10-17). In this example, assume that step 1 is active (the dot in the step 1 symbol indicates that this is the active state). The sequence will proceed along the path 1-2-3-5 if transition condition "A" becomes true before transition condition "B"; the sequence will proceed along the path 1-4-5 if transition condition "B" becomes true before transition condition "A".

Sequential function charts have the most potential for use as a sequence diagraming tool. They show the sequence graphically, they do a good job of showing concurrent activities, they are adaptable to generation on an engineering workstation (there may be no commercially available software packages at this time), they are flexible enough to handle procedure changes in recipes, the conversion from sequential function chart to other batch languages is relatively straightforward, they do a good job of enforcing the operation/phase/control step hierarchy, and there is an international standard (IEC 848) that shows how to prepare them (Ref. 11). In addition, the sequential function chart implementation in the international standard being developed for programmable controller languages (Ref. 12) is derived from IEC 848. Using structured English in conjunction

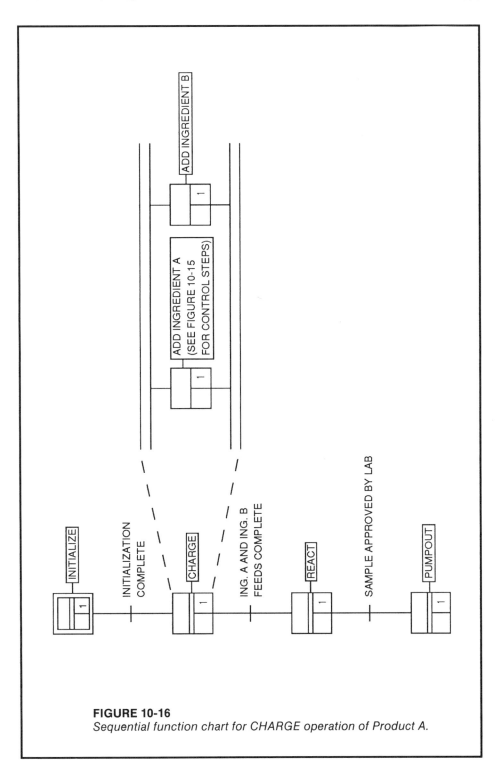

FIGURE 10-16
Sequential function chart for CHARGE operation of Product A.

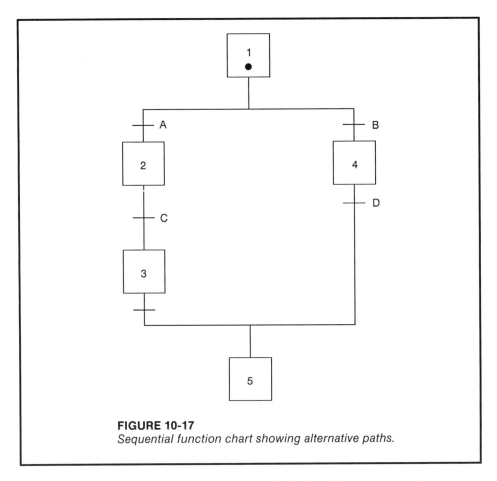

FIGURE 10-17
Sequential function chart showing alternative paths.

with sequential function charts means that, if the batch language is also sequential function chart, the only conversion necessary is from the structured English statements to the actual batch language (e.g., ladder logic or structured text).

Batch Sequencing Techniques   A number of different techniques
are used to provide batch sequencing:

1. Manual sequencing
2. Ladder logic
3. Function blocks
4. Status-oriented languages
5. Decision tables
6. General-purpose programming languages
7. Batch-oriented programming languages
8. Flowcharts
9. State diagrams

   • Sequential function chart diagrams
   • Modified state transition diagrams

Manual Sequencing A surprisingly large percentage of sequential control is being done manually, with the operator physically opening valves and starting pumps. The operator usually follows a written set of instructions, e.g., a batch sheet. This type of operation inherently introduces significant variability into the final product, e.g., usually in the batch cycle times.

Ladder Logic Ladder logic, which has its roots in relay logic, is undoubtedly the most familiar of all the programming languages for PLCs. Many DCSs also have ladder logic capability. Ladder logic is not a good choice for most batch sequencing applications, although it does work and is applied to many simple batch systems.

Some programmable controllers have built-in sequencers, but the capabilities and ease of use of these sequencers varies widely from one manufacturer to another. These sequencers generally function just like a state table, where a number of steps are available and a number of outputs can be turned on or off at each step of the sequence. A number of manufacturers have no specific sequencer block, but they can provide a sequencer based on a counter, which almost all programmable controllers include. A sequencer can also be developed using the latch relay functions that most controllers have. In this case, one latch relay is needed for each phase of the sequencer. It is important in most batch processes that the control system not lose the current step in case of a power failure. The latch relay provides that capability. In any case, additional ladder logic is needed to determine when to advance the sequencer, when a step is complete, and so on.

It is also possible, though not recommended, to implement a batch sequence in ladder logic using combinational logic (logic that depends only on the present values of inputs and outputs) instead of sequential logic (i.e., no memory elements are used). If the designer is not extremely careful with the logic design, it is possible with combinational logic for outputs to get turned on at the wrong times. For example, in sequential logic a transfer from a reactor might be permissible if the sequence is in the COOL phase and the reactor temperature is equal to or less than 100°F. It is always good practice to verify that the system is in the correct operating phase before allowing certain actions to take place. In this example, this prevents the transfer inadvertently being actuated anytime the temperature is below 100°F, which could be any time the reactor is not operating. Those kinds of cases occur much more easily when combinational logic is used, because there may be no maintained COOL state (such as with a latch relay). In addition, unless memory elements are used, the current state of the system will probably be lost on a power failure, which means the operator may not have the information needed to safely restart the batch.

Function Blocks This approach to batch control uses software-structured function blocks to implement both regulatory control and sequential control. The blocks are configured with a fill-in-the-blank display and connected with software links. Function blocks are well established in the regulatory control area and are the basis for regulatory control functions in many distributed systems and single-station digital controllers. However, when this approach is applied to complex batch processes, it tends to be limited by both the number of software blocks available and by the ease of use of these blocks for sequence control. As a result, the usual applications are for smaller batch processes.

These implementations usually use sequencer blocks provided within the programmable electronic system (PES). The logic for stepping the sequencer is developed in auxiliary logic devices (e.g., AND and OR gates). As with programmable controllers, there is absolutely no standardization on how these sequencer blocks are implemented. Some sequencer blocks very closely mimic the state table; others do not.

The use of function blocks will work for small systems where changes are not made frequently. However, they do not have the flexibility to handle complex batch processes where procedure changes are necessary.

Status-Oriented Languages This type of language has been used for many years and is a version of the state table (basically a version of the electromechanical stepping switch). The numerical step numbers (most manufacturers' implementations identify the different states as "steps" instead of "phases") are listed on the left-hand side and the discrete outputs across the top. This "matrix" of steps and outputs is programmed by inserting "ones" and "zeros" at the intersections of the steps and outputs (Ref. 13). A "one" says that the output will be actuated during that step; a "zero" says that it will not.

The simplest version of the drum programmer is a device called a drum timer. This device controls a number of discrete field devices. These devices will be turned on or off depending on which step the drum timer is in. In this case, the only condition for advancing from one step to another is time.

For most process applications, the device must also be capable of being stepped by events, e.g., the system is in Phase 4 and the batch temperature is less than 100° F. The programmer may also be advanced based on an operator action.

Many hardware types of drum programmers address only the normal sequence of events. It is not easy to modify them to take into account the abnormal events that are common in some batch systems and to take into account the interfacing necessary with the regulatory control function. One implementation of the state table approach to batch sequencing using programmable controllers does provide this capability (Ref. 13), but it uses six different state tables to give it the flexibility to perform batch logic. Each of the tables has three different sections: the step description section, the block information section, and the step data section. The steps required to run the batch process are named in the step description section. Once they are named, they are the same for all six tables. The block information section is different for each type of table.

The following are the six state tables used in this batch package (Ref. 13):

1. Discrete Output State Table. This table is used to show which outputs are energized or deenergized at each step of the sequence. The block information gives the addresses for the discrete outputs or control relays that are controlled by the various process steps. The step data section defines the characteristics of the block data for the given table. The block data are the ones and zeros that determine if an output is turned on during a given step.

2. Analog Output State Table. This table is used to define and control analog values that can be used as outputs to the process or as remote set points to other loops. The block information section contains the output address for the analog value to be stored along with the scaling factor to be used for the output. The step data section contains the analog values for each output. If no value is specified for a given step, the output value is the same as it was in the previous step.

3. Ramp Block State Table. This table is used to ramp an analog signal either up or down. The block information section defines the analog output address, the scaling factors, and the ramp update rate (allows one to configure the coarseness of the ramping function). The step data section contains the starting point for the ramp, the amount that the analog value will change with each ramp update, and the upper limit of the analog value. If the starting point for the ramp is not specified, the analog value will continue ramping from the value in a previous step.

4. Integration Block State Table. This block is used to totalize an analog value and determine when a set point has been reached. A discrete output will be activated at this point. The block information section contains the analog input address, scaling factors, update rate, and the address of the discrete output that will be activated at preset. The step data section contains the target values for the different steps and a reset feature so that the integrator can be reset at the beginning of a step, if necessary.

5. Threshold Block State Table. This block is used to turn an output or a control relay on or off based on an analog input target value and the direction of the input value change. A deadband around the target value can also be specified. The block information section contains the analog input address, scaling factors, deadband factor, and discrete output address. The step data section contains the threshold value that is used for comparison. This value, along with the deadband, determines when the discrete output will be turned on.

6. Loop Block State Table. This table defines step-based regulatory control loop requirements. It is used in conjunction with loop tables that are configured in the operator interface. The block information section contains the number of the loop and a time delay value for alarming. The step data section is set up to define the loop mode (cascade, manual, or output), the set point or output value, and the high and low alarm limits for the loop. A loop table editor screen is included so that the loop parameters for any of the 16 loops can be configured. Those 16 loops can be assigned to any of the available processes defined. They can be manipulated through the Loop Block State Table.

Once the above tables are configured, there must be some way to determine how the process will sequence from one step to the next. This is done through the Transition Table, which has three different sections: the trigger block, the jump block, and the input mask section.

The trigger block causes the process to go to the next step of the process. It can be either event-driven or time-driven. The jump block causes the process to jump to any valid step based on a watchdog timer that the user defines. The input mask section contains the information that determines which block, trigger, or jump is active in the Transition Table. If the mask is true, the process will step based on the trigger block. If the mask is false, the jump block is active. A jump will occur to a predefined step when the watchdog timer times out.

This batch package also contains two different types of calculations. This first type is step-based and occurs at the end of a process step. One use for these might be as correction factors for the next step of the process. The second type is a continuous calculation that is turned on by a discrete I/O point. It will continue to calculate as long as this discrete point is on.

Status-oriented languages are relatively easy to use, easy to understand, and work well for simple batch processes. However, some of the other higher-level languages can handle more complex process operations and have much more flexibility.

Decision Tables At least two manufacturers have batch language packages based on the use of decision tables. One of these implementations uses the decision table shown in Figure 10-7. The author's feeling is that decision tables are fine for simple batch processes. However, many batch processes today need more flexibility than this approach to batch sequencing can provide.

General-Purpose Programming Languages Any of the higher level languages (e.g., BASIC, Pascal, and FORTRAN) can be used to program batch processes as long as they have the ability to make calls to the input/output devices. However, unless they have been designed for process control and include built-in routines to handle regulatory control and sequence control, the programming can become very tedious. Another disadvantage is that they don't enforce the procedure/operation/phase/step hierarchy; it is the designer's responsibility to structure the program to provide some semblance of this hierarchy. They are also difficult to read and understand.

General-purpose programming languages are not a good choice for batch sequencing.

Batch-Oriented Programming Languages For some systems, special batch software has been developed. Most of these take the form of a BASIC-like or a Pascal-like language. The commands available in these languages are much more limited than in a general-purpose programming language, and the commands have special meaning when used for batch sequencing. The following are some typical commands available in one of these languages (Ref. 14):

Operator	Function
A. tron	Turn devices on
B. troff	Turn devices off
C. send com	Transfer data and messages
D. delay until	Synchronize step processing
E. if then else	Decision/action or decision/branch
F. repeat until	Loop until true
G. go_to	Unconditional branch

Although these types of programming languages don't enforce the hierarchy of operations/phases/control steps, they do make an attempt to enforce some structure in the program, they are specifically designed for batch control, and the resulting program is considerably more readable than a program generated with a general-purpose programming language, e.g., BASIC.

The batch-oriented programming language would work quite well in conjunction with a high-level graphical, batch sequencing language such as sequential function chart. This language would then be used to actually implement the control step logic (e.g., replace the structured English statements).

Flowcharts A relatively new language is a flowchart language that runs on a personal computer; the personal computer interfaces directly with the I/O (inputs/outputs) from various manufacturers of programmable controllers (the programmable controller is not required, only the I/O). This is a graphical control language that uses decision flowcharts to directly control a machine or process (Refs. 15 and 16).

This system provides two different levels of flowcharts: a functional flowchart that is used to initially diagram the system and a detailed flowchart that contains all the information necessary to make the machine or process function. The detailed flowchart is derived from the functional flowchart. The overall control scheme usually ends up as a hierarchy of flowcharts that can run concurrently or sequentially. The flowcharts can communicate with each other, and one flowchart can control another.

The following are the block types that are interconnected by flow lines to create the detailed flowcharts:

1. Control Block. This block causes actions to take place, such as turn on or turn off an output.

2. Decision Block. This block tests the condition of specific inputs, outputs, timers, flags, or function keys.

3. Compare block. This block tests the relative values of two numbers.

4. Wait Block. This block pauses execution of a flowchart for a specified period of time.

5. Move Block. This block is used to transfer numbers from one place to another in the system.

6. Exit Flowchart Block. This block allows for the concurrent execution of flowcharts and other language routines.

7. Display Block. This block is used to generate interactive menus that are used by the operator to control the machine or process.

8. Comment Block. This block is used to add comments to the flowcharts throughout the program.

This language has some advantages for those who are familiar with flowcharts. Since the original sequence is diagramed on the functional flowchart and that information is not lost when the functional flowchart is translated into a detailed flowchart, no time is wasted doing the sequence diagraming. The main concern is not with the language but with the hardware. Is a personal computer rugged and reliable enough to use as the main controller in a batch process? It is unclear at this time how regulatory controls, process interlock logic, and other similar logic is handled with this system. It appears that this flowchart language is primarily directed at systems that use discrete inputs and outputs.

State Diagrams State diagrams are built around a model of the process that is actually being controlled. Each block in the state diagram contains a series of statements that outline what is going to happen. After the steps in each block are executed and the required transition conditions are met, the program moves on to the next block. This is an example of a very high-level language that uses English-like statements plus graphical representation in a series of blocks. The following are some advantages of state diagrams (Ref. 17):

- Programming productivity is increased.
- Troubleshooting is easier.
- Program modifications are quick and easy.
- The program is almost self-documenting.
- The program runs faster because the only sequential logic solved is the logic for the active step and the transition conditions following that step.

Graphical programming is receiving a lot of attention at the time of this writing. Some graphical programming techniques allow control engineers to integrate discrete and regulatory control actions with sequential control using a sequential function chart format. Everything at the engineering programming level is in graphical format. The graphical format allows the user to define functional levels, PID loops, and alarms; it also helps the user define state transition requirements. One set of conditions must be met before transfer to the next functional level can occur. The objective of graphical programming packages is to talk to engineers and technicians in a simple language they can quickly master. Then they can spend more time on control strategy refinement without wasting days learning programming environments.

Sequential Function Charts

Each manufacturer that uses state diagrams in batch control packages appears to have a different implementation. That should eventually change, because, at the time of this writing, the IEC (International Electrotechnical Commission) was very close to having a programming language standard completed for programmable controllers (Ref. 12). Since one of those languages is sequential function chart, and since a number of manufacturers are advertising sequential function chart implementations designed in accordance with this proposed standard, it is inevitable that these implementations will invade the batch control system world (at the time of this writing, one DCS manufacturer has advertised a sequential function chart language for batch sequencing in their DCS; this sequential function chart language complies with the proposed IEC standard).

The ability to nest levels of sequential function charts provides an easy way to enforce the hierarchy of operations, phases, and control steps (see Figure 10-18). This figure shows unique boxes for each of these elements (as discussed under

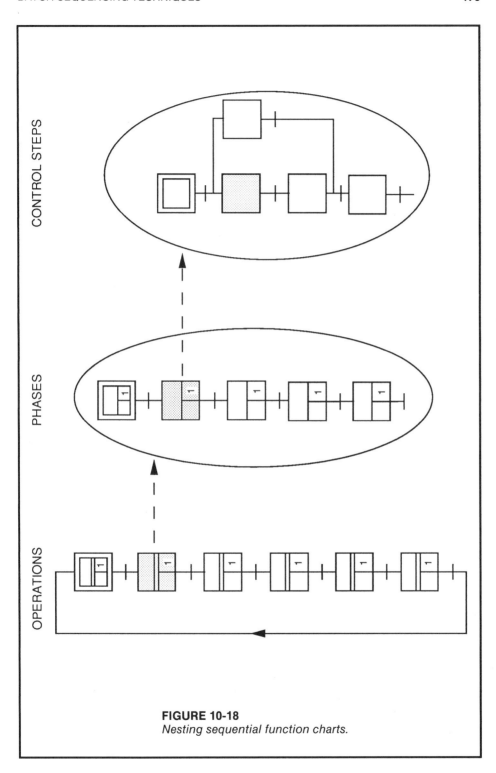

FIGURE 10-18
Nesting sequential function charts.

"sequence diagrams" earlier in this chapter). The double horizontal line indicates an operation, the single horizontal line indicates a phase, and a box with no horizontal line indicates a control step. The number in the lower right-hand corner is the unit being used. Current implementations of sequential function chart programming do not use this format; one reason is that very few of them have been designed expressly for batch control.

No operation, phase, or control step numbers are shown the sequential function chart in Figure 10-18. This is because these numbers get in the way of rearranging the sequential function charts in systems that need a great deal of flexibility. If a phase needs to be moved somewhere else in the sequence, the sequential number must be changed. A name for the operation, phase, or control step should be sufficient.

Another potential opportunity for sequential function charts is as an operator interface. Figure 10-19 shows an example. The operator would see the complete set of operations and the phases associated with the active operation overlayed (presumably using windows) onto the process graphic display. The active operation and phase would also be highlighted. The advantage of using the sequential function chart as part of the operator interface is that it lets the operator know where the batch has been, where it currently is, and where it is going. If the operator needs additional information (e.g., control steps), this information can be found on another display.

The sequential function chart language is not a complete language; it handles only the sequential portion of the program. One or more other languages, e.g., ladder logic, is needed to actually implement the control steps, process interlocks, regulatory control, etc.

Program execution time can be shortened using sequential function charts because only the active logic is solved on each scan. However, not all logic is sequential. Much of it is purely combinational, e.g., many process interlock circuits. It is very important that this logic be executed on each controller scan. This logic would be written in some other language, e.g., ladder logic, function block, structured text, or instruction list (these are the other four languages provided in the IEC programmable controller language standard).

Sequential function chart programming has some exciting possibilities for batch control. This will be especially true if a manufacturer develops a batch language around this language and allows the user to use both a batch-oriented programming language and/or ladder logic as the secondary language.

Modified State Transition Diagrams
One manufacturer offers a modified version of the state transition diagram in its distributed control system (Ref. 18). It looks like a state transition diagram, but the states and transitions are defined in the same manner as with Petri nets and sequential function charts. Figure 10-20 shows an example of how this state diagram might look, using the operations from Product A. Three levels of hierarchy are available in this state diagram, so the overview (see Figure 10-20) could show operations, the next level down could show phases, and the final level could show control steps. Three levels of hierarchy are sufficient for batch control,

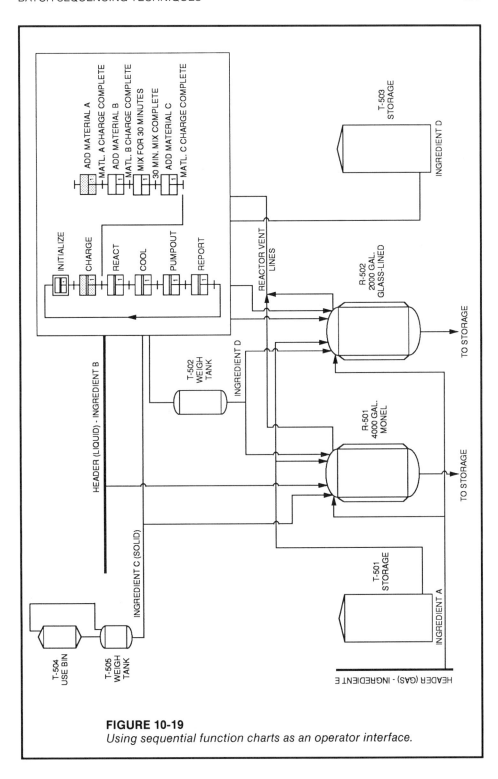

FIGURE 10-19
Using sequential function charts as an operator interface.

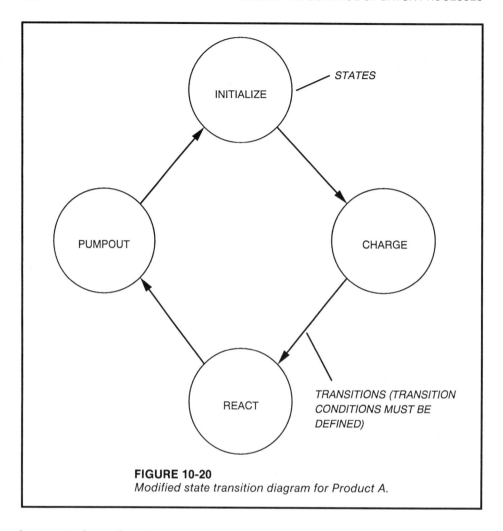

FIGURE 10-20
Modified state transition diagram for Product A.

because it does allow the enforcement of the operation/phase/control step hierarchy. Multiple transitions out of a state are permitted, so that alternate paths can be selected based on the transition condition that becomes true first.

How Are Procedures Implemented?   A procedure in a batch
recipe will be made up of operations, phases, and control steps (see Figure 10-21).

Operations Operations are generally not programmed directly in logic; they are merely divided into the appropriate number of phases. They are very useful for providing long-term hold points within the execution of a batch. They also provide a high-level combination of phases to implement a more complex function (e.g., CHARGE) that can be executed completely within a unit. Operations are not split across different units; they are the highest level of the procedure hierarchy that must be executed completely within the same unit.

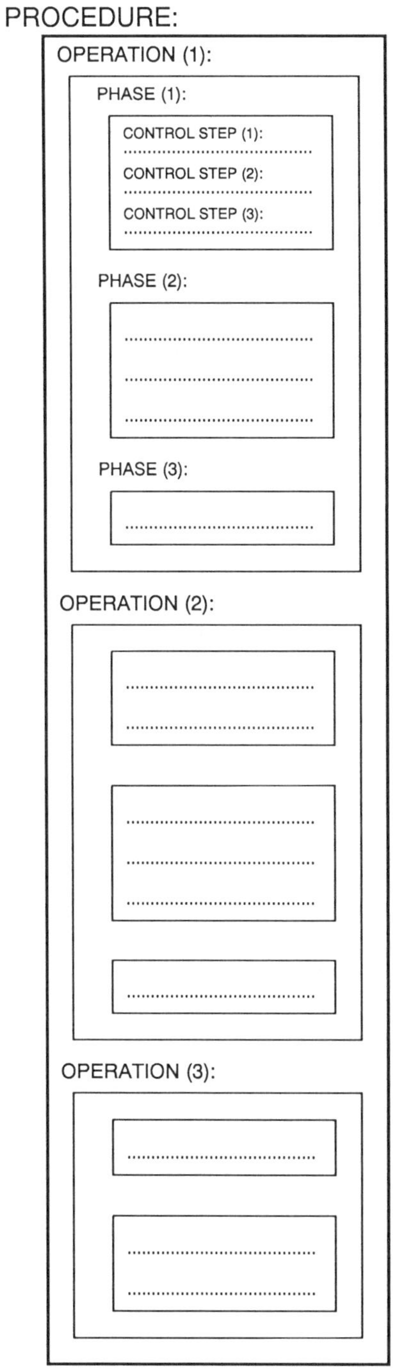

PROCEDURE:

OPERATION (1):

PHASE (1):

CONTROL STEP (1):
....

CONTROL STEP (2):
....

CONTROL STEP (3):
....

PHASE (2):

....

....

....

PHASE (3):

....

OPERATION (2):

....

....

....

....

....

....

OPERATION (3):

....

....

....

FIGURE 10-21
The components of a procedure.

Phases The phases in an operation may be implemented directly in logic, e.g., when a sequencer is used to advance from one phase to the next. An implementation of this type results in a very superficial definition of a phase.

The NAMUR Committee (Ref. 19) describes a phase as consisting of three parts: a "Control Part," a "Parameter Part," and a "Communications Part."

Control Part

This part of the phase consists of one or several sequence chains in which control steps, follow-up conditions, and output commands are fixed. These define the control step sequence for normal operation by giving (Ref. 19):

- control step chain,
- AND/OR breakdown,
- follow-up conditions, and
- control instructions

for normal uninterrupted execution of a phase. They also define the control step sequence for initialization, which accomplishes tasks that must be carried out only once at the beginning of the phase. Finally, these sequence chains define the control step sequence for abnormal conditions. Monitoring is required in parallel with the executing procedure and must include provisions for action in case abnormal conditions arise.

Parameter Part

This consists of (variable) parameters for follow-up conditions and commands. For a chemical reaction, these parameters might be (Ref. 19):

- ingredient name,
- normal phase duration,
- operational parameters (e.g., quantities, set point and limiting values for process quantities, durations),
- basic states of equipment,
- required level before activation of an agitator, and
- required temperature before addition of catalyst.

With regard to operating personnel and required qualifications, these parameters might be (Ref. 19):

- delay time (until sampling, etc.),
- acceptable range of analysis values,
- visual testing, etc.,
- acceptable action initiated by the operator,
- operator requirements,
- charge data for the batch log, and
- text output for operation and abnormal conditions logs.

Logistics parameters might include (Ref.19):

- maximum storage period,
- storage temperature range,

- reservation and use of equipment and paths, and
- location data (from, to).

Communication Part
The final part of a phase is used for:

- announcing the end of the phase,
- announcing an abnormal condition,
- describing the current state of a phase, and
- preparing data for the batch log.

Control Steps The control step is the smallest functional unit of a program sequence chain in a phase. It is generally concerned with partial control and consists of one or more control instructions, usually in connection with logical structures of the type:

IF....THEN....ELSE

For example:

If analog value greater than limiting value
THEN close valve AND print text

The commands that are used to implement control steps generally fall into five categories (Ref. 1):

1. Commands that manipulate contact outputs, contact input desired states, devices, and flags
2. Commands that interface with the regulatory control functions
3. Commands that perform arithmetic calculations
4. Commands that communicate with operators, supervisors, etc.
5. Commands that make decisions and control the direction and timing of control steps

The control step is activated whenever the follow-up conditions assigned to it are met. The control step precipitates internal and external actions by means of the control instructions contained in it.

Generalized Phase Implementation   Shaw (Ref. 20) defines a well-designed batch program as one that includes five basic sections. These sections are the INITIATION section, the CONTROL section, the OPERATOR OVERRIDE LOGIC, the ERROR-FAULT-HANDLING section, and the TERMINATION section. These five sections apply directly to each phase in the batch program.

Initiation The INITIATION section of the batch program is used to verify required preconditions. This ensures that the program won't execute at the wrong time or create a problem by its execution. Whenever a phase is initiated, whether by operator request or by some automatic means, three basic questions should be considered before actually executing the phase (Ref. 20):

1. Is this phase permitted? Does the requester have the right to ask for this phase to proceed?

2. Should it be performed? Is it okay to execute this phase at this particular time? It may be that this phase is allowed only with certain products or at certain points in the sequence. If so, compliance with these restrictions can be tested here.

3. Will it be successful? This question deals with resource checking. If the phase requires that a given piece of plant equipment be available or that a certain quantity of raw materials be available, a check for these things can be made at this point in the program. Why start an addition to a batch reactor if it is known that there are insufficient raw materials to complete the addition?

The initiation section might be the time when the operator has to enter charge quantities. It usually is also the point where the program would check to see that all interlocks are satisfied before allowing the phase to continue.

Control The CONTROL section is the logic that actually manipulates the plant equipment and causes the processing of the raw materials into final product during the normal execution of the phase. A major requirement of the CONTROL section is to keep the operator informed of exactly where the batch program is in the sequence. This requirement can be satisfied if the program advises the operator of every major control action being taken by the batch program.

There is also a need for some control that can be used by the operator to alter the flow of the batch program. HOLD and FAULT LOGIC are two ways to implement operator control. If the operator has some means to signal two separate events to the batch program, the program can be designed to interrupt its normal flow and return control to the operator or take a branch to predefined fault logic. This will allow the operator to successfully manipulate the program execution in the event of problems or when alternate processing actions (e.g., bypassing a phase, inserting a new phase, overriding the linking conditions between phases, terminating a phase, or restarting a phase after an interruption) are required.

Operator Override Logic The OPERATOR OVERRIDE LOGIC section of the batch program works in conjunction with the CONTROL section and serves two basic purposes:

1. It monitors the process if a "hold" is in effect and will cause a safe shutdown if the process becomes unstable or otherwise dangerous.

2. It also allows the operator to re-enter his main processing (CONTROL section) logic at whatever phase is appropriate after the "hold" condition is canceled. This prevents the operator from having to complete the batch manually.

Error-Fault-Handling Logic The ERROR-FAULT-HANDLING LOGIC section defines the control steps that must be executed to handle abnormal conditions, e.g., the case where process conditions could arise that require normal processing to be aborted for safety reasons and special fault-handling or even emergency shutdown actions to be implemented. These fault conditions should normally be tested by the batch logic, but the operator can detect some faults that the batch control system may not be capable of detecting.

Termination The TERMINATION section of the phase must signal that the phase is complete and, if necessary, restore the plant equipment to a condition that allows it to be used for the next phase.

Operational Modes and Operational States

It has always been difficult to define the difference between a mode and a state; what the difference is between manual, semiautomatic, and automatic modes; what the consequences are of an emergency shutdown; etc. The person(s) who is designing the batch control system usually has the responsibility to establish guidelines for these areas. The sequence diagraming techniques and the batch languages discussed earlier in this chapter are generally applicable to the normal (run) state of the batch process. The real question is: how is the relationship between the normal (run) state and the other states and modes of the system defined. It appears that some form of the state diagram may offer a possible solution to this problem.

State Transition Matrix One DCS manufacturer (Ref. 21) has made an attempt at defining a technique for establishing the relationship between the normal (run) operational state and other operational states and operational modes of the system. They provide a special form of the state transition diagram called a state transition matrix that can be used to define this relationship (see Figure 10-22).

GEMMA Another approach is called GEMMA (Refs. 22 and 23), which is a Design Guide for Start and Stop Modes. GEMMA is a graphical checklist that allows the designer to define from the beginning all of the operational modes and operational states of a machine or process and what they mean to the machine or process. GEMMA groups all the different modes and states of a machine or process into: production procedures, stop procedures, and failure procedures.

Production procedures include all modes and states that are used to obtain added value expected from the machine or process and that are indispensable for production. Stop procedures account for the times when a machine is stopped for external reasons, e.g., end of the work shift, lack of raw materials, etc. Failure procedures describe all the internal reasons for stopping the machine or process. The disposition of these three types of procedures on a GEMMA is shown in Figure 10-23 (Refs. 22 and 23).

Production Procedures
Within the production procedures, GEMMA defines six states and/or modes:

1. F1 Normal Production. This is the normal operating state for the machine or process.
2. F2 Start-up. This state is used for any initialization requirements, e.g., pressurizing with nitrogen, prefilling a weigh tank, etc.
3. F3 Shutdown. This state allows for emptying and cleaning before stopping the process or between batches.

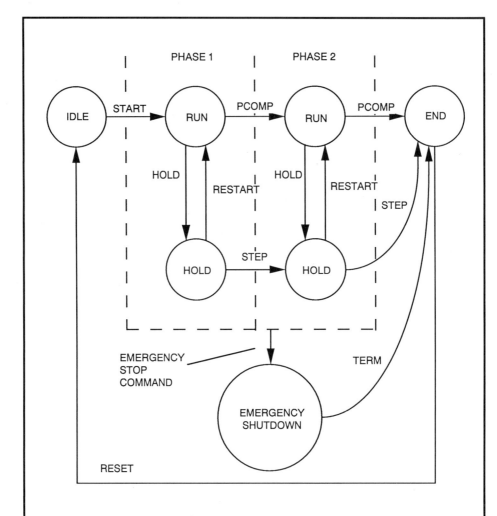

FIGURE 10-22
State transition matrix for operational modes and operational states.

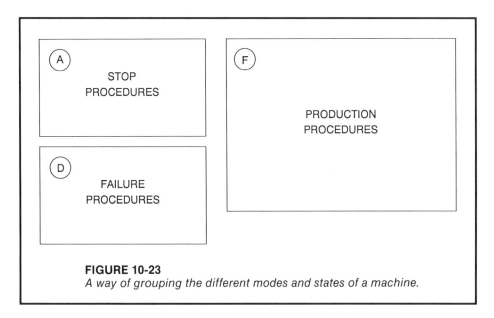

FIGURE 10-23
A way of grouping the different modes and states of a machine.

4. F4 Unsequenced Test Mode. This mode allows the machine or process to be sequenced without following the usual sequence of operation (e.g., a JOG or LOCAL mode).

5. F5 Sequenced Test Mode. In this mode, the cycle can be followed phase by phase in the normal sequence. The machine or process may or may not be producing during this mode.

6. F6 Calibration Mode. This mode allows the elements, loops, and devices installed in the system to be adjusted, tested, recalibrated, etc.

Stop Procedures

Seven stop states have been identified by GEMMA:

1. A1 Initial State Stop. This corresponds to the zero energy state, where the process is shut down but the control system is still energized.

2. A2 Requested Stop at the End of the Procedure. A2 is a transient state to A1. At the end of the normal production cycle, the machine or process stops and then transfers to the A1 state.

3. A3 Requested Stop in a Determined State. This is a transient state to A4. Now the machine or process will stop at some intermediate stage of the procedure.

4. A4 Obtained Stop. In this state, the machine or process is stopped at some other state than the end of the production cycle.

5. A5 Preparation to Restart after a Failure. In this state, all requested actions after a failure take place, e.g., flushing the system.

6. A6 Production Reset to the Initial State. The machine or process is set back to the beginning of the production cycle (either manually or automatically).

7. A7 Production Reset in a Determined State. The machine or process is set to a position ready to resume production from a predetermined state (either manually or automatically).

Failure Procedures

GEMMA has identified three failure states:

1. D1 Emergency Stop. This state takes all the necessary actions to protect people, the environment, and production equipment from unsafe occurrences.
2. D2 Troubleshooting and Repair. This state allows the machine or process to be examined after a failure and to take actions to allow a restart.
3. D3 Derated Production. This state allows the machine or process to continue production, even after a failure. The production rate may be derated; the machine or process may have to be operated manually. This might be the case where a failure in the system has occurred, but the operator must take the batch to a safe state where it can be held for a period of time.

The GEMMA Relationship Figure 10-24 shows the relationship between the various procedures, operational modes, and operational states (Ref. 10-22). The heavy dashed line shows all modes/states actually involved in production. This drawing should be considered as a starting point for the designer. Operational states and operational modes can be eliminated if not required; additional ones can be added. The designer must then establish the transition conditions necessary to move from one operation mode and/or operational state to another.

With the current batch control system offerings, the designer has the responsibility to implement these modes, states, and transition conditions within the control system. As this area receives more attention, more manufacturers will provide techniques, such as the state transition matrix, to minimize the effort required by the batch control system designer.

EXERCISES

10.1 What problems would be encountered in the CHARGE operation of Example 10-1 if ingredient A flow totalizer reached its preset before ingredient B flow totalizer? How could this problem be solved?

10.2 In the ADD INGREDIENT C phase of Example 10-1, what other technique could be used to determine that the transfer line between the pneumatic conveying system and the reactor is clear other than time? Which gives the more positive indication that the transfer line is clear of solids?

10.3 Convert the flowchart of Figure 10-1 to a decision table.

10.4 Develop Petri net diagrams and sequential function charts for the REACT operation of Example 10-1.

10.5 Compare time sequence diagrams with the sequence matrix and list relative advantages and disadvantages of each.

10.6 What are the disadvantages of using structured English logic as the overall sequence diagraming tool?

10.7 Discuss the relative advantages and disadvantages of Petri nets as compared with sequential function charts.

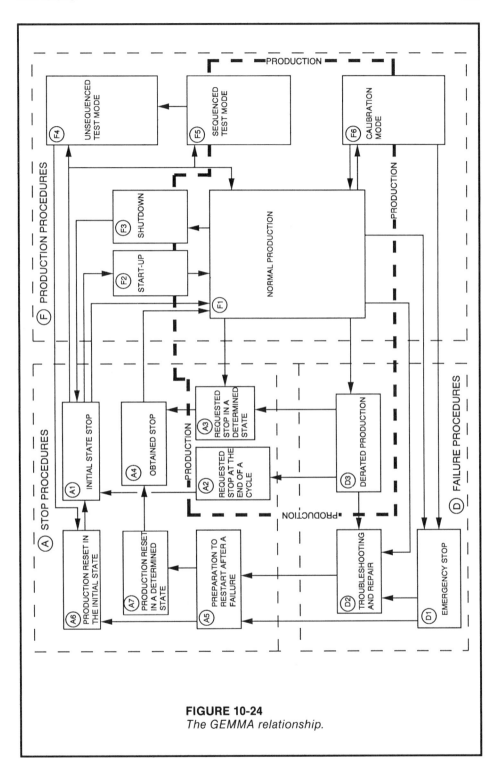

FIGURE 10-24
The GEMMA relationship.

REFERENCES

1. Rosenof, H. P., and A. Ghosh, *Batch Process Automation: Theory and Practice*, Van Nostrand Reinhold Company, New York, 1987.

2. Ghosh, A., "Modular Structuring of Batch Control Logic," ISA/82, PAPER #82-840.

3. ISO 5807, Information Processing — Documentation Symbols and Conventions for Data, Program and System Flowcharts, Program Network Charts and System Resources Charts, International Organization for Standardization, 1985.

4. Sakaki, Y., and K. Matsunaga, "A Decision Table Approach to Sequence Control of Batch Processes," ISA/86, Paper #86-2698.

5. Rosenof, H. P., "Diagraming Method Simplifies Sequential Control Documentation," *Control Engineering*, March 1981.

6. Application Note AP$:021, "Developing a Batch Control Strategy Using Batch Formalism and Time Sequence Diagraming," Fisher Controls, October 1983.

7. Habib, A, "Sequence Matrix Simplified Software Documentation," *INTECH*, July 1990.

8. Barnard, J., "State Transition Diagrams: Specifying Programmable Controller Logic without Relay Ladders," *InTech*, October 1985.

9. Weingarten, W.; R. Filer; P. Lewis; and W. Weingarten, "Improved PLC Programming Techniques," *Programmable Controls*, May/June 1988.

10. Cotter, S. M., and A. T. Woodward, "Designing Better Programs for Controllers," *C&I*, November 1986.

11. IEC 848, "Preparation of Function Charts for Control Systems," International Electrotechnical Commission, 1988.

12. "Draft — Programmable Controllers, Part 3: Programming Languages," International Electrotechnical Commission, December 1988.

13. "TIBATCH Control System," Texas Instruments, 1986.

14. Duff, S. B., and R. E. Nelson, "Advanced Technology Reduces Batch Hardware and Software Implementation Costs," ISA/87, Paper #87-1276.

15. Groden, B. M., "FloPro: A New Programming Language for Industrial Control," Proceedings of the 17th Annual ESD/SMI International Programmable Controllers Conference & Exhibition, April 12–14, 1988.

16. Barb, M., "Using a Personal Computer for High-Speed, Real-Time Machine Control," *Control Engineering*, November 1988.

17. "The State Language Revolution," Adatek.

18. "CAPE Software," Data Acquisition Systems, Inc., ICON 1000 System.

19. "Development of Sequence Controls for Charge Processes with Variable Formulation from Pretailored Functional Modules," NAMUR Committee, July 1985.

20. Shaw, W. T., "Structured Design Produces Good Batch Control Programs," *Control Engineering*, November 1983.

21. Sugiyama, H.; Y. Umehara; and E. Smith, "A Sequential Function Chart (SFC) Language for Batch Control," ISA/89, Paper #89-0700.

22. Cloutier, G., and J-J. Paques, "GEMMA, The Complementary Tool of the Grafcet," Unknown Source.

23. "ADEPA:GEMMA, the Run/Stop Modes Study Guide," Unknown Source.

11
Batch Management

Introduction   To meet the diverse needs of today's marketplace, the trend is towards small-batch multiproduct plants, where each unit handles numerous different products and each product passes through several units during the execution of the batch. With conventional batch control systems, each unit and equipment module may be controlled separately. However, with the new batch plants, the challenge is to (1) synchronize sequential, regulatory, and discrete control in several units, (2) control all equipment working in parallel, (3) utilize each unit and equipment module effectively, and (4) maximize throughput—all to achieve total management of equipment and resources (Ref. 1).

The user should have the ability to set up a production schedule, monitor actual production against that schedule, and make changes as necessitated by delays in any batch. The operator must have the ability to (1) establish/modify the plan for what batch is in what vessel throughout the day, week, or month, (2) determine what batch is currently in each vessel and the time remaining in that vessel, and (3) monitor the plan and current status for any particular batch (Ref. 2).

What Is Batch Management?   In the batch model of Figure 4-7, the Train/Line level (Process Supervision) is the interface between the process control levels and the higher-level business systems. The Train/Line level functions as a supervisor and coordinator for the Unit, Equipment Module, and Loop/Device/Element levels. In the control model of Figure 5-1, Batch Management is the interface level between the control activities associated with direct process control (e.g., safety interlocking, regulatory/discrete control, and sequential control) and the higher level management control activities (e.g., recipe management and production scheduling). This relationship is shown in Figure 11-1 (Ref. 3).

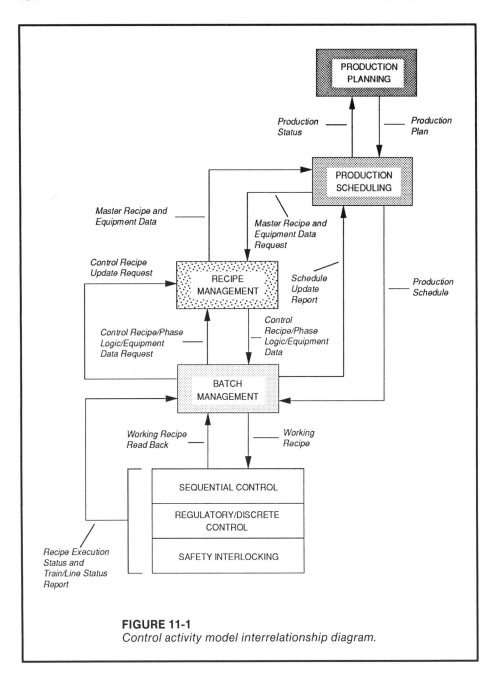

FIGURE 11-1
Control activity model interrelationship diagram.

Production Scheduling The production scheduling activity matches production requirements (i.e., the production plan and the master recipes) with the availability of raw materials and units and organizes unit utilization as a function of the time required to perform a batch and any product incompatibilities.

This results in a production schedule, which is passed to batch management, that shows what to make and where to make it. This scheduling activity needs information on what materials are needed to manufacture a given product, what equipment in each train/line can be used to manufacture this product, and what the operating rates for the various trains/lines are. It gets this information from the recipe management activity. This activity also updates the production planning activity on a periodic basis.

Production scheduling is discussed in more detail in Chapter 13.

Recipe Management The recipe management activity maintains a data base on master recipes, control recipes, and phase logic for various units within the trains/lines associated with this activity. It also maintains data on operating rates for the trains/lines as a whole, in addition to the times required to accomplish the operations that can be run in a particular unit. This activity provides master recipe data and equipment data to the production scheduling activity. It provides control recipes, phase logic (where the implementation needs this information), and equipment data for the batch management activity. This equipment data is more detailed (e.g., it provides times required to execute an operation in a particular unit; this information is used for dynamic scheduling) than the equipment data supplied to production scheduling. It also updates the control recipes stored in its database based on a request from batch management.

Recipe management is discussed in more detail in Chapter 12.

Batch Management Batch management receives the production schedule from the production scheduling activity and determines what resources are required to manufacture these products. It requests control recipes from recipe management for the products included in the production schedule. This could be a new control recipe if the product has not been manufactured before. It modifies these control recipes as necessary and downloads the recipes to the process supervision and process control levels (sequential control, regulatory/discrete control, and safety interlocking), which then execute the batch. Batch management performs a similar role in relationship to the control model that the Train/Line level performs in the batch model; it supervises and coordinates the control activities that are performed at the lower levels. It also monitors the execution of the batches (recipe execution status), collects batch data (e.g., process variable values, batch tracking, and equipment status within the train/line), and changes resource allocations as necessary to carry the batches through to completion.

Batch management may be associated with trains/lines or it may be associated with some kind of equipment path—a distinction between what is a physical or a logical line. Batch management is only looking at a set of units associated with a batch; therefore, production scheduling is responsible for deciding which batch management system will be used for each batch of product.

A batch could be suspended and resubmitted to production scheduling for finishing later. Therefore, records on the batch status must contain information about the state the batch was in at the time it was stopped, in addition to other data that is collected as part of the batch history. In some plants, a batch can be suspended and removed from the processing equipment (packaged for temporary storage) and be out of the control of batch management. Therefore, batch history information should be associated with the working recipe so that it can easily be retrieved when the batch is reprocessed.

A batch process is usually made up of a number of units and equipment modules (such as storage tanks, premixers, and reactors) that constitute a train/line. Batch management looks at how a batch of product routes through various units and makes sure that each batch goes through the various units in the right sequence. A batch management system should allow operators to look at the entire train/line, see various batches going through the various units, and identify where each batch is, what it's doing, and its state (Ref. 4).

The batch management system selects, assigns, and releases units; provides batch supervision and tracking; generates the working batch recipe; and provides for on-line collection of batch history (Ref. 5). A batch management system assigns units to each batch being processed, releases the unit when all associated operations are completed, and supervises the production flow from one unit to the next.

Kano lists some functions required by the batch management system (Ref. 1):

- *Recipe Scheduling.* Recipe execution schedules are based on the production schedule; they are entered manually by the operator or automatically downloaded from a supervisory computer.
- *Recipe Dispatch.* A scheduled recipe is dispatched (started or initiated).
- *Recipe status management.* The status of the currently active recipe is managed: if the unit is now being used by another recipe, then the next procedure to use the unit must wait for the first recipe to finish. It is usually desirable that the statuses of the recipes and the units be managed separately, since there are so many possible status combinations. It is usually sufficient to monitor for statuses such as ready (wait until the start conditions are satisfied), active (operation/phase now being executed), logging (now gathering data), complete (recipe execution ended), and aborted (abnormal end due to unit problems).
- *Recipe management in "operations" extending across several unit controllers.* In many batch control systems, the units used in a recipe may extend over several unit controllers. In this case, the recipe is divided into operations, where each operation corresponds to a unit. This will involve the movement of batch data to several unit controllers and the start of operations in other controllers. In this case, the overall process may be managed by a specific unit controller (e.g., the unit controller that includes the first operation), by a cell controller, or some other controller.
- *Transmission of recipe-end data to a higher level activity.* At recipe end, the results data is acquired, and it may — as required — be transmitted to a higher level activity, e.g., a batch historian in the recipe management activity.
- *Management of free units.* Usually, the unit used by an operation is fixed; but where there are several identical units that may be used inter-

changeably, a batch may be started as soon as any of them becomes free. However, just because a unit is free does not mean that it can be used; other conditions may have to be met, such as sharing the load evenly between all the units. It may be necessary to manage such cases using a supervisory computer.

A Batch Management Model
A batch management model is shown in Figure 11-2, which is a more detailed breakdown of the batch management block of Figure 11-1. Four primary functions are concerned with making a batch of product: collecting and managing batch data, managing batch resources, selecting a control recipe and transforming it into a working recipe, and initiating and supervising the execution of the batch.

Collect/Manage Batch Data The *collect/manage batch data* activity provides data collection and management associated with batches of material as they are processed in a plant. Batch data maintained by the system include the recipe information required to manufacture the product and the actual results achieved for each batch (data at batch end). This capability supports:

- continuous data collection for each batch, batch-end data collection, "snapshot" data collection at any point in the batch process, event/alarm tracking (includes alarms complete with trip, acknowledge, and clear times; recipe download events; operator loop changes; detailed configuration and system changes; abnormal operation status; etc.), and reporting;
- the simultaneous monitoring of many different batches of material;
- the monitoring of relationships among batches of material as the materials separate and merge within the process (batch tracking);
- operator-entered comments into the batch records during or after production (these comments become part of the retained batch information);
- the storing of a history of all feedstocks, intermediates, and end products for material and batch genealogy.

Very high reliability is needed in data collection, for both event- and batch-associated data. If data is not accurate, it won't get used for managing the plant resources, and the stored data is worthless. This goes beyond merely the collecting of data; it also includes the archiving and retrieval of data. Data must be associated by batch events (and across multiple batches) and not only on time-based retrieval. The user needs to be able to define the data that should be collected during the batch.

The operator should have the ability to enter data (with the appropriate date, time, and the unit where the batch executed) into the database. The following are examples of data that has a different time/batch/unit stamp that the operator must have the ability to enter into the records:

- laboratory data that is not available at the time of the batch,
- data such as manual readings (e.g., a local reactor pressure) that are not immediately available; and
- operator-entered data that tells the system what time/batch/unit it is.

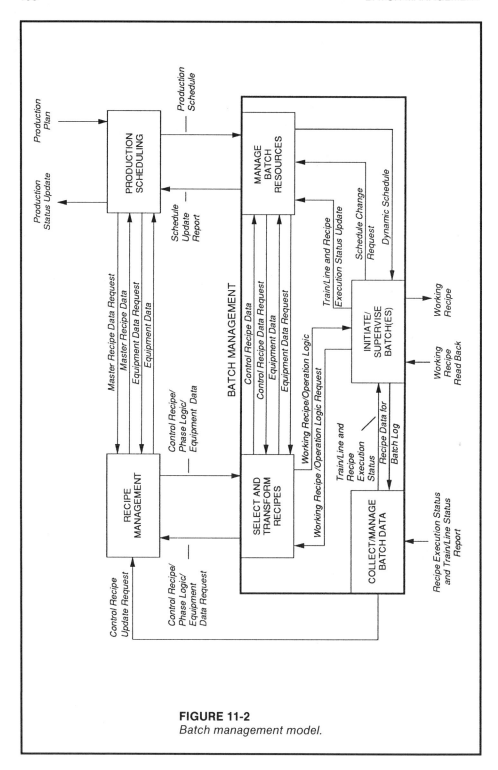

FIGURE 11-2
Batch management model.

Lower-level activities must be able to accrue the data until the data can be passed on to a storage device at a higher-level activity (other implementations could also prevent data loss). A secure way to get this information to the higher-level business systems must be available, e.g., MRP (material requirements planning) packages.

The user must have the ability to generate reports; both preformatted and custom formats (free format) must be available. The capability to allow trends/data from remote sources to be embedded in the reports is necessary, e.g., an SPC (statistical process control) chart from another control system.

Manage Batch Resources The *manage batch resources* activity is responsible for making sure that resources are available so that a batch can be manufactured as dictated by the production schedule. However, it should be realized that the production schedule generated by the production scheduling activity is usually a rough pass at a schedule. For example, it may specify what train/line to manufacture the product in but not what units should be used or the size of the batches. Therefore, dynamic scheduling must be accomplished within this activity. At the time of this writing, this dynamic scheduling is usually done manually. In the future, the dynamic schedule should be generated by computer so that the optimum use of the batch resources can be obtained (see Chapter 13).

The production schedule is not a dynamic document; the production schedule may be generated once a day, once a week, or so forth. However, batch management is an on-line activity; it needs to work as close to real time as possible. This means that the schedule may need to be adjusted several times a day because of equipment problems, processing problems, etc. That is the function of dynamic scheduling.

The *manage batch resources* activity also provides a mechanism for determining how shared resources will be allocated to the various batches. This may be as simple as "first there, first served," i.e., the first batch that needs the resource gets the use of that resource. However, often, priorities must be met in determining how shared resources should be allocated. For example, one batch of product is more valuable than another batch of product; the most valuable product may get the use of the common resource even though the other batch is ready to use the resource first.

This module receives the production schedule from the production scheduling activity and schedule change requests from the *initiate/supervise batch(es)* module; it provides the dynamic schedule to the *initiate/supervise batch(es)* module. It also receives the status of the equipment in the trains/lines and the status of currently executing batches; it updates the production scheduling activity on the status of the batch plant. This module needs the control recipes and equipment data on the various units so that it can generate the dynamic schedule; it receives this information from the *select and transform recipes* module.

Select/Transform Recipes The *select/transform recipes* module provides the capability to select a control recipe from recipe management, to modify that control recipe to make it a working recipe (e.g., by sizing the batch), and then to forward that control recipe to the *initiate/supervise batch* module. It can also retrieve equipment data information from recipe management as requested by the *manage batch resources* module. On receipt of a working recipe request for a specific set of production equipment from the *initiate/supervise batch(es)* module, the *select/transform recipes* module in the batch management system allows the operator to request a control recipe for a specific set of equipment from the recipe management system. This control recipe can then be modified, if necessary, to create a working recipe that is sent to the *initiate/supervise batch(es)* module.

The following are some desirable features of the *select and transform recipes* module (Ref. 6):

1. Operators must be able to modify recipe information without corrupting the integrity of the control recipe.

2. A complete audit trail must be developed that details recipes selected and equipment used.

3. Operators should be able to make recipe changes without costly software modifications.

4. The operator should have the ability to access any recipe.

5. The operator should be able to change a recipe on line.

The control recipe should contain at least a list of equivalent equipment or the name of a list; it may, or may not, contain the exact equipment. This may be left up to batch management to decide when the working recipe is created. The equipment size is specified at this time because the formula portion of the control recipe is sized. Some of the value of the control recipe is that it gives batch management a list of available resources; it sizes the batch, thus affecting the schedule. Batch management allows a user to modify the procedure and formula on the fly, essentially modifying the working recipe.

If there are equipment problems during the execution of a batch, this module may receive a request for operation logic to run on a particular unit from the *initiate/supervise batch(es)* module. It then requests the phase logic from recipe management for that operation and unit and provides that information back to the *initiate/supervise batch(es)*] module.

Initiate/Supervise Batch(es) The *initiate/supervise batch(es)* module down-loads a working recipe to the batch control system, initiates the batch, and then monitors the batch as it executes to make sure that it travels through the various units in the correct sequence. It also tells the *collect/manage batch data* module what data needs to be collected on each batch. If multiple destinations (i.e., multiple reactors) for the recipes are possible, the operator may need to select the appropriate destination for downloading. Some security checks are necessary at this point (Ref. 7):

1. Have the system compare the selected recipe with a list of allowable control programs and inhibit final downloading until the operator activates the appropriate control programs.

2. Have the system make sure that the selected recipe is compatible with the selected process equipment.

The *initiate/supervise batch(es)* module controls the transportation of batches and the selection and booking of process equipment, either automatically or according to operator commands. The actual transport of batches between process sections can be carried out fully automatically or semiautomatically. This module receives the dynamic schedule from the *manage batch resources* module and requests the needed control recipes from the *select and transform recipes* module. It continuously receives updates on the status of both the equipment and the batches from the lower levels for its own use; it also provides this information to the *manage batch resources* module so that its effect on the schedule can be determined.

If there are equipment problems that would prevent a batch from completing, this module can request operation logic from the *select and transform recipes* module and a change of equipment from the *manage batch resources* module so that the batch can continue. It can then download this information to the control system.

The following are some desirable features of the *initiate/supervise batch(es)* module:

1. Batches can be configured to start automatically at pre-entered dates/times, to be triggered manually upon reaching earliest possible start date/time, or they can be triggered by an input from a lower level activity.

2. The operator can be notified in advance of scheduled conflicts in the usage of both units and shared equipment.

3. A status display can be provided that shows the operator the progress of recipe downloads as commands are being sent to the unit controllers.

4. After downloading the information, an automatic read-back and verify function can be invoked to confirm the data transfer (unless it can be shown that the security of the transmission is such that the read-back verification is not necessary).

5. The operator can change the list of scheduled batches by adding batches to the list, deleting batches from the list, or modifying the order of the batches in the list. This should be possible on line, subject to a variety of necessary manufacturing permissives.

6. The operator should be able to change the units that will be used in executing the batch while the batch is running.

7. Batch execution status and train/line status can be monitored on a continuous basis and before and after each recipe download to assure proper control and execution of batches.

8. A recipe cannot be loaded into an incompatible reactor or to a process already running.

9. The operator has the ability to start or abort an operation on a unit.

10. The operator can add/remove a batch of material to or from a unit.

11. The operator can retrieve real-time data on batch and unit activities.

Executing a Batch
The time or the sequence that a batch should be initiated is entered into the list of scheduled batches manually or automatically

(Ref. 1). Note that a particular recipe can be implemented more than once by entering that recipe multiple times in the list of scheduled batches. The number of times a recipe is executed is not a recipe parameter; it is a production scheduling parameter.

When the scheduled start time or sequence has been reached, the recipe is downloaded to the control system. To verify that the downloading occurred correctly, the recipe may be read back from the control system and compared to the original recipe in the *initiate/supervise batch(es)* module. When the downloading is confirmed as correct, a "start batch" command is sent to the control system.

The execution progress of the recipe should be displayed on the operator's console; this progress should be updated as events occur throughout the execution of the recipe.

Once the execution of the recipe is started, the *initiate/supervise batch(es)* module manages the sequence of execution, checks conditions for transition from unit to unit (e.g., whether the unit to be used for the next operation(s) is free or not), and synchronizes the use of any shared equipment.

When execution is completed, a batch end signal is sent to the *collect/manage batch data* module, which uploads the actual results data (this data could be sent continuously throughout the execution of the batch; this is an implementation problem). When the data has been collected, the batch is complete, and the recipe can be removed from the *collect/manage batch data* module.

How Much Batch Management Activity Is Required? Several

different levels of interaction are required with the batch management system, depending on how recipes are implemented in the batch control system. During execution, the working recipes are typically performed as phases within the operations, assigned to units, and processed sequentially or in parallel. The recipes act on the process via the basic measuring and control functions (dedicated or freely programmable functions).

The following are some of the ways recipes are being implemented in batch control systems:

1. The procedure logic for the working recipe for each different product is software coded into a unit controller. Formula parameters are downloaded when a working recipe is ready to be executed. This implementation requires very little interaction with batch management as the batch is being executed other than collecting data for reports and the batch status displays. However, it requires a lot of memory in the unit controller since all the procedure logic must be resident in the controller. It is also not very flexible; if an equipment problem occurs, the operator may be forced to complete the batch manually.

2. The phase logic for all the possible phases that can be executed for the desired products is software coded into the unit controller. Part of the formula parameter file that is downloaded is an order of execution for the phases required for a particular working recipe. The complete order of phases must be downloaded at the start of the batch. This requires less memory than the first system described

above, because complete procedures do not have to be coded into the unit controller, which means that phase logic does not have to be duplicated. However, it is not very flexible, because the order of phases for the complete procedure must be downloaded at the beginning of the batch. As in system 1 above, if an equipment problem occurs, the operator may have to complete the batch manually. This system also does not require much interaction with batch management as the batch is being executed.

3. This system is implemented very similar to system 2 above, except that the order of phases for the complete procedure does not have to be downloaded at the beginning of the batch; the order of phases is downloaded an operation at a time. This system provides much more flexibility than the first two systems. If an equipment problem occurs, the operator may have to operate on manual, but only until the present operation is completed. The next operation can be downloaded so that different equipment will be used to implement the operation, which allows the operator to bypass failed equipment. This system also provides the ability to split the procedure among several unit controllers, operation by operation. This system requires a higher level of interaction with batch management as the batch is being executed.

4. This system downloads the procedure an operation at a time to the appropriate unit controller. When an operation is downloaded, the phase logic is included as part of the file that is downloaded. This requires the least amount of memory in the unit controller, because the only phase logic that resides in the unit controller is that which is needed for the present operations being implemented. This system also provides the flexibility of being able to execute the recipe over several different unit controllers. To provide the ultimate flexibility, the system should allow several operations to be executed at the same time, where each of those operations is part of a different working recipe. Partial downloads should be possible; for example, while an operation for one working recipe is executing, the system should allow an operation for another working recipe to be downloaded without stopping the execution of the first operation. This system requires a high level of interaction with batch management as the batches are being executed. This makes it possible for concurrently running recipes to access the same units successively, which means that several batches can be run interleaved in the same train/line, thus achieving optimum utilization of the train/line capacity.

Building and Downloading Working Recipes   Figure 11-3 shows the on-line operation of building control recipes from phases and parameters (when necessary), generating the working recipe, and downloading the working recipe to the control equipment for execution.

Modification of a recipe takes place in a fashion similar to development by an authorized operator. In this case, no new recipe heading is required; only the data for the modification is necessary. It is essential that the system also allow modifications to recipes that are already being executed.

A recipe from the library of completed recipes can be assigned to a suitable unit or train/line by calling up the recipe identification; this can be done manually by the user or by a master computer.

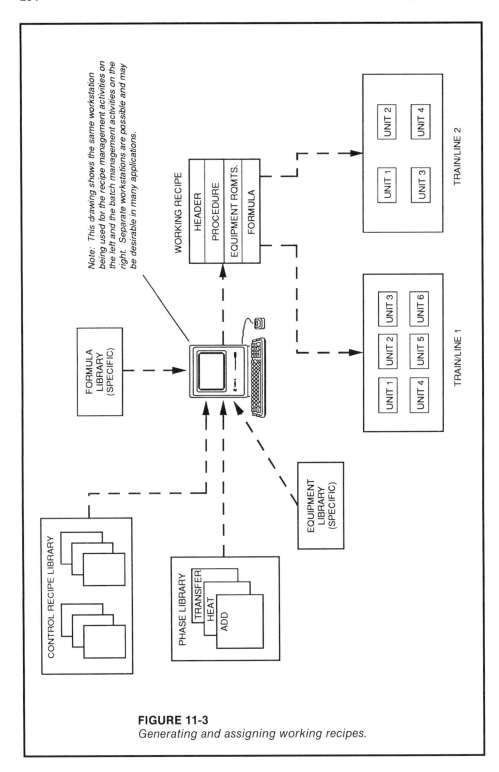

FIGURE 11-3
Generating and assigning working recipes.

EXERCISES

11.1 Why should the batch history database reside with the recipe management activity?

11.2 Explain why the production scheduling activity needs a different level of detail for equipment data than the batch management activity does.

11.3 Explain why the operator may need to enter date/time/unit stamped data into a batch record.

11.4 What are the advantages of having a batch management system that can do partial downloads of recipe information?

REFERENCES

1. Kano, T.; T. Hidai; and D. Mexxatesta, "Activity Control for Recipe Management," ISA/89, Paper # 89-0540.

2. Staples, R. A. C., "Cost Effective Batch Control System Using Programmable Controllers," ISA/87, Paper #87-1129.

3. ISA/SP88-1989-MM-5, Minutes of SP88 Batch Control Systems Standards Committee Meeting, December 6, 7, and 8, 1989.

4. Tolfo, F., "An Introduction to Modular Batch Automation," *Control Engineering*, September 1989, Vol. II.

5. Hurd, E. T., "Reducing Software Development Costs through Modular Batch Automation," *CONTROL*, November 1989.

6. DiMattio, C. J., "Optimization in Discontinuous (Batch) Process Manufacturing: A Case Study," Honeywell IAS Users Group, 1989.

7. "Development of Sequence Controls for Charge Processes with Variable Formulation from Pretailored Functional Modules," NAMUR Recommendations, July 1985.

12

Recipe Management

Introduction A recipe is a collection of information that tells a batch control system how to process the raw materials to make the desired final product. Usually, a recipe exists for each final product to be produced. A recipe, as defined in Chapter 2, is a combination of the "formula," the "procedure," the "header," and the "equipment requirements." But this alone is not always enough information to allow the control system to make a batch of product. A "unit/equipment module descriptor" is often needed to provide the data that defines the actual process equipment assigned to the batch. In addition, some "operator-entered data" often is needed to process the batch. The recipes contain product-oriented information and are used to make different products in the same equipment.

The formula, the unit/equipment module descriptor, and the operator-entered data are externally defined data structures. The formula contains all of the set points, constants, limits, and logical states to be used by the set of procedures in the production run. Multiple processes may be operating asynchronously in parallel, all using the same formula. Although the batch procedures may use formula, unit/equipment module descriptors, and operator-entered data, they must never change that data.

How recipes are created and maintained is a critical element of a batch control system. What information is contained in the recipe and how much control the recipe has over the various operations determines the flexibility of a batch system.

Recipe Classifications Several types of recipes could be used in a batch automation system (see Figure 12-1). The "basic recipe" is one that contains process-related information, such as the procedure (operations and phases only), but with no specific designation of actual equipment or control system entities to be used. This is typical of a recipe that might exist at the Corporation level in a multiplant organization. It is a generic recipe in that it is not equipment- or plant-specific; it contains formula parameters, but they are specified as normalized amounts.

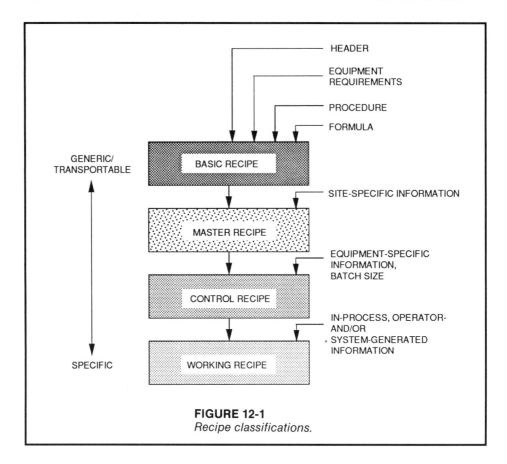

FIGURE 12-1
Recipe classifications.

The "master recipe" is most likely to exist at the Plant level. The master file contains a number of recipes with original product-related data to make different types of products or the same product with a number of variations. The master recipe is a basic recipe that has been made plant-specific. It still is unlikely to have a designation as to specific equipment or control systems. It is plant-specific in that it uses standard consumptions of the various ingredients used to make the final product. As such, it is used as an input to the "production scheduling" activity. For example, a basic recipe may have been developed in a pilot facility at the Corporation level where a particular raw material was available as a 30% solution. However, the plant has this raw material available only as a 20% solution. The basic recipe must be modified to reflect this change.

The "control recipe" is a master recipe with production equipment assigned; it is structured in the necessary control system format. It resides in a system file and is linked to actual or virtual process equipment and control system parameters. At this level, the ingredients may still be specified in percent rather than in absolute values. Although the control recipe is specific to the actual plant equipment, it may be specific to only a specific class of equipment. This allows the use of "generic" control recipes that simplify the recipe building task and also minimize the amount of recipe storage space required (see "Unit/Formula Parameter Relativity" in this chapter). Before the control recipe can become a working recipe, the specific unit(s) that will actually be used to process the batch must be specified, and the batch must be sized for the desired amount of product required (the normalized values of formula parameters will become actual values).

A batch management package allows the operator to select a control recipe, make necessary changes based on lab data and equipment characteristics to produce a "working recipe," and then download the working recipe to the basic process control system (see Chapter 11). This recipe is then used for producing the batch . The working recipe is a control recipe that operates in real time in the control system that makes the batch of product. Even at this level, the operator still needs to be able to make changes to the recipe as situations occur throughout the execution of the batch.

A recipe management package should maintain a database of master recipes for various products, formulas and procedures that are used to produce various products, and specific information on the batch equipment (e.g., units) that can run each operation within the procedure. It must also allow a control recipe to be constructed from the master recipe using the formulas, procedures, and equipment-specific information, along with the addition of header information. These control recipes must also be stored in the recipe management system. In addition, the recipe management package may have to store equipment-specific phases that can be used to convert master recipes into control recipes. The recipe management package must allow the database to be accessed by the batch management system so that control recipes can be selected, modified (if necessary), and downloaded to the basic process control system in a flexible, optimal, and secure method.

The selection and downloading of recipe parameters to controllers, based on production scheduling, is being successfully implemented with computers. The automatic downloading of recipe parameters reduces the chances for human error and reduces the manual labor previously required.

Recipe Contents

Table 12-1 shows the contents of the basic recipe (Refs. 1 and 2); both NAMUR and current ISA SP88 recommendations are shown.

Since the master recipe is still generic (i.e., it is not equipment-specific), its content will be the same as the basic recipe.

Table 12-2 shows the contents of the control recipe (Refs. 1 and 3). Note that the NAMUR control recipe is much shorter than that of SP88 because NAMUR assumes that the formula parameters and equipment assignments have been folded into the procedure once the control recipe stage has been reached.

The working recipe is basically a copy of the control recipe with specific equipment assignments and actual ingredient amounts instead of normalized amounts. A control recipe becomes a working recipe once a specific batch identification is assigned, and the working recipe begins to accumulate batch history at the same time. The working recipe still can contain options for equipment requirements to permit dynamic allocation of equivalent equipment during the execution of the batch.

TABLE 12-1
Contents of a Basic Recipe

NAMUR	ISA SP88
FORMULA HEADING	**HEADER**
Basic formula number	Recipe identifier
Product number	Version number
Operator	Version date
Version markings	Version author
Development and modification data	Product identification code
Apparatus requirements	Product description
	Procedure abstract
	User defined information (safety requirements and handling information, authorized plant sites, customer name, security classification, etc.)
	Comments
REQUIRED APPARATUS	**EQUIPMENT REQUIREMENTS**
Acceptable apparatus types	Equipment list with required characteristics
Capacity	User-defined information
Cold volume	Comments
MATERIAL REQUIREMENTS LIST	**FORMULA**
Product number	INGREDIENTS
Quantity (standardized)	Identification
Material identification	Description
Total quantity required per ingredient	Grade code
Standard setup (= total of inputs less losses)	Quantity (absolute or normalized)
Theoretical yield	Engineering units
Quality characteristics	Quantity tolerances
	User-defined information (operation/phase where used, equipment where used, specifications, etc.)
	PROCESS VARIABLE VALUES
PROCESS INSTRUCTION	Identification
	Description
BASIC OPERATIONS	Value
Dosing, mixing, etc.	Engineering units
	Value permissive range
PARAMETERS	User defined information (variable type, operation/phase where applicable, etc.)

(continued)

TABLE 12-1
Contents of a Basic Recipe (continued)

NAMUR	ISA SP88
Quantity required for a component	Comments
Set point and limiting values of	
physical quantities	PROCESS OUTPUTS (PRODUCTS
Durations, etc	AND BYPRODUCTS)
	Identification
LINKING	Description
Sequence	Quantity (yield, absolute or normalized)
Division (running sequentially	Engineering units
and/or simultaneously)	User-defined information (product specifi-
	cations, product destination, etc.)
	Comments
	PROCEDURE
	List of operations and phases shown
	in proper sequence
	Comments

Recipe Structures

Batch processes operate according to a set of variables that may be changed with each batch; that set of variables is the recipe. The arrangement of these variables is called the "recipe structure" (Ref. 4). Most batch control systems have multiple recipes with variable formulas. Some have variable procedures and others deal only with a single fixed procedure. This leads to two general types of structures (Ref. 4):

- those that require the recipe to fit within a predefined master sequence and
- those that allow the sequence to vary.

The difference between the operator interface and internal construction of the predefined master sequence recipe and variable sequence recipe can be considerable. When operations and phases are written in a master sequence recipe, the control systems engineer knows what is happening before, during, and after the operation of each phase. In a variable sequence recipe, the control systems engineer does not know everything that is going to happen beforehand; the sequence must be written in a more general manner. There are advantages and disadvantages to each type.

Master Sequence Recipe The procedure is built into a master sequence, which is one sequence that includes all the phases that will actually be used. The ingredient types and amounts may vary. However, if a charge is to occur at a particular point in the batch, that charge must be part of the master sequence.

A master sequence recipe is sufficient when the sequence is fixed, but not when the sequence is changed according to product. For example, if the decision is made to make another product that doesn't fit this rigid structure, there is a problem with using a master sequence recipe (e.g., maybe the materials are added in a different order in the new product).

EXAMPLE 12-1

Problem: Develop a master recipe for products A and B in Table 9-3. Show phases only.

Solution: The master sequence for these two products is shown in Figure 12-2.

TABLE 12-2
Contents of a Control Recipe

NAMUR	ISA SP88
FORMULA HEADING	**HEADER**
Apparatus number	Working recipe identifier
Basic formulation number	Working recipe version number
Lot number, product number	Control recipe identifier
Production dates	Control recipe version number
	Master recipe identifier
	Master recipe version number
	Basic recipe identifier
	Basic recipe version number
	Version date
	Version author
	Product identification code
	Batch identification code
	Product description
	Procedure abstract
	Batch information requirements (collection, status, and report)
	User-defined information
	Comments
	EQUIPMENT REQUIREMENTS
	Equipment assignments or specific equipment options
	User-defined information
	Comments
PROCESS INSTRUCTIONS	**FORMULA**
Phase names	INGREDIENTS
Order, sequential/parallel	Identification
Process parameters	Description
Test conditions that must be fulfilled during a phase	Grade code
	Quantity (absolute, calculation, or assayed)
	Engineering units
	Quantity tolerances
	User-defined information

(continued)

TABLE 12-2
Contents of a Control Recipe (continued)

NAMUR	ISA SP88
	PROCESS VARIABLE VALUES
	Identification
	Description
	Value
	Engineering units
	Value permissive range
	User-defined information
	PROCESS OUTPUTS (PRODUCTS AND BYPRODUCTS)
	Identification
	Description
	Quantity (expected yield, absolute)
	Engineering units
	User-defined information
	Comments
	PROCEDURE
	List of operations and phases shown in proper sequence for the assigned, or possible, equipment choices
	Comments

Example 12-1 shows the master sequence as it would be implemented by a sequencer block in a DCS or a PLC, neither of which normally have the flexibility to operate parallel phases. This means that phases must be defined to include combinations of the normal phases to provide this parallel capability, e.g., ADD ING. A/MIX/ADD ING. B.

Some mechanism must also be built into the master sequence to allow phases to be skipped when certain products are made. For example, product A does not use ingredient C, so that phase must be skipped. When material charges are involved, an easy way is to enter a charge value of zero for the ingredient that will not be used. The logic must recognize that a zero charge quantity means that this particular phase is not required and then must step the sequence to the next phase. Another way is to set a flag (e.g., a bit status) when the formula parameters are entered and have the logic recognize it as meaning that this particular phase is not required.

Variable Sequence Recipes With this method, the recipe is written as a sequence of phases, e.g., ADD A, HEAT, COOL, etc. The recipe then consists of a list of phases. Associated with the use of each phase is a set of variables that have to be interpreted according to the phase logic, as shown in Table 12-3. Recipes written in this way do not require that all sequences be defined with the initial

TABLE 12-3
Phases in a Variable Sequence Recipe

PHASE	PARAMETER 1	PARAMETER 2
Heat	230 (Temp. SP, °F)	2 (Ramp, °F/min)
Hold	230 (Temp. °F)	30 (Max. time, min.)
Add A	3200 (lbs)	

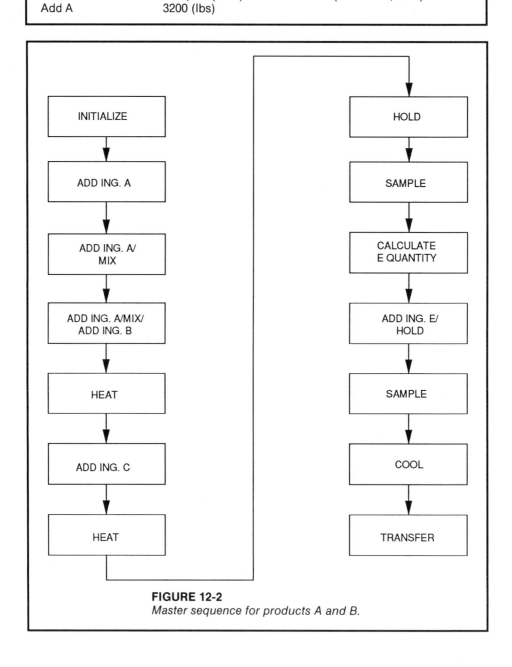

FIGURE 12-2
Master sequence for products A and B.

program. They are more accommodating to the development of new processes. However, the software for variable sequence recipes is more complex. Synchronization between units is also more difficult.

Unit/Formula Parameter Relativity
Generic names (aliasing) are often used in generating control recipes. Unit relativity is the use of generic, unit-relative names to refer to control loops and devices that are repeated on many units. Often it is not possible to fix the unit used for recipe execution because of scheduling considerations, because a unit is under maintenance, or for other reasons. In this case, the operator simply displays a list of usable units and then selects the one desired from among them (see Chapter 11, Batch Management).

For example, a temperature controller on each of two units can be referred to by a unit-relative name such as TIC-XXX. When the batch sequence is executed on reactor R-501 (Unit 1), the batch logic would access regulatory loop TIC-101. The same sequence running on reactor R-502 (Unit 2) would access regulatory loop TIC-201.

TAG ID	UNIT	UNIT RELATIVE NAME
TIC-101	Unit 1 (R-501)	TIC-XXX
TIC-201	Unit 2 (R-502)	TIC-XXX

For the most flexibility, the formula parameter files for the various products should allow the same interchangeability (formula parameter relativity). This means that local variables can be assigned to target values, which may be tied to unit aliases. For example, consider a HEAT phase where the final temperature should be 350°F for Unit 1 and 360°F for Unit 2. The heating target for Unit 1 (reactor R-501) could be assigned to a local variable (HEAT1 = 350°F); for Unit 2 (R-502) the local variable would be HEAT1 = 360°F. The procedure could then simply set the set point (alias TIC-XXX) equal to the local variable (HEAT1) without mentioning a physical address or actual number. The unit and formula parameter files direct the information automatically.

Recipe Management Requirements
Successful recipe management in a batch control system requires capabilities in (Ref. 5):

- engineering implementation,
- operator use,
- ongoing revision and maintenance, and
- documentation/validation.

Engineering Implementation Actual implementation and use of a recipe management system involves three activities: recipe definition, operational characteristics, and data configuration entry (Ref. 5).

The contents of each recipe must be defined. For each product or grade, a list of required recipe parameters (e.g., operation/phase/control step sequence, formula parameters, and equipment characteristics) and their values must be created. These parameters are individually named by the user and are accessed throughout the system by that name.

The operational characteristics must be determined to identify what sort of operator actions will be allowed within the recipe management system. The conversion from basic recipe to master recipe should be straightforward. The conversion from master recipe to control recipe could be considerably more complex depending on how the system is implemented. For example, does logic for actually implementing the phases reside in the recipe management system? If so, methods must be provided to allow control recipes to be developed using the master recipes, existing control recipes, and phases. Some limit on what data can be entered is often required. When multiple process units are used to make the same products, should the system automatically scale recipes to different unit capacities? The answers to these types of questions determine the structure of operator interaction.

After the operating characteristics have been defined, the next step is to actually enter the data into the recipe management system. This can be done in either an on-line operating mode or an off-line engineering mode.

Operator Use   Operator interactions with the recipe management system include recipe selection and recipe editing (Ref. 5). Typically, the operator would simply select the master recipe or control recipe to be modified from a recipe summary display. If necessary, the operator then makes necessary changes to the recipe to meet the needs of the particular batch (e.g., editing a master recipe, editing a control recipe, or creating a new control recipe).

Ongoing Revision and Maintenance   Maintenance of the recipe database includes the following functions (Ref. 5):

1. Protecting the recipes from unauthorized changes, e.g., with a keylock or password system
2. Copying the recipes to other systems as needed
3. Maintaining updated copies of any edited recipes
4. Determining allowable destinations for recipes, e.g., which recipes can be used with which equipment

Documentation/Validation   Documentation is needed by both Engineering and Operations groups. It provides a means for maintaining copies of the recipes (from basic recipes to control recipes) in an electronic source file as well as on hard copy.

Validation involves verifying that the recipe still exists as designed and produces statistically repeatable results.

Formula Management or Recipe Management   Most of the
"recipe management" packages that are included by manufacturers in their batch control systems are in reality only "formula management" packages. A formula management package allows the formula parameters to be changed but

not the procedure. The procedure is either hardwired or is coded via software into the unit controller. A "true" recipe management package allows both the formula parameters and the procedure to be changed, which makes the package much more complex. Both packages must allow changes in the equipment assigned to the batch and must allow the batch to be identified with a header.

Formula Management Packages For a single product plant, the formula management package can be extremely simple. For example, if the batch plant made only product A (see Example 10-1), the only adjustment (formula parameter) the operator may need could be the batch size. The procedure could be implemented using electromechanical relays and stepping switches (hardwired), or it may be implemented in a multifunction controller in a DCS or in a PLC (coded in software). In either case, the procedure cannot be changed by the operator. This would be true if none of the other formula parameters needed to be changed.

This example is not realistic in most batch plants. There are often changes in the quality of raw materials or the need to continually optimize the quality of the product produced. This requires changes to ingredient quantities, operating conditions, and so on. Then the operator needs to have access to most of the formula parameters. The formula parameters are often presented to the operator in the form of a table that simply shows a list of the parameters. The operator then has the ability to change those parameters as necessary (he may not have access to all the parameters, only a select few). Those formula parameters are directly linked to the procedure. Figure 12-3 shows an example of how the formula parameters might be related to the procedure, using product A from Example 10-1.

Recipe Management Packages Recipe management packages need to have much more flexibility than do formula management packages. This was one of the goals of the NAMUR Committee: to create a universally followed recipe structure on a modular basis so that the frequent and complex task of recipe updating can be accomplished relatively easily through configuration rather than programming (Ref. 6). Having this capability will make the use of the variable sequence recipe much simpler.

Developing a Phase Library

Figure 12-4 shows the first step: developing a phase library (Ref. 6). New batch processes are often developed in a laboratory environment by a chemist who works with the operating data needed to make the product, but who is not generally concerned with the equipment needed in a plant environment.

Documents are generated that are mostly a description of the operation in addition to main chemical and thermodynamic data. The project team (see Chapter 15) must take this information and develop phases and associated parameters with specific equipment in mind. These phases could be developed for one particular unit or for a general class of units (generic). These are put into a phase library. This step has been reported as being the step that is the most time consuming (Ref. 7).

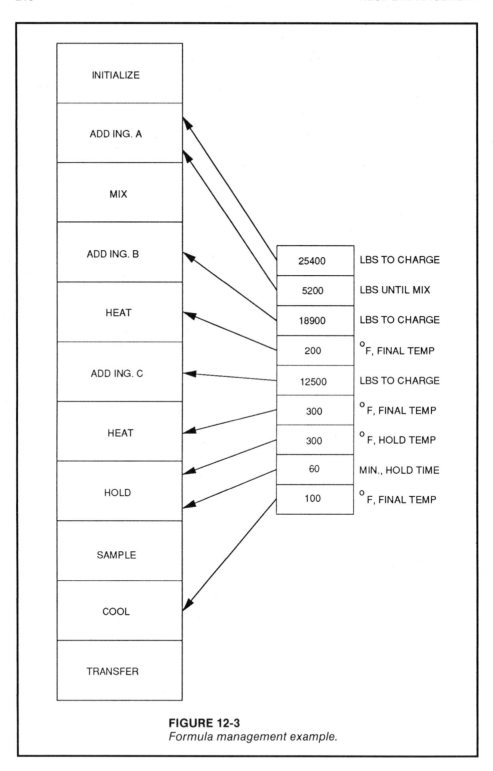

FIGURE 12-3
Formula management example.

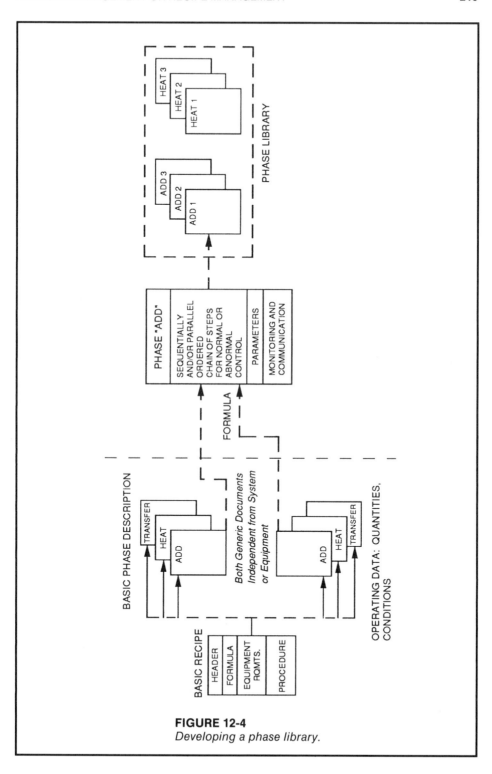

FIGURE 12-4
Developing a phase library.

The phases are developed and are available for use as a collection of phases (operations) to which parameters can be assigned. From them a user can configure a given recipe and can assign parameters for material and process quantities as well as location and equipment designations.

In general, the user should not be able to make modifications to the preprogrammed phases.

Building Control Recipes

Figure 12-5 shows the building of procedures and associated data from libraries of phases, units (equipment), and parameters into control recipes.

The recipes are assembled and administered by the user, who has the option to:

- build a recipe from phases, units, and parameters;
- insert and modify phases, units, and parameters; or
- allocate a control recipe to a specific system.

New recipes can be assembled by operating personnel from existing phases. Operating personnel must be able to use the phases individually or to assemble them as a sequence of phases (an operation) in a sequential structure, in a parallel structure, or in mixed sequential/parallel structures. Graphical configuration of the sequence of phases is certainly most desirable. Although this operation can be accomplished in the batch control system itself, it is probably better done off line in a separate engineering workstation.

A recipe that already contains a procedure (this recipe has a class designation that will allow it to be matched with the appropriate unit(s)) is called up by an operator. Then the formula parameters for the various phases are input. The system must offer the possibility of testing the parameters that have been input for upper and lower limiting values. In case the new recipe is produced by copying another formula, parameter input is simplified. The new parameters are produced by modifying the current parameters. Finally, some equipment assignment is necessary to make this a true control phase. This could be a generic assignment to a class of equipment, e.g., Class 1 consists of three units: reactors R-501, R-502, and R-503; the control recipe could also be assigned to a specific unit, e.g., a control recipe for the unit that consists of reactor R-501. A control recipe would not be capable of being assigned to equipment that does not have the same class designation.

Maintaining separate files for units, procedures, and formulas reduces the complexity of batch configuration and programming. Instead of developing a unique file for every product and every hardware combination, each component (unit, procedure, formula) has to be configured only once. These components can then be mixed and matched—in any combination needed—to make specific products in specific plant units.

The control recipe produced is stored in a storage medium and is ready for use on a train/line when needed (see Chapter 11, Batch Management).

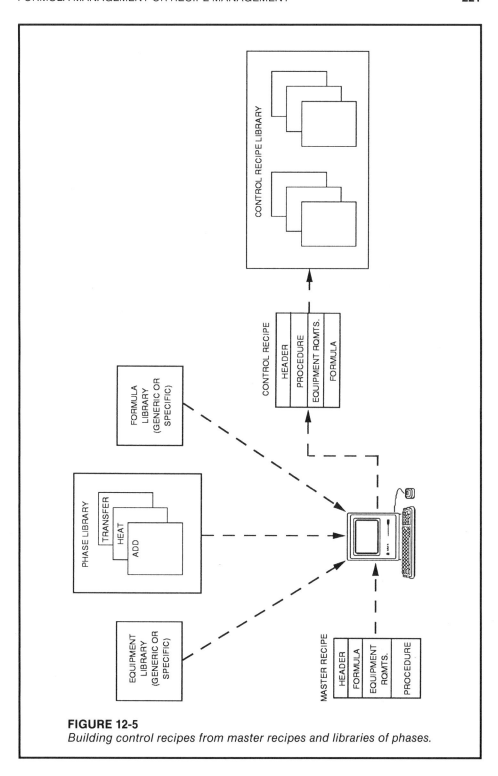

FIGURE 12-5
Building control recipes from master recipes and libraries of phases.

EXERCISES

12.1 Develop a master sequence for products A, B, C, and D in Table 9-3.

12.2 A fifth product, E, is being considered for manufacture in the same reactor system as products A, B, C, and D in Table 9-3. The details on the manufacture of product E are:

Product E (Possible)
- Initialize
- Charge A
- When enough A has been charged to cover the agitator, turn on the agitator, start charging B. Ratio B to A so that they complete charging at the same time.
- Charge preset amount of catalyst D.
- Raise temperature to 300°F as rapidly as possible while minimizing overshoot.
- When reactor is at 300°F, start E feed. Feed E at the maximum possible feed rate to minimize cycle time as long as pressure and temperature do not exceed their respective set points. Vent valve must be closed during E feed. Raise temperature to 450°F during E feed based on % of total E fed.
- Sample to lab and start cooling to 400°F.
- Calculate amount of C to be charged based on lab analysis.
- When temperature is at 400°F, start feeding C. Hold at 400°F during C feed.
- Hold for 30 minutes.
- Sample to lab and start cooling to 100 °F as rapidly as possible to quench the reaction.
- When lab analysis is OK and temperature is 100°F, pump to storage.

How does the addition of this product complicate the batch sequencing?

12.3 List some advantages of using unit/formula parameter relativity.

12.4 Can a working recipe be generic?

REFERENCES

1. "Development of Sequence Controls for Charge Processes with Variable Formulation from Pretailored Functional Modules," NAMUR Recommendations, July 1985.

2. ISA/SP88-1990-3, Minutes of SP88 Batch Control Systems Standards Committee Meeting, February 14, 15, and 16, 1990.

3. Preliminary Minutes of SP88 Batch Control Systems Standards Committee Meeting, June 25, 26, 27, and 28, 1990.

4. Rosenof, H. P., "Building Batch Control Systems around Recipes," *CEP*, September 1982.

5. Smith, E. M., and E. Whitmer, "Recipe Management in a Distributed Process Control System," ISA/87, Paper #87-1171.

6. Carlo-Stella, G., "Batch Control Technology: Market, State of the Art and Perspective in the Eighties," Batch System International, 1988.

7. Uhlig, R. J., "Experience in Implementing Batch Automation Systems," SP88 Meeting, Brussels, Belgium, April 23–26, 1990.

13

Production Scheduling for Batch Processes

Introduction The operation of a modern multiproduct batch production system involves a great deal of scheduling and coordination, but most of this allocation is still being done by humans (Ref. 1). However, a batch production system offers greater optimization opportunities than does a continuous plant. Although the product recipe and vessel allocation are fixed in a continuous plant, there is flexibility in both of these areas in a batch production system. There are also larger product quality variations, more scheduling conflicts, and bigger demands on plant operators in batch processes (Ref. 2). In addition, bottlenecks in a batch production system shift with the product mix in the system, operating priorities, material and labor availability, and marketing goals. The ability to do scheduling and coordination with computer assistance can significantly improve batch process throughput and profitability (Ref. 3).

However, scheduling is made difficult by the large number of raw materials used and products manufactured in a complex batch plant, the long lead times of raw materials, the short lead times of customer orders, and the constraints imposed by the production equipment and quality control considerations (Ref. 4). Therefore, there are constant tradeoffs between customer service, operating costs, and inventory holding costs.

Reasons for Scheduling Proper scheduling of a batch production system is necessary for several reasons (Refs. 5 and 6):

1. To maintain performance of the production system and minimize idle time
2. To minimize equipment changeover by scheduling batches consecutively
3. To minimize disruption in batch cycles by scheduling clean-in-place operations
4. To maximize equipment utilization

5. To assist the operator in making choices on product transfer, recipe handling, and equipment allocations
6. To allocate constrained resources
7. To minimize inventory
8. To allow preventive maintenance
9. To meet market demand
10. To feed downstream units efficiently

Scheduling Techniques

Batch scheduling in the plant environment should require the same data on time and capacity whether it is done manually or by computer, but too often the cost components are not adequately handled by manual scheduling techniques.

Manual scheduling involves a great deal of manual manipulation of information and is heavily dependent on the experience and intuition of the schedulers (Ref. 4). Some of the complexities that make the manual scheduling job difficult are (Ref. 7):

- sequence-dependent clean-in-place operations required between the manufacture of various products,
- inventory concerns caused by the need to maintain inventory levels within certain targets in order to respond rapidly to customer orders while recognizing that storage vessels have finite capacities and that inventory-holding costs can be very significant,
- availability of raw materials and operator/resource availability,
- poor product quality and variable batch cycle times,
- operating preferences for making certain products in particular pieces of equipment,
- the discrete sizes of process units, which means that the scheduler may have to decide whether to manufacture 6000 gallons of product by making either four batches of 1500 gallons each or six batches of 1000 gallons each, and
- scheduling objectives, such as meeting customer due dates while maintaining target inventory levels or maximizing throughput while reducing inventory levels.

Even with all the problems inherent with manual scheduling, most batch plants are still scheduled using human schedulers. This is because scheduling of batch process units is a very complex procedure, and a great deal of information is required to do it effectively. For example, some of the information required is: customer orders, forecast demands, expected receipts of raw materials and packaging materials, current inventories of products, and recipes. The cost of developing an effective computer-based scheduling package is very high, and the results of some of the attempts have been discouraging. However, many of the obstacles have either been eliminated or reduced in size by the steady reduction in the cost of computing power, the growing familiarity of plant and management personnel with computer aids, and a recognition of the benefits of computer-aided manufacturing control (Ref. 7).

However, data is available in an automated batch control system to allow the user to get a better handle on automated batch scheduling. The control system should be able to accumulate process data on each batch as it is processed through the various batch units (Ref. 1). Then cost data can be put together to tie down variable costs (e.g., energy), the specific processing costs (raw material required for a given batch size), and the fixed costs (chemicals, catalysts, and manpower). Some units will be more efficient than others. For example, a reactor with poor agitation may require more catalyst than a vessel with good agitation; it may also require more manpower in operator attention.

The number of vessels or processing units, throughput capacity per campaign length, and demand in capacity units all have to be known before the equipment can be adequately scheduled. However, automated batch scheduling will not provide the full range of possible benefits if all information is not available through electronic means. For example, there may be some information that must still be entered manually (e.g., the Production Plan). This may be because those other parts of the hierarchy have not been automated or because there is no communication between that level of the hierarchy and the Production Scheduling level.

Just because an automated batch scheduling system has been implemented doesn't mean that the human scheduler has been eliminated. Many of the techniques discussed below still require the human scheduler to interface with the scheduling system in order to achieve optimal scheduling.

Linear Programming Linear programming allows the user to optimize a system of linear equations to a linearized cost function, all bounded by series of constraints. However, their equation setup can be complex and often not meaningful to the end user. Bozenhardt (Ref. 1) has applied a simplified linear programming tool called the "transportation algorithm" to batch scheduling.

Linear programming tries to achieve an optimal solution based on achieving the lowest-cost system; but it is often difficult to place dollar values on some of the benefits that can be achieved in a batch system, e.g., delivery reliability and delivery response. The optimal solution from a cost standpoint may optimize short-term returns from the system, but it might not achieve the long-term return desired. For example, what is the effect of poor customer satisfaction if materials are not delivered on time, even though this may represent the lowest short-term manufacturing cost for the supplier?

MRP (Material Requirements Planning) This technique was originally developed for the discrete parts and assembly industries but is now being applied to batch processing by a number of companies in the process industries (Ref. 7). Information required by the MRP system includes the due dates for each product, normal processing time at each production stage, and a standard lot size for each batch. The processing times are usually based on standard production lead times.

Musier and Evans (Ref. 7) list the following advantages that using MRP can provide:

1. Reduction of inventory because of a better match of order quantities and plant production and better timing of inventory replenishment
2. Improved customer service
3. Lowered manufacturing costs because of the above benefits and a reduction in personnel
4. Improved plantwide communication and coordination of activities

They also provide the following limitations to using MRP as a plantwide planning tool (Ref. 7):

    1. An MRP system does not optimize, so it cannot generate, evaluate, and select scheduling alternatives when there are limited production resources.

    2. The production order initiated by the system might be unacceptable or even infeasible because MRP generally assumes that capacity is available to make the products (i.e., the system has infinite capacity).

    3. MRP cannot represent material recycles that are often encountered in batch production plants.

    4. Material, resource, and storage constraints are not considered.

    5. Implementation difficulties may occur because many products in batch plants have an inverted bill of materials (i.e., one or several ingredients are combined or separated into multiple end products) and MRP was originally developed for assembly processes.

Simulation Simulation is the process of creating a representation or "model" of the operation of a system on a digital computer by providing the computer with a description of the physical components of the system and the logic associated with the operation of the system. The model imitates the responses of the actual system in relation to events that take place over time. Once the system model has been developed, it is available to act as a laboratory through which experiments can be conducted to predict how the system will operate under various scenarios (Ref. 8).

In applying simulation, a model of the system under study is constructed using a simulation language. This language simplifies the process of building the model by providing special model-building tools. This is not a dynamic-type simulation that looks at reaction dynamics, the response of control loops, and so on. This is discrete event simulation where discrete or identifiable units (e.g., a batch) are moved through processing steps with time.

A queue is a basic concept used in discrete event simulation; it is a need waiting for a resource (e.g., a reactor waiting for a weigh tank to come free). In this case, the resource is a piece of equipment; it could be an operator, a safe environment, etc. The need could be an operation waiting to be initiated, an order for a particular product, and so on. The size of a queue could range from limited to infinite. If a batch is finished and is waiting in a reactor for an available tank truck so it can be pumped out, it is in a queue. In this case, the queue is limited to one, since the reactor can hold only one batch at a time. A storage tank can generally hold a larger, although still finite, number of batches, while an outdoor drum storage area may be considered for practical purposes to have a queue of infinite size.

Another factor that is important in discrete event simulation is stochastic variation (Ref. 9). It represents the random variation with time of various parameters within the process (e.g., the time it takes to sample the batch, deliver the sample to the quality assurance laboratory, and receive the results back). The use of stochastic variables allows the simulation to more accurately represent the actual performance of the batch process rather than use fixed values for all the variables. When stochastic variables are used in the simulation, different results will be obtained each time the simulation is run.

A discrete event simulation package is used to develop a model that looks at the material flow through the system and the resources (people, reactors, etc.) necessary to make the product. Discrete event simulation is a tool that allows the entire manufacturing process to be previewed on a computer screen before decisions are executed. It can provide a real appreciation of the complexities involved in the system and the interrelationships that will be driven by those decisions. For example, it can be used to (Ref. 9):

- provide valuable insight into how batches should be sequenced,
- determine capacities of a train or line, and
- identify bottleneck steps in a train or line.

Running the model using different values of various parameters (e.g., different product mix) allows inferences to be drawn about overall system performance based on various types of performance measures, such as equipment utilization, throughput, and in-process inventories.

Simulation can be used successfully to create and evaluate production schedules. The simulation model provides a computer replica of the batch production system. The scheduler can then run the model in the computer and look at a number of different production scenarios. Based on the performance information provided as a result of the various simulation runs, a feasible schedule can be developed based on the constraints specified in the model. The detailed interaction of various production limitations (e.g., the number of operators available, the product mix to be manufactured, etc.) can be included at any level of detail.

Expert Systems Many sophisticated production rules must be followed in a batch system, and this implies the use of a real-time expert system. An expert system is a computer program that uses the knowledge of a human expert and a reasoning process to solve problems in a given application (Ref. 10). The knowledge from the expert is stored in the "knowledge base"; the reasoning procedure is known as the "inference engine." Once the knowledge is entered into the system, the expert system can recommend a production schedule for the operation of the batch equipment (Ref. 11). Plant production personnel would have to enter the target production goals for the time period being scheduled. The advantage of the expert system approach over the linear programming approach is that the knowledge entered into the expert system can be more than mere cost data. Requirements for items such as delivery reliability and response can be given equal weight with cost items.

Knowledge-Based Simulation Artificial intelligence (expert systems) is being incorporated into simulation software, resulting in knowledge-based simulation systems.

Although linear programming and discrete event simulation techniques can be very useful, these techniques alone may not be sufficient to build the scheduling and coordination system for a particular application. Quite often, special rules have to be followed; for example:

- Don't make Product B immediately after Product A without cleaning out the reactor because a catalyst is used to make Product A and it poisons the catalyst used in Product B.
- Don't fill reactor A as full as reactor B because it does not have good enough agitation.

The cost of developing an expert system to perform the total scheduling process could be very costly and time-consuming. But expert systems can be combined with the discrete event simulation technique to provide a very cost-effective and high-performance scheduling package (expert systems can also be combined with linear programming techniques). Some companies are currently involved in developing scheduling packages that combine discrete event simulation and expert systems. The discrete event simulation package effectively acts as a "front end" for the expert system; the expert system provides optimal scheduling based on the rules built into the knowledge base.

A Scheduling Hierarchy

Successful control of a batch production system requires planning, execution, feedback, and flexible response. Scheduling is needed at different levels of the functional hierarchy. One possible scenario is shown in Figure 13-1. This scenario assumes that the company has multiple manufacturing plants that make the same or similar materials. This hierarchy could change significantly based on the way the corporation is structured.

Scheduling at the highest level (usually the Corporation level in the Batch Model discussed in Chapter 4) is used to assign production orders to the various manufacturing plants. At this planning level, the horizons may be measured in weeks or months.

The Corporation scheduling package would send the Production Plan down to the plant to the Production Scheduling system that is installed on the Plant computer. This system would check inventories against the production demands and determine what raw materials need to be ordered. It would use the Master Recipe that resides at the Plant level and would include standard consumptions of raw materials.

This Production Scheduling system would probably reside on the Plant computer, which would schedule production in the various "Areas" of the plant. This scheduling package would probably not be run more than once a day, and it might be run only once a week.

At the Batch Management level, it is necessary that production scheduling more closely approximate "real time," i.e., dynamic scheduling. At this execution level, horizons are measured in shifts, hours, or even minutes. It is here that

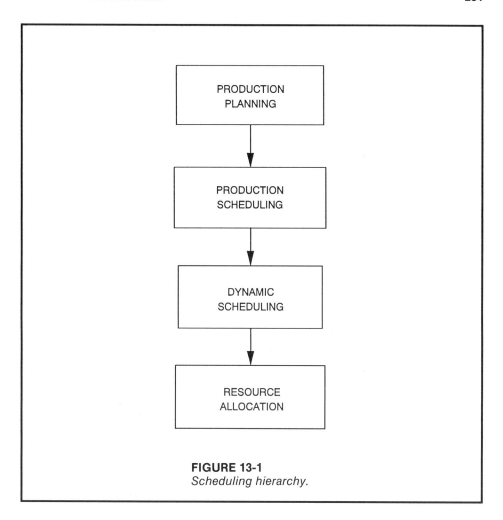

FIGURE 13-1
Scheduling hierarchy.

detailed scheduling based on the specific resources and requirements of the batch production system is the key to control of the batch system. At this level, the scheduling package would need to be run any time an activity is not completed within a specified time limit, whether that activity is delayed or whether it is completed ahead of time; and that activity can affect the schedule of other systems in this area.

There may also be a need for the operator to do some limited equipment reassignment or resource allocation at the production train/line level. This may be necessary because of a malfunction in equipment, availability of raw materials, and the like, and the batch is a critical one that must be completed on time. This will most likely be a reason to rerun the dynamic scheduling package to see what the total effect on the production schedule will be.

The key to control of the production system is a comprehensive system that links higher-level planning and order release, detailed scheduling, and batch system data collection. Planning and orders start the chain, detailed scheduling organizes the system for producing the required materials, and a data collection system is the source of timely information that allows the scheduling and order release activities to be fine tuned.

Scheduling Activities
Verhulst (Ref. 3) defines four broad classes of activities that have to do with overall plant coordination and scheduling: unit and train/line dispatching, resource planning, resource allocation, and schedule optimization.

Unit and Train/Line Dispatching The control system for the batch train/line system must know when to start and stop operations in the various vessels in order to achieve the production scheduling objectives. Therefore, mechanisms to start and stop operations in the batch control system environment must be included that will respond to both clock time and the occurrence of specific events. The control system also must be able to report back to the Production Scheduling system the actual results against the scheduled plan.

Resource Planning There are many different constraints on the schedule for a typical batch plant:

1. Availability of shared tankage, refrigeration resources, electrical, steam, cooling water, and so on

2. Availability of raw and intermediate materials for the process

3. The process equipment itself, since most plants have relatively well defined reaction trains that use equipment in prepiped configurations

4. Product processing characteristics, such as ramp/soak times and mixing times

5. Equipment performance characteristics, because it makes no sense to operate the batch train/line at 10,000 lbs/hr capacity if the packaging system can process only 4,000 lbs/hr of product

Resource planning must economically optimize the use of the equipment to produce the desired mix of products.

Resource Allocation The resource allocation system is a mechanism to prevent a piece of equipment from being used by more than one user at a time (shared equipment). This can be much more complex than merely preventing contention for the use of a shared piece of equipment. It may be necessary to decide which product is the most deserving of access to the shared equipment, so a simple first come, first served algorithm may be insufficient.

Schedule Optimization Scheduling a batch train/line can often be justified more than just once a day or once a shift. Ideally, the plant schedule should be adjusted whenever a certain activity is not completed within the time established for the activity and when that, in turn, has a downstream impact on schedule. This should include activities completed ahead of schedule as well.

EXERCISES

13.1 List some things that complicate scheduling of batch production plants.

13.2 Why does contention for shared resources require more than just a first come, first served algorithm?

13.3 Why should the dynamic scheduling system generally be run every time an activity is not completed within the time established for that activity? What levels of the scheduling hierarchy does this impact?

REFERENCES

1. Bozenhardt, H., "Multilevel Integrated Batch Control," *CEP*, December 1985.

2. Chowdhury, J., "Batch Plants Adapt to CPI's Flexible Gameplans," *Chemical Engineering*, February 15, 1988.

3. Verhulst, J. D., "Batch Plant Scheduling and Coordination," ISA/88, Paper #88-1582.

4. Thomas, L. R., and D. E. Shobrys, "Planning and Scheduling Lube Blending and Packaging," ISA/89, Paper #89-0409.

5. Bozenhardt, H., "Process Optimization via Scheduling Batch Processes," ISA/88, Paper #88-1402.

6. Rosenof, H. P., and A. Ghosh, *Batch Process Automation*, Van Nostrand Reinhold Company, Inc., New York, 1987.

7. Musier, R. F. H., and L. B. Evans, "Batch Process Management," *Chemical Engineering Progress*, June 1990.

8. Grant, H. F., "Simulation for Interactive Shop Floor Scheduling," Source Unknown.

9. Morris, R. C., "Simulation of Batch Systems," ISA/87, Paper #87-1260.

10. Nelson, W. R., and J. P. Jenkins, "Expert System for Operator Problem Solving in Process Control," *CEP*, December 1985.

11. Charpentier, L. R., and M. A. Turk, "Batch Decision Support System Enhances Safety of Reactor Operation," ISA/86, Paper # 86-2515.

Part IV
Batch Control System Design

14
Overall System Requirements

Introduction The design and selection of a batch control system requires a more detailed analysis of plant control and operation than is the case for a control system for a continuous process. Each batch control system tends to be unique; all possible combinations of normal equipment operations and failure modes need to be considered.

Batch control systems should be capable of supporting the following general-purpose utilities (Ref. 1):

1. Data entry by means of dedicated push buttons and soft keys
2. Overview/group/loop display facilities
3. Comprehensive trend/recall/archiving capability
4. Mimic/graphics capability supported by a picture builder, vector routines, and shape library
5. Menu-driven configurable firmware/blocks for direct digital control loops
6. Management information systems capability

Since batch control systems do tend to be more complex than control systems for continuous processes, most batch control systems also support the following utilities (Ref. 1):

1. A batch master to handle recipe allocation, batch scheduling, and contention arbitration for shared units
2. Recipe capability to include formulation, operating conditions, status information, and recovery operations
3. Structured batch control language to support a hierarchy of operations, phases, and control steps
4. Process-oriented instruction set with comprehensive firmware interface
5. Integrated display/logging facilities for alarm/event/status information
6. User-friendly editor/menu driver for sequence development

7. Flexible monitor and trace facilities for sequence testing supported by simulator and model library capabilities

8. Report generator with facilities for menu-driven format/layout and for free format data entry

There should be very good interaction between the regulatory control package and the batch package. The batch package must be able to manipulate the set points, tuning parameters, etc., of the regulatory control functions as a function of any number of logic variables in the batch package. Batch control systems also need the ability to check the status of large groups of devices and make logical decisions based on the result.

The implementation of batch automation is made difficult by complex control requirements, and most control system configurations are dependent upon process equipment. Also, many types of control equipment can be used to implement batch control systems. The selection of hardware for implementing the control system is very difficult because of the many types of control equipment available and because technology is rapidly changing the control equipment.

Control System Alternatives

A tremendous variety of systems on the market can be used to implement batch process control, ranging from single-station, microprocessor-based digital controllers (SSDCs) with built-in logic capability through PC-based systems and programmable logic controllers (PLCs), up to minicomputer- and microcomputer-based proprietary process control systems that may or may not be distributed. The number of control system alternatives available today is staggering, and it makes the selection process very difficult.

Carlo-Stella (Ref. 2) shows the hardware usage in batch control systems as a function of the degree of automation and the size and complexity of the system (see Figure 14-1). He defines a small batch application as having less than 10 control loops per production system, 25 or fewer analog inputs, 25 or fewer digital inputs, and 25 or fewer digital outputs. A medium batch application would have between 10 and 25 control loops per production system and 26 to 100 each of analog inputs, digital inputs, and digital outputs. The large batch application is anything above these two levels.

Early computer control systems used central minicomputers and mainframe computers that were directly connected to field inputs and outputs. These have fallen out of favor, primarily because of the total lifetime cost of the system. It generally took a team of computer people to program these systems and then support them as the computer vendor evolved the system software. Many process control users also were concerned about having everything tied up in one computer system and required some type of redundancy to keep from losing control of the whole plant on a computer outage. The cost of duplicating the important parts of the system increased the purchase and hardware maintenance costs. Providing analog backup, which also involved high costs, was another early solution. Because the hardware and software were unique to the particular vendor, users tended to get locked into one vendor when they purchased one of these systems.

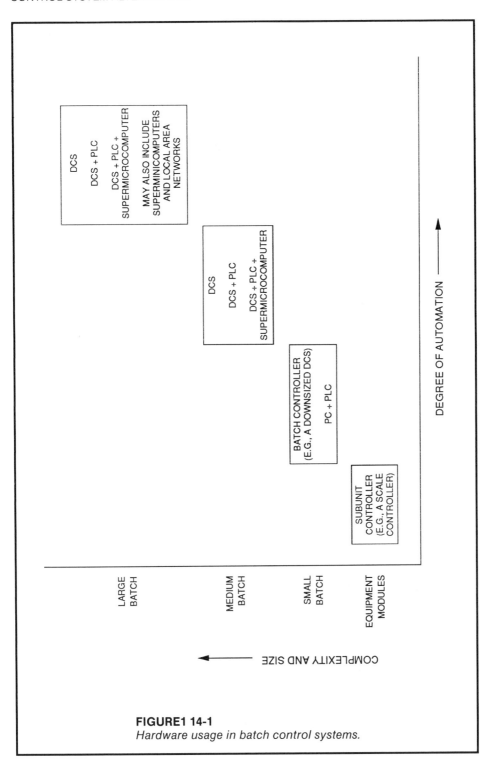

FIGURE1 14-1
Hardware usage in batch control systems.

The emergence of distributed control systems (DCSs) solved some of these problems. The cost of backing up critical multiloop controllers was much less than backing up whole computers. The fact that the programming languages used in DCSs made the programming task much easier basically eliminated the need for the programming team. The compatibility problem still remained, as it does today, because each vendor's system is proprietary and is different from any other vendor's system.

Not all new installations have used distributed control. Many new control systems, particularly small batch systems, are using single-station digital controllers (SSDCs) combined with low-cost versions of CRT operator consoles that are designed explicitly for these systems.

Programmable controllers (PLCs) are also finding wide use in batch processes, primarily in the small to medium batch systems. Many PLC vendors have added limited regulatory control functions to their PLCs, although those functions are usually not as complete as the control algorithms used in distributed control systems.

PC-based systems appear to be very cost-effective. Their hardware is cheap and familiar; proprietary systems software is now available that enables users to develop their own applications software. Personal computers are also being combined with programmable controllers and single-station digital controllers to provide very effective batch control solutions for small batch processes. There are still concerns among many process control users about the reliability of the hardware, the robustness of the systems software, long-term support, and overall systems safety.

Cell controllers, whether they be based on proprietary architectures or on general-purpose computers, are going to have a major impact on the batch control systems of the future.

The majority of the systems are of a distributed nature and are using a variety of architectures and strategies for communications. There is still a feeling among many users, however, that the ideal batch control system is still somewhere in the future.

Reliability

Reliability   A batch control system must be able to fail safely on loss of power; it must also recover gracefully when power is restored. What the control system must do in each of these cases is generally quite different. Different courses of action may be required based on the length of the power outage. Another problem is that the state of a batch cannot be determined solely from measurements at a particular instant of time. The total history of the batch must be known so that it can be used to determine the state the batch was in prior to the failure. This doesn't mean that the batch will be restored to this same state; the batch history is necessary to determine a course of action for the batch.

Operator Displays

Operator Displays   The role of the operator in the batch environment continues to receive attention. This is because the complexity of the plants that can be placed under the supervision of an operator, the large amounts of information available, and the number of possible decisions make the job more demanding in a batch facility than in a continuous facility.

The entire batch process must be reviewed from the standpoint of normal and abnormal operation to determine the type of information required and its organization for operator display, as well as to ensure that the operator is provided with sufficient controls. Standard console designs and display formats that are used in continuous systems are of limited value here, since batch plants are unique. The analysis should also determine that input and output signals are available to satisfy the control requirements and that the means for coping with a power failure, air failure, or equipment failure have been provided. By the end of this analysis, the size of the system (in terms of inputs and outputs, the operator console, and the required batch language features) should be fairly well defined.

Special operator's functions are needed to enable an operator to communicate with the batch control system, e.g., how to select a recipe, change recipe parameters, assign batch size and number, and start a batch. With a CRT display and data entry console, the operators and engineers should be able to display process schematics with dynamic data and control loops as well as monitor, modify, and, if necessary, intervene in the automatic control of the plant equipment.

Data Logging
A history module is generally needed that can store historical data, such as process data, laboratory data, and calculated data. The historical data must also be capable of being displayed or printed at the operator's station. During system configuration, the process engineer can format all the historical data required by the various functional groups within the plant.

Data storage affords the ability to handle the recipes as well as the control system parameters for multiple products, enabling rapid changes in formulations. Data logging capability is also important because of the emphasis placed on batch records in many processing applications.

EXERCISES

14.1 Why do some users have concerns about the reliability of PC-based batch control systems?

14.2 Why are cell controllers going to have a major impact on the batch control market?

14.3 Why are the regulatory control algorithms used in PLCs generally not as complete as the similar algorithms used in DCSs?

14.4 List some reasons why the life cycle cost of early batch control systems based on central minicomputers and mainframe computers was high.

14.5 List some reasons why the implementation of batch automation is difficult.

REFERENCES

1. Love, J., "Batch Process Control," *The Chemical Engineer*, June 1987.

2. Carlo-Stella, G., "Batch Control Terminology: Market, State of the Art and Perspective in the Eighties," Batch Control Systems International, 1988.

15

A Typical
Design Approach

Introduction The design of a batch control system begins with a definition of the demands imposed on the plant and proceeds to successively lower levels of the system hierarchy. The definition of the batch control system should proceed in parallel with the plant definition (Ref. 1). Then each level of control can be viewed as supporting the level immediately above it. This is a "top down" design approach that begins with a performance specification that is based on the desired operating objectives for the batch plant. The result will be an installed batch control system that will result in tangible and intangible economic benefits, instead of just being the latest technology.

This is different from the "bottom-up" approach that is normally used (Ref. 2). With the normal approach, hardware requirements are specified in great detail, beginning with an evaluation of various vendors' products by an equipment selection team. Although the resulting control system will meet the expectations of the equipment selection team, it probably will not meet the economic objectives of top management. This is because the equipment selection team and top management had different expectations.

Assembling the Team It is not an easy matter to specify a batch control system. It is also not a job for one person. Too many things are involved in a batch project.

A project team should be formed with the responsibility to determine the overall control system objectives, the basic requirements of the system, and operational philosophies, and to resolve any conflicts concerning the design of the control system. The team should define the control requirements for the batch process, remembering that this should be done without any consideration for particular systems or suppliers. However, it is necessary to have an idea of what types of systems are available. Other important needs of the system, e.g., those relating to things like safety, quality control, management information needs, etc., also have to be defined.

All members of the team must be in agreement with the requirements developed to this point. Some point in this stage of the design process would be a good time to perform a preliminary hazard review of the system, e.g., a hazard and operability study (HAZOP). However, a set of process and instrument diagrams (P&IDs) would be a big help for this step. The results of the hazard analysis should be incorporated into the design at this point.

When using a team approach to problem solving, it's important to define the expertise of the individuals involved so that the problem can be divided into subsets according to each team member's specific talents (Ref. 3). At least five different types of expertise are needed for this team:

1. Production management (e.g., an understanding of how the system will actually be run in the plant environment)

2. Equipment operation (e.g., a knowledge of process equipment, what is currently used at the given plant, and what is currently available)

3. Instrument operation and control (e.g., knowledge of the actual plant and an understanding of what the plant's current capabilities are in instrumentation and where management would like to have them go in the future)

4. Process technology (e.g., intimate knowledge of the actual process)

5. Plant resource management (e.g., an understanding of resources such as people, utilities, and maintenance that are available within the plant)

The Top Down Design Approach

Once the team has been established, a structured analysis of the problem should be started, approaching the problem from the top and working down. Many people try to approach the design of batch control systems from the bottom up, which is not the most desirable way. If the design of a batch control system starts at this bottom level, there is a danger of getting caught in such a mass of details that the team will get frustrated.

A more effective approach to the structured design of the project is a multi-level procedure based on the previously mentioned five levels of engineering expertise (Ref. 3). Then each team member has the opportunity and flexibility that comes with working from a position of knowledge. This will result in a batch control system design that takes collective advantage of the individual areas of expertise; it will include many useful details that may otherwise have been overlooked.

With this top-down approach, the team can view the batch control system as a tool to help the plant meet its desired performance objectives (Ref. 2). Now the mission of the team is to meet these economic objectives; installing the new batch control system is just a means to that end. Christie (Ref. 2) recommends that the team find answers to the following questions before the system is specified:

1. Is the plant capable of meeting the desired performance objectives? This means the team must validate the performance objectives to make sure they are feasible, which may involve a study of the batch plant's physical equipment. Equipment changes, in addition to the new batch control system, may be required.

2. Will existing instrumentation be adequate at the new operating conditions? This question applies when the project is a retrofit of an existing system. For example, if improved product quality is an objective, on-line analysis equipment may be necessary rather than relying on periodic laboratory analysis.

3. How will performance against the new economic objectives be measured and enforced? This involves thinking about the role of each person in the organization and how they affect the day-to-day economic performance of the batch plant.

4. How should real-time data be reconciled with existing management information systems and PC networks? Is a link to the MIS (management information system) department necessary, so that periodic reports can be sent or so that necessary instructions (e.g., production scheduling requirements) can be downloaded? How much access to the data within the batch control system should be provided to people on local PC networks? What kind of data access security should be provided?

All these questions must be answered before a purchase specification is prepared. Figure 15-1 shows a project program evaluation and review technique (PERT) chart that gives the necessary steps that need to be taken (Ref. 2). Resolving all the necessary issues will probably involve all areas of the plant organization. Additional expertise may be needed in addition to that provided by the team members.

The top-down approach involves a lot more work and may require a larger investment (Ref. 2). However, if the performance objectives are met, this may mean that the batch plant has the capability to compete with similar systems at competitors' plants.

The Functional Model

One of the first things to be determined is what functions have to be included in the system. Figure 15-2 is an example of the batch hierarchical model of Chapter 4, with functions identified at each level. Remember that this is not intended to be a physical model. Once the team defines what functions must be included and how those functions will be implemented, then a physical model can be developed.

This drawing shows three levels of communications networks: the office and engineering network, the plant backbone network, and the production system (process control) network. In actuality, a fourth level should be added below the process control network: the "field bus" network, which is being developed by ISA's SP50 Standards Committee along with some other similar groups throughout the world. The field bus is intended to connect field devices to the unit controllers at the process control level.

Defining the System Requirements

The control activity model from Chapter 5 is reproduced here as Figure 15-3. System definition starts at level 6; the Corporate (Production Planning) level is not considered here. As each level is defined, it dictates a particular method of documentation (Ref. 1).

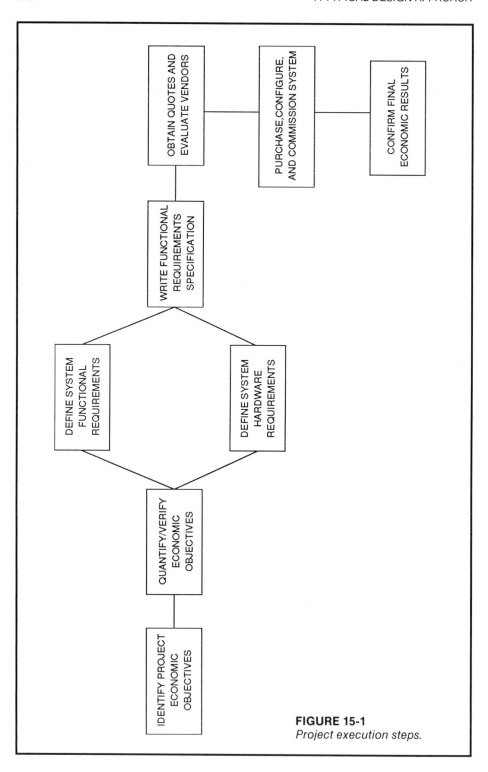

FIGURE 15-1
Project execution steps.

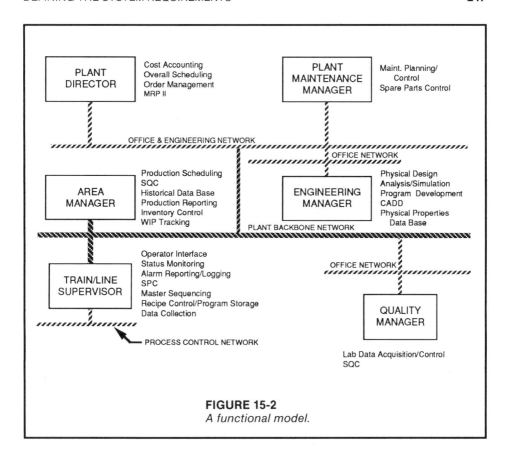

FIGURE 15-2
A functional model.

At some point early in the system definition, some decisions need to be made concerning how the batch process will be partitioned. Batch processes are typically subdivided into functional groups of equipment called units and equipment modules, which perform essentially independent tasks. Some processes will have multiple units and equipment modules of the same type (e.g., several reactors or weigh tanks) that operate in parallel. The number of units should not necessarily be associated with the number of vessels. This partitioning is necessary in order to define what products can be made in what units and equipment modules. Without this partitioning, it is impossible to complete the definition of the recipe management section.

The functional requirements of the control system must be determined, such as:

- required regulatory control algorithms (e.g., PID, cascade, feedforward, dual-mode, etc.);
- sequence control capabilities, such as the type of batch language required; and
- communications and display requirements, including the need for a data highway, number of operator consoles, etc.

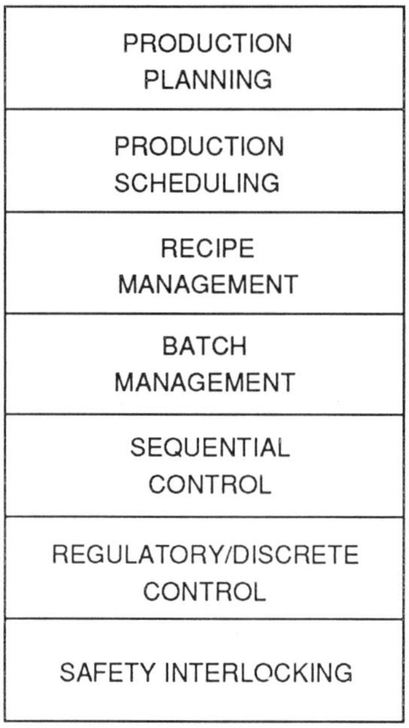

PRODUCTION PLANNING
PRODUCTION SCHEDULING
RECIPE MANAGEMENT
BATCH MANAGEMENT
SEQUENTIAL CONTROL
REGULATORY/DISCRETE CONTROL
SAFETY INTERLOCKING

FIGURE 15-3
Control activity model.

Production Scheduling The team must decide how scheduling will be handled. They may decide to implement scheduling using a manual system or automatically by computer. In either case, the format of the production plan that is sent down to the Plant from Corporate must be known. In addition, the information that will be sent to Corporate from the Plant must be defined, including the format of that information.

Recipe Management Recipe management requirements (e.g., where the recipes will be stored, the number of recipes, and the general structure of a recipe) must be defined. At this stage of the design, the recipe structure will likely define the procedure only down to the phase level, since the phase logic cannot be defined this early in the design.

Needed maintenance functions must also be specified, e.g., add a recipe, modify a recipe, develop a new recipe, etc.

Batch Management Many things need to be defined at this level. Examples are operator displays, data to be collected from each batch, tracking requirements, how the batch management system will interface with batch control (e.g., sequential control, regulatory and discrete control, and safety interlocking), reporting requirements, and so on. Different types of documentation will be needed to define each of these requirements.

Sequential Control The sequential control requirements will be supported by some type of sequence diagramming, e.g., process timing diagrams, time sequence diagrams, and sequential function charts. State transition diagrams may be necessary to define the interface between the operational states of the system and the sequential control logic.

It is necessary to give an operator the ability to intervene in a batch process. However, it must be a critical situation before an operation can be halted the instant he/she requests a hold. Therefore, operations are divided into phases, where each phase is made up of one or more control steps that perform equipment-oriented functions. Phase boundaries provide valid, unprogrammed hold points in the control step sequencing. They also provide a convenient way to subdivide an operation. A phase boundary does not have to be a valid hold point; however, a valid hold point may occur only at a phase boundary.

Failure monitoring and failure sequencing are included in the operation of the system. Multiple process alarm conditions and failure interlocks allow triggering of alternate control step sequences, which may hold or shut down a unit. Failure monitoring and sequencing are normally included at the control step level of the sequence.

Regulatory and Discrete Control Documentation will consist of input/output lists, block diagrams of control loops, display specifications, process and instrumentation diagrams (P&IDs), binary logic drawings, and so on.

An operation is an individual set of instructions that defines how a unit is to be controlled and monitored. Discrete and regulatory control tasks must be coordinated within the operation. Normally, many different operations can be performed on one unit, and many units use similar or identical operations. An operation is never split across more than one unit.

Safety Interlocking The requirements for safety interlocks would typically be defined using either binary logic diagrams or ladder logic drawings.

Control System Implementation
When the team starts looking at where control functions will be implemented, their range of choices has two extremes, generally referred to as "push-up" and "push-down" (Ref. 4). In the "push-up" approach, a control function is implemented at the highest possible level in the hierarchy, which would probably be at the Area level. This approach uses the basic process control system primarily as a process interface and backup system for the process computers. Any function critical to the operation of the process would either be implemented at the Basic Process Control System level or would be backed up by a function implemented at that level. Most simple, stand-alone loops still tend to be implemented in the basic process control system with

this approach unless there is a real advantage of implementing them in the computer.

In the "push-down" approach, a control function is implemented at the lowest possible level in the hierarchy. Some adhere to this philosophy, apparently because they have had better experiences with functions implemented in basic process control systems than they have had with process computers. If enough of the functionality can be pushed down into the basic process control system, process computers become unnecessary.

However, many users prefer to follow a "middle-of-the-road" approach, in which functions are implemented where they make the most sense. One technique for determining where functions should be located is to evaluate the consequences of a component failure. In general, critical, on-line control functions are not implemented in a central computer because of reliability problems with these general-purpose computers. Although no generally accepted set of rules for making that determination has been developed, the following are some possibilities to consider (Ref. 4):

1. Those functions critical to continued operation of the process should be implemented in the basic process control system.

2. Functions that must be performed quickly or frequently should be implemented in the basic process control system.

3. Simple functions should be implemented in the basic process control system; complex functions should be implemented in the process computer. However, what is "simple" and what is "complex" is not well defined.

4. Configuration of the basic process control system should allow the operator to cover the most ground in an emergency. Complexities such as cascading should be added only if the resulting configuration is more robust during process upsets.

5. Supervisory functions, e.g., optimization of the batch process, should be implemented in the process computer.

6. Control functions that must be modified or enhanced from time to time should be implemented in the process computer. The idea is that functions implemented in the basic process control system should be thoroughly tested and then left alone. The team should address this issue and determine what functions need to be "fixed" by configuration and what is "flexible" (e.g., specified as a recipe parameter).

The Physical Architecture

Eventually, the team will get to a position where they will define a physical architecture for the overall control system. If they determine that computing devices are needed at each level of the functional model, the resulting architecture could look like the system shown in Figure 15-4. This architecture assumes the use of "open systems" for communications, so MAP and TOP are identified as the networks to be used at the various levels. As before, the field bus is not shown.

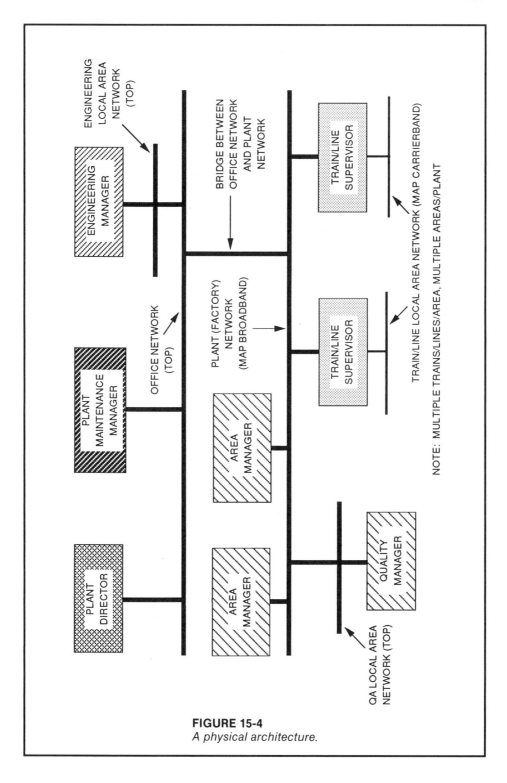

FIGURE 15-4
A physical architecture.

The team will also have to define the architecture of the basic process control system, where the real-time process control is implemented. Figure 15-5 is an example of an architecture, based on MAP carrierband communications, that might be implemented. The safety interlocking system is shown as a separate unit controller; it is unlikely that the user would want to combine this unit controller with any of the other unit controllers.

When the top down design phase is complete, engineering then proceeds in the opposite direction, from detailed to general. This allows the development of the system to take place in stages, i.e., a level or two at a time. This phase of the system design is discussed in more detail in Chapter 19, "Specifying a Batch Control System."

EXERCISES

15.1 What areas of expertise might be needed on the batch control system definition team other than the ones discussed early in the chapter?

15.2 Assume that the MIS group starts implementing the business systems from the upper levels of the control activity model and the process control group starts implementing the batch control systems from the lower levels of the control activity model. How do you assure that they will eventually meet at some common point in the middle levels of the control activity model?

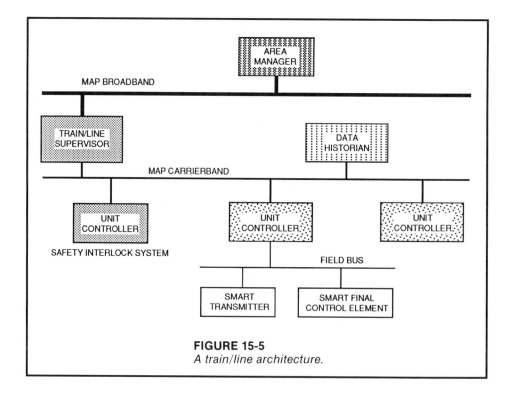

FIGURE 15-5
A train/line architecture.

REFERENCES

1. Rosenof, H. P., "Successful Batch Control Planning: A Path to Plant-Wide Automation," *Control Engineering*, September 1982.

2. Christie, D. A., "The Top-Down Approach to Successful Process Control Projects," *CONTROL*, October 1989.

3. Martin, P. G., "Designing a Batch Control System," *I&CS*, October 1987.

4. Ramaker, B. L., and C. L. Smith, "Criteria for Distributing Functions in Distributed Control Systems," Fifth CMA Process Computer Users Forum, May 5–7, 1986.

16

Batch Control System Hardware

Introduction Batch control systems have evolved over the years to accommodate plant needs. These applications range from small control systems up to large and complex systems with significant input/output (I/O) requirements. Six types of computer-based systems are now used in automating batch operations:

1. General-purpose computers, e.g., minicomputers and super microcomputers
2. Distributed control systems (DCSs)
3. Programmable controllers (PLCs)
4. Single-station microprocessor-based digital controllers (SSDCs)
5. Personal computers (PCs)
6. Cell controllers

The functional distinctions between these is diminishing. For example, PLCs now handle analog as well as digital signals. SSDCs, driven by microprocessors similar to those used in PCs, have extended computational, logic, and database capabilities that reduce the need for an external computer or supervisory control station. And distributed control systems, once built around a central computer, have become more modular and now even use the PC as a resource.

However, these products do not offer the same capabilities to the user. The SSDC is easily configured as a process controller. Configuration for logic function, however, is not as simple, usually requiring the use of a higher-level language. Relay ladder logic and timing are simple to implement in a PLC, but configuration for PID control is cumbersome. And the PC, despite all of the latest software and hardware development, still is best at providing data management and supervisory capabilities.

In a typical batch process plant, a balance of regulatory, discrete, and sequential control is needed. In a large batch plant, control needs are well served by a true distributed control system in which both analog and digital I/O and the various types of control functions can be mixed as desired.

Competition between distributed control systems (DCSs) and programmable controllers (PLCs) for control of batch applications will intensify significantly during the next five years as users increase their use of batch control systems.

General-Purpose Computers

Many batch control systems in the past were totally controlled by a single general-purpose computer, such as the DDC (direct digital control) system shown in Figure 16-1. Because of some inherent problems with the DDC system (e.g., reliability and high life-cycle costs), the trend today is toward distributed control systems, with the general-purpose computer performing specialized applications, e.g., batch scheduling. Usually, the general-purpose computer is not involved in the real-time control of the process.

Note that some small systems are being offered based on PCs with direct field I/O; these offer the same configuration as the DDC systems based on general-purpose computers and with all the inherent problems of the DDC system.

Since most PLC manufacturers provide an interface to their data highways for general-purpose computers, a general-purpose computer can very easily be used in a batch control system in conjunction with PLCs, where the PLCs would sit on their own proprietary data highway. The general-purpose computer would provide the operator display for the system.

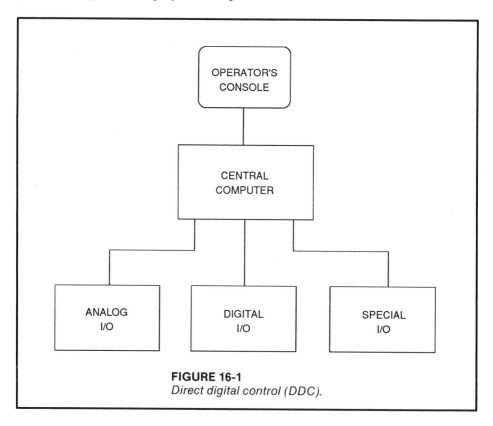

FIGURE 16-1
Direct digital control (DDC).

Distributed Control Systems (DCSs)
Distributed control systems (DCSs) were originally designed to satisfy the needs of continuous processes. The controllers were based around the PID control algorithm, with numerous supporting regulatory algorithms such as summers, multipliers, selectors, and so on. The early DCS did not do a good job of addressing the requirements for discrete and batch control applications. Since batch processes typically need regulatory, sequential, and discrete types of control, other equipment was needed to fill these voids, e.g., programmable controllers. Most DCS vendors have incorporated PLCs into their systems to satisfy the demands of discrete control requirements. The high-speed ladder logic of the PLC is usually being performed independently of the functions being performed in the rest of the DCS. Typically, the integration of the PLC into the DCS has been limited to data exchange. The programming of the PLC is usually accomplished via a separate piece of equipment, e.g., a PC. The operator can monitor and control selected points in the PLC from the DCS operator interface, but the program cannot be modified except through the separate PLC programming device.

Today's DCS has evolved into a flexible and powerful integrated control system that supplies data acquisition, advanced process control, and batch control capabilities. Batch control is usually accomplished with a vendor proprietary language designed specifically around the database structure of the given system. A distributed control system in its basic form (see Figure 16-2) consists of the following (Ref. 1):

1. Operator stations that use microprocessor-based CRT displays and keyboard communication with control devices and displays

2. Remote multifunction microprocessor-based controllers

3. A digital data link (data highway) that connects the multifunction controllers with the central operator stations

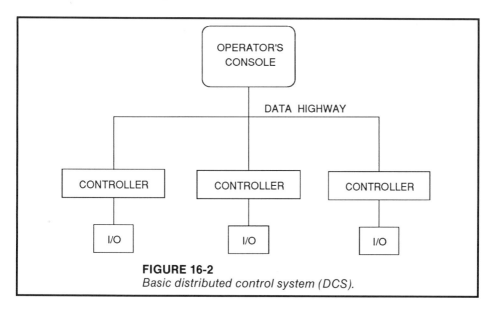

FIGURE 16-2
Basic distributed control system (DCS).

The first priority of the DCS is to provide superior operator interfacing and real-time process control. This is, in fact, the strength of the DCS. The system architecture provides for distribution and connectability of control devices and computing platforms throughout the plant. The flexibility of implementation of sequential control and integration among the various types of control is also an additional strength. Because of the distributed nature of the system, a single failure typically will not shut down the entire operation.

The DCS architecture provides a single window to the process and control system so that it can (Ref. 2):

- monitor and manipulate the process,
- retrieve historical data (batch history is required to facilitate display and analysis of key characteristics within a batch and between batches of similar types),
- configure the system,
- build schematic displays,
- develop control programs, and
- diagnose system failures.

The DCS installations of the past were usually more expensive than a PLC-based system and a dedicated operator interface. Today, DCS manufacturers are finding that, as PLCs and operator interfaces become more powerful, their DCS products must evolve to remain competitive.

The traditional DCS manufacturers and some new competitors are offering smaller distributed control systems that fit at or slightly above the largest "canned" operator interface units and are smaller in size than the large DCS offerings. These smaller systems contain much of the power of the larger systems but are oriented toward smaller applications. They provide fewer graphic displays, I/O, and front end devices. These systems will find use in almost any batch control application that requires a reasonably powerful operator interface and/or supervisory control functions.

Programmable Controllers (PLCs)

Early PLCs were developed to replace relays, timers, counters, and other discrete devices, so there were no analog requirements. All inputs and outputs were strictly ON or OFF. All analog signals had to pass through transducers or sensors to provide on/off signals similar to what relay systems had to use.

Since they were developed out of the needs of the automotive industry, early programmable controllers had to meet their criteria. They had to be (Ref. 3):

- easily programmed and reprogrammed in the plant,
- highly reliable,
- small,
- able to communicate with a computer, and
- inexpensive.

The biggest application of PLCs has been in the discrete parts manufacturing industries, but PLC manufacturers see a large potential market in the process industries. PLCs have long had the capability to do sequencing; as the PLC became more popular, manufacturers expanded their hardware capability and brought in analog modules that could be directly connected to the process variables. Special input modules, such as thermocouples and RTDs, were also designed. Since then, they have become even more flexible, with the addition of process control algorithms, intelligent modules, advanced communications interfaces, and so on. With this combination, it would seem natural to apply PLCs to batch control systems. In fact, a number of PLC manufacturers are advertising this capability.

The PLC's ability to work in harsh plant environments in real time, along with its flexibility and relatively low cost, have made it a popular choice among users. For example, PLCs may be used in data acquisition applications, as stand-alone controllers, or as part of larger, distributed systems. In addition, some of the low-cost units can be used as front end I/O devices for use with microprocessor-based control systems to provide a very cost-effective control system.

The wide use of relay ladder logic programming on the PLC is based on its being used as a replacement for the relay, which used ladder diagrams to represent the relay logic. The programming symbols and documentation are based on pictorial representations of relay contacts. Although relay ladder logic programming is useful for logic manipulation, it loses much of its effectiveness when it is used in process control applications.

Because the primary use of a PLC is as a real-time front end controller, it has not had good programming and documentation capabilities. Initially, manufacturers provided special programming stations, but these are special-purpose and relatively expensive; the recent trend has been to use PCs for PLC programming and documentation.

PLC manufacturers allow for communications between several PLC units and remote computers, but, in general, through proprietary bus structures and special protocols. The problem that remains is the lack of standardization. For a remote computer to communicate with a PLC, the peculiarities need to be bridged. The hardware connections may be the relatively standard RS-232 serial interface, except the proprietary software protocols and internal memory structures inhibit almost anyone except the manufacturer from attempting effective communication. Today, the focus has shifted to simplifying the networking of these systems by making them more compatible with each other. Some PLCs are now available with Manufacturing Automation Protocol (MAP) interfaces.

Single-Loop Microprocessor-Based Digital Controllers (SSDCs)
Although these digital controllers are often called single-loop controllers, most have at least two controllers built in, so they have the capability of implementing a cascade control system. Most also have the capability to take in digital inputs, perform some logic, and send out a digital output to other devices. They can also perform some math functions and implement advanced control loops. Note that all of these functions cannot be accomplished at the same time in a single controller from all manufacturers. Some require the use of more than one controller.

Single-station digital controllers (SSDCs) were originally designed for simple closed-loop control. The controllers are based on a PID algorithm that determines the control output based on a comparison between set point and process variable. Process variable, set point, and output are usually displayed on the controller faceplate for the operator interface. The operator interface can either be local, via the controller faceplate, or remote, via a PC or general-purpose computer, since many SSDCs also have communications capabilities. Some manufacturers have designed special-purpose SSDCs with more sequential control capability, more data acquisition capability, and the like. These various types of SSDCs can be combined in the same system using the manufacturers' proprietary data highways.

Advantages of using SSDCs in batch control systems are single-loop integrity for critical loops, low initial cost, ease of configuration, built-in auto/manual station, and controller faceplate displays for process variable, set point, and output.

Personal Computers (PCs)

In U.S. industrial plants, PCs are proliferating on the desks of managers, engineers, and operating supervisors, where they are making information available to those responsible for operating decisions. Before a PC is selected for an industrial application, it's important to consider packaging for the environment, field-ready I/O, and software (Ref. 3).

Types of PC Packaging Basically, three types of personal computers are being used in control systems. The first is the standard PC that can be purchased from the local computer store; it is a very cost-effective option. This hardware should be used only in a clean environment such as an office or a clean control room. These machines are generally very dependable but lack any real protection against a harsh environment.

IBM, as well as other manufacturers, saw the need for a more industrially hardened machine and developed computers with heavier-duty housings, better filtering, better shielding, ruggedized hard disks, a more reliable power supply, serial ports with transient suppression, and the like. Though functionally the same as the models in the local computer store, these models are better suited for rougher environments.

The most common configuration for control devices in U.S. industrial plants is the rack-mount. National Electrical Manufacturers Association (NEMA) enclosures are generally required by plants with corrosive environments. Compatible manufacturers were first to come out with this type, with IBM following. They tend to look like a PLC in a rack.

Field I/O for PCs Four main methods are used in applying field I/O in PC-based systems (Refs. 4 and 5):

1. The lowest cost method (which sometimes suffers from noise problems) is the direct plug-in "lab style" I/O board. Here, the board resides inside the PC rack.

2. The second approach involves the remote operation of a dedicated I/O subsystem. This offers better noise immunity but, depending on the manufacturer, may have slow speed updates (serial-driven systems) or packaging that's inferior to a typical PLC's I/O.

3. I/O coprocessors involve attaching a separate box to the PC and contain varying degrees of intelligence. I/O coprocessors unburden PCs of some time-consuming chores and incorporate many real-time capabilities needed for monitoring and control applications. In the future, industrial users will purchase an increasing number of I/O coprocessors for simple data acquisition and for monitoring and control applications.

4. The last method involves configuring a low-cost PLC or SSDC as the I/O subsystem. Here, cost and speed factors must be carefully considered.

PC Software   There are a number of good data acquisition packages but less is available in the control area. Some packages provide good operator interface functions, and some mimic a PLC environment.

Database offerings are on the increase, but industrial offerings designed for database applications are not common. However, almost every modern industrial application requires some form of database. Recipes, manufacturing specifications, production logs, and quality control are but a few examples of database applications common to almost every process.

Reasons for Increased Usage of PCs   The PC's role in process control products is becoming increasingly popular for several reasons. First, a PC with capabilities comparable to the minis or mainframes of yesterday can be purchased for minimal cost. Second, the quality and features of both the PC operating system and third-party software have improved steadily since the PC's introduction, yet costs have stayed low. Third, improvements such as better displays and printers have made the PC more usable. Finally, low-cost PC coprocessors can now bring together the resources of the SSDC and the PLC with those of the PC.

PC Applications   The PC finds uses as an operator interface, a smaller supervisory unit, and a data acquisition station. PC-based real-time control solutions, especially for dedicated applications, are also in place and are becoming more common as new software solutions arrive.

With a PC connected to a distributed control system or data highway, process engineers and supervisory personnel can access data from various controllers, subsystems, or operator workstations without interrupting operational routines. Currently, most control companies offer hardware interfaces to connect PCs to their control systems. MAP interfaces are available for PCs.

In general, PCs are used as follows (Ref. 5):

1. Engineering Console.   The largest application of PCs in manufacturing is as an engineer's console. Most control companies sell consoles needed to configure the system for specific uses. PCs offer ample computing power, storage

capacity, and flexibility. The most important tasks of the engineer's consoles are (Ref. 5):

- control system configuration, e.g., design of ladder diagrams for PLCs and control schemes for SSDCs;
- building the process database;
- building plant graphics or management reports;
- custom application programming; and
- system documentation.

Currently, PCs are used to configure all types of control devices, from SSDCs to PLCs to DCSs.

2. Data Acquisition. At the time of this writing, data acquisition is the second largest application of PCs in industrial plants. Because it involves no real process monitoring or control, data acquisition became one of the earliest process uses for microcomputers. The PC may be connected directly to the process through I/O boards, through I/O coprocessors, or via interfaces to data highways.

3. Operator Consoles. Improved graphics technology has stimulated the use of PCs as cost-effective operator consoles. They are increasingly being used as replacements for traditional operator consoles (sold by control companies with their systems) because of low cost, versatility, and advanced graphics interfaces. This usage is also being accelerated by an abundance of inexpensive, new process graphics software and the efforts to industrially harden and environmentally protect PCs. However, many PC-based operator workstations lack the capabilities that are provided with the operator workstations in DCSs (e.g., dedicated operator keyboard, data historian, and good reporting capabilities) (Ref. 2).

4. Monitoring and Control. PCs offer adequate computing power and data storage for monitoring and control applications. They are normally limited, however, to relatively simple and direct process monitoring due to their general lack of speed and responsiveness for real-time control. In the foreseeable future, PCs cannot be expected to replace other major types of control devices for the following reasons (Ref. 5):

- Since the office market is much larger in size, it will continue to drive PC technology.
- Lack of a universally accepted real-time operating system limits their application in many industrial plants. This may change as UNIX achieves greater acceptance as an operating system for PCs.
- Most of the manufacturing software currently available is written for MS-DOS operating systems, which lacks real-time and multi-tasking capabilities.
- PCs lack modularity or diversity for the control of numerous different types of manufacturing processes.
- Many process industry companies are concerned about the safety and reliability of PCs in industrial applications.

5. Plant Management. PCs are beginning to assume a major role in plant management because of the abundance of applications software. Manufacturing resource planning (MRP II) software is readily available in modules covering such functions as scheduling, inventory control, maintenance management, energy management, production control, forecasting, and so forth. These systems are being increasingly interfaced with other real-time process controls through communications networks. When connected with plantwide information systems, PCs make plant operating data available to a variety of engineers, managers, supervisors, and operating personnel. This is becoming increasingly essential in order to make timely, informed decisions.

6. Statistical Process Control/Statistical Quality Control (SPC/SQC). Because of a number of innovative software packages, PCs are being used in many statistical process control or statistical quality control applications. Programs for computing standard deviations, production trending, and the like have made SPC/SQC the dominant use of PCs in overall plant management.

Cell Controllers (Train/Line Supervisors)   The cell controller (train/line supervisor) in Figure 16-3:

- provides a link between broadband and carrierband MAP;
- drives the operator console;
- performs alarm management;
- implements SPC;
- handles batch tracking and reporting;
- monitors overall operation of the cell;
- performs batch sequencing;
- controls the global database and collects data;
- provides configuration capabilities; and
- allows expert system applications.

The cell (train/line) level is the essential level in the information system because it is the bridge that connects the process control subsystem to the plant level information processing subsystem. The cell controller collects data from the machine level, organizes it for display to operating personnel for real-time local decision making, and transmits summary data to the higher-level information subsystem. It usually does not interact with the process at the input/output (I/O) level.

Cell controllers operate between two diverse worlds (Ref. 6). They extract real-time data from lower-level devices and format such data for use on higher-level computers. They also accept direction from above and distribute data to lower-level devices.

Though cell controllers were first conceived for discrete parts manufacturing industries, the control companies were quick to realize their potential for batch applications as well. As a result, several control companies are now busy implementing batch functions in their cell controllers.

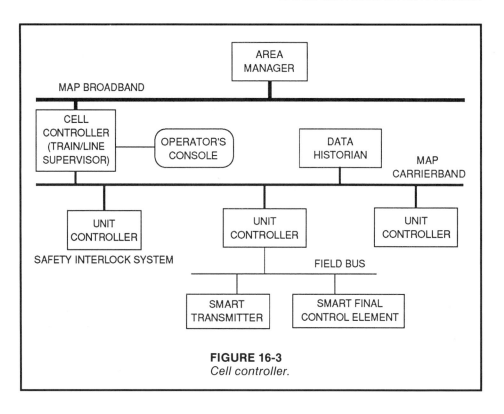

FIGURE 16-3
Cell controller.

There are a number of reasons why cell controllers will be popular with batch users (Ref. 7):

1. Although programmable logic controllers are strong contenders for simple batch applications, they lack capabilities in data storage, recipe management, and operator interface.

2. Distributed control systems are expensive and, in general, are a proprietary solution.

3. Most cell controllers, based on super micros or minicomputers, complement PLCs and SSDCs with capabilities that require considerable computing power.

4. Cell controllers with built-in batch programming languages will help control companies in making PLCs and SSDCs appeal to more users.

5. Cell controllers, when networked with PLCs and regulatory control devices, offer improved interface capabilities with computers for performing supervisory functions.

6. Cell controllers allow control companies to offer complete unit and supervisory level solutions to meet user needs for plantwide integration.

A definition of a cell controller is:

A device that is responsible for the operation of a group of manufacturing resources — manpower, machines, and materials — required for the manufacture of a product or related component parts, provides the methods required to improve quality and increase productivity, and offers *open systems* communications and information-processing capabilities.

Note that most cell controllers offered today do not include the *open systems* capability. However, to achieve maximum penetration into the batch control market and to compete with other batch control offerings (e.g., DCSs and the PC/PLC combination), this will be a strong selling point, and perhaps a necessary requirement, for this class of products.

The term "cell controller," used to describe a class of devices that oversee a cluster of related machinery or processes that constitute a work cell, first came into prominence during the planning of a GM plant. According to the National Electrical Manufacturers Association (NEMA), the minimum tasks of a cell controller are (Ref. 8):

- to communicate production information with either an operator, a higher-level device, or both;
- to coordinate and supervise at least one other independent production device that handles machine or process I/O; and
- to locally store and retrieve production information.

A study by the Automation Research Group found that users want a cell controller to perform the following four key functions (Ref. 9):

1. A cell controller must be able to communicate with many control devices, e.g., programmable controllers. This capability may be provided through an RS-232 type of serial interface or through an interface to a local communications network or data highway. In addition, users want a cell controller to communicate with higher-level computers or plant networks.

2. Based on directions received from an operator or a higher-level computer, a cell controller is required to monitor and direct the operations of all the control devices in a cell.

3. It must be able to collect and store data locally for a period of time depending on the nature of the manufacturing cell. Local data storage capability offers security in the event of a failure to link with the higher-level computer, and it provides a database for cell management functions.

4. Most manufacturing users want a cell controller to perform management functions, such as report generation, materials tracking, and device maintenance scheduling.

Cell controllers handle primarily two kinds of data: historical and real-time. In supervisory applications, a cell controller will gather and store information that will be used at a later time to report on system performance and problems for statistical and trending analyses. In control-oriented applications, a cell controller will handle data that will be used for alarming, graphics displays, and so forth.

The data in a cell controller database should be only what the cell needs in order to function. Other information is better stored in a higher-level computer. As some vendors and users see it, the area manager would be used to maintain information directly relating to the cell controllers it supervises. It would maintain and store material-handling data, inventory data, and any other data for which a cell controller does not have frequent need.

The major cell controller functions that utilize the real-time database are alarming, process graphics displays, and device status notation.

Historical data is typically used in statistical analyses, in trending, and for tabular reporting. Trending provides an ability to track key process or manufacturing variables over time, providing a responsive indicator on the performance of a particular production operation.

The following are some important characteristics that should be looked for in a cell controller system to derive maximum benefits (Ref. 10):

1. The platform should be designed as an automation system and not simply adapted from some other environment. It should have both information processing and real-time performance capabilities. This permits efficient and effective application of the system.

2. There should be a platform family of processors that is scalable to suit a variety of processing power requirements. It should support extensibility and flexibility and provide for node power enhancement.

3. Distributed processing capabilities are necessary so that they fit geographically distributed manufacturing operations.

4. An open architecture is required to take full advantage of multiple product sources for the best available and improving technology. This facilitates multivendor compatibility and permits use of existing third-party packages based on UNIX, SQL, MAP, and other de facto standards.

Many hardware solutions are being offered to handle the cell controller functions, such as the following:

1. Programmable controllers. A number of PLC manufacturers are offering their products as cell controllers. However, very few of these devices can provide the capabilities needed to meet the requirements of cell controllers.

2. Personal computers. These devices are probably used more than any other computing device to perform cell controller functions. However, personal computers lack the computing power and the multitasking operating system needed to effectively function as cell controllers.

3. Distributed control systems. A DCS is an expensive, proprietary solution to the needs of the cell controller. However, many of the current DCS offerings provide all the capabilities needed to function as cell controllers At least one DCS manufacturer offers a MAP gateway (broadband and carrierband) to allow the DCS to be connected into a MAP network.

4. Specially designed systems. A number of manufacturers have introduced specially designed cell controllers that can meet most of the needs of the batch industry at this level. The problem is that these systems have been designed to meet the needs of the discrete parts industries. They usually lack features such as adequate recipe-handling and storage capabilities, analog data handling, etc., that are so vital to batch control.

5. General-purpose computers. The largest potential in the cell controller area lies with general-purpose computers, such as the super microcomputers and minicomputers. Techniques are needed to get around the problems of real-time data collection.

The primary benefits of the cell controller in the manufacturing environment include the following (Refs. 11 and 12):

1. Permits cost savings by improved control of the manufacturing process, reduced inventory, and work-in-process (WIP) levels
2. Improves product quality and reduces scrap through statistical process control (SPC) techniques
3. Increases manufacturing flexibility and improves utilization of machines and facilities
4. Improves overall machine reliability and response when used as part of a distributed intelligence architecture
5. Continues operation if the plant computer fails (it does not need to be supported by higher-level devices; it can still control and supervise the production of material)
6. Enables decisions to be made at lower levels
7. Reduces the distance data must travel (machines respond faster to commands; it also reduces data traffic throughout the plant when acting as a data processor, concentrator, and as a data filter)
8. Functions as a bridge between shop floor and plantwide networks
9. Allows hardware and data to be distributed to best suit an individual facility
10. Acts as a building block for future automation

Small Batch Applications

Controlling small batch control processes has been a difficult problem for the control engineer. If the process has a large analog component, distributed control systems have been ideal. But since they tend to be costly, their use has been limited to large jobs. If the process has little analog control and limited operator interface requirements, programmable controllers (PLCs) can be good choices. However, small batch jobs often have several analog loops and the need for good operator interface, so the engineer using the PLC usually ends up installing conventional analog controllers, switches, indicator lights, and the like. Costs and complexity increase as the engineer puts together the various components. The result is often a very unsatisfying control system.

SSDCs For very small batch applications, SSDCs can provide the analog and sequential control capability along with a proven, process-oriented operator interface (the controller faceplate). Since many of these controllers (manufactured by the same company) can communicate with each other, they can eliminate the cost and difficulty of hardwiring signals between units. However, for SSDCs to be applied by themselves to a batch application, the sequencing requirements must be fairly simple.

The PC/PLC Combination There is a big opportunity to combine the speed and performance of the PLC with the versatility and data-handling capability of the PC.

Most PLCs were designed for stand-alone control, with very limited operator interfacing. Typical operator controls were usually limited to push buttons and annunciator lights. After programming and documentation, the most urgent need filled by PCs for PLCs was as operator interfaces.

Color graphics are now commonplace on PCs; detailed graphics representations of a process or factory function can be implemented relatively easily. Bar graphs, pie charts, simulated annunciator panels, or a drawing of the actual process layout or machinery can all be displayed in vivid colors for effectiveness. I/O on the PLC can be tied directly to color or shape changes or movements on the PC screen, providing a very effective operator display.

The PC/PLC combination tends to be particularly well-suited for batch process control. Sequencing, recipe handling, interlocking, and alarming can be readily implemented. Data logging and simple regulatory control functions can be handled with relative ease. However, this system may have to be augmented with SSDCs where a lot of regulatory control algorithms (e.g., PID or cascade) are required.

There are also some disadvantages to this approach:

1. When the user decides to use more than one vendor, the user takes on the responsibility for integrating the multiple hardware and software platforms. As revisions evolve over the life cycle of these systems, the support and upkeep of these systems may very well be more than for a fully integrated system (e.g., a DCS).

2. These systems still do not provide the same functionality as is provided by a DCS (e.g., speed, operator interface sophistication, time-tagged data, reliability and availability, etc.).

The PC bridges the gap between PLCs and the rest of the world. The PLC continues to do real-time, front end control, while the PC provides a host of functions (Ref. 13):

1. Acts as a programming and documentation station
2. Provides the functions of an effective operator interface station
3. Supervises and coordinates several PLC units, even across proprietary protocol boundaries
4. Provides hard disk storage for real-time and historical data logging
5. Allows analysis of logged data through the use of commercial software packages
6. Acts as the primary networking interface upwards into the mainstream data processing and communications environment

The PC effectively acts as a cell controller in this application.

PCs and PLCs should be considered partners, not competitors, in control for some good reasons:

1. In most process control applications, inputs must be monitored in real time, so the control device must be able to respond quickly, sometimes in milliseconds.

2. Personal computers, including the hardened plant floor versions, have a very difficult time handling real-time I/O because of their operating systems. These computers generally use the DOS operating system, which is single-tasking.

3. PLCs are designed to handle high-speed I/O very efficiently. A PLC can interpret a large number of input signals, use the information to control a large number of outputs, and repeat that process many times per second.

4. PLCs provide a wide array of I/O modules that meet the needs of industrial applications. Most PLC vendors provide analog, digital, and special-purpose I/O that cover the gamut of requirements found in automation and process control applications. In addition, I/O supplied by a PLC manufacturer is ruggedly designed for plant floor operation.

5. The PLC's continuing role in real-time control applications is also assured by its relatively low cost and ease of maintenance when compared to a comparable PC-based system.

6. In addition to providing the timing, sequencing, and logic functions for basic machine control, a PLC is in the ideal position to collect data from a production process and send it to a PC.

With internal PID capability, the entire array of control requirements for the small batch process can be satisfied within a single control device. The PID algorithm is implemented in ladder logic and can be applied to many simple regulatory control problems. An advantage of having the PID algorithm resident within the PLC is that it is tightly integrated with the logic and sequential control. This means that desired control interaction is much easier to implement than in modular systems in which these different control strategies reside in different hardware platforms throughout the architecture. However, the biggest drawback is that the PID algorithm is usually difficult to use and configure. Setting values into the PID parameters frequently involves continual reference to user's manuals.

Since the PLC provides the regulatory control capability in this control scheme, these capabilities must be discussed:

1. Some PLCs perform the PID algorithm in the same processor in which the logic is performed. This tends to slow down the operation of the PLC. If the PID algorithm is going to be performed within the PLC, there should be a dedicated microprocessor in the PLC that handles PID loops, calculations, data handling, and so on—the same things that slow down the PLC scan. These separate microprocessors must communicate with each other to allow calls to logic from regulatory control functions and vice versa.

Another option for handling PID loops and calculations is through intelligent I/O modules. These are stand-alone units installed in a slot or slots in the PLC I/O structure. They have their own built-in microprocessors and can communicate with the PLC's processor via the I/O structure, but they don't tie up the logic processor with these additional functions. PID modules are available that can handle multiple PID loops; BASIC modules are available that can do calculations and data handling.

2. The user should investigate this analog control capability very carefully. Usually these systems implement a basic PID loop, but very often they don't incorporate features that are important in batch control systems, e.g., a method to handle reset windup. In addition, they are often not set up to handle advanced control loops, such as feedforward control, override control, and so forth.

3. Although most PLCs are available now with some math capability, many do not have floating point math capability. Trying to do sophisticated math calculations can become very cumbersome when the PLC has only limited math capability.

Connecting a PC to a PLC can be a very easy task. The hardware interface, in most cases, is RS-232 or RS-422, so the connection is straightforward. Multiple PLCs can also be networked with one or more PCs. A number of PC-based process control packages come complete with drivers for PLCs and attempt to mimic conventional microcomputer-based distributed control systems. However, personal computers still have a significant speed shortcoming when compared with DCS systems.

Since most people have not actually designed and implemented a system using PLCs and PCs, certain guidelines should be followed (Ref. 3):

1. In general, PLCs do a good, reliable job at discrete control and an increasingly better job of analog control; a PC is best at displaying data, handling data, and making reports. Both types of hardware should be used within its capabilities.

2. Use proven packaged software, where possible, instead of custom software. Custom software with good documentation can be very expensive. It may not be worth having a feature if that feature has to be obtained through custom programming.

3. Understand the difference between programming and configuration. Programming means writing a program to perform a certain function in BASIC, FORTRAN, etc. Configuration means taking packaged software and using its commands, e.g., fill-in-the-blanks, to tailor it to fit the application.

4. Provide capacity for future expansion, as well as communications capabilities.

5. Involve maintenance and/or operations personnel in the design criteria phase of the new system. They can provide helpful information, and it may help them feel more comfortable with the new control system.

6. Segment control so that each piece of the process and each piece of the system is as independent as practical. Control hardware (PLCs) should function independently from the monitoring hardware and software (PCs).

7. Consider selecting a standard brand of PLC and using it throughout the plant. It should be able to communicate on a data highway.

The PC/PLC/SSDC Combination PCs seem to be good at data management, PLCs best at discrete logic, and SSDCs best at performing analog control. The ideal control system solution for a typical process, then, seems to be a combination of all three hardware products. The distributed architecture concept of this approach to process control offers numerous advantages, including low cost, flexibility, ease of operator interface, and capacity for expansion.

The same disadvantages that were discussed under "The PC/PLC Combination" apply to the PC/PLC/SSDC combination.

The three functional components in a typical PC-based control system of this type are the SSDC, PLC, and the PC. The following are the functional roles of each of the system components in a small system (Ref. 14):

1. SSDC
   - Analog input display and monitoring
   - Regulatory control
   - Batch control, including simple custom sequencing
   - Continuous process calculations (i.e., totalization, etc.)
   - Selectable multiloop, multivariable control
2. PLC
   - Discrete I/O interface
   - Interlock/safety logic
   - Complex sequence control
3. Operator Workstation (PC)
   - Operator interface to SSDC and PLC
   - Pictorial interface to process via graphics displays
   - Means to receive/acknowledge alarms
   - Engineering workstation for on-line programming and configuration of controllers
   - Data archiving and analysis
   - Document storage and control
   - Report generation and alarm logs

The operator must be able to operate the plant from the PC, and the engineer must be able to configure the PC and control system elements. Also, it is important that management information (plant data) be made available through the PC, and the PC should provide supervisory control. Here, again, the PC is playing the role of a cell controller.

Although some existing PC-based systems use an alphanumeric keyboard for both the engineer (configuration) and the operator (control), a dedicated functional keyboard for the operator provides an easier and more secure interface with which to view and operate the process. Operators, especially in alarm conditions, do not like conventional computer typewriter style keyboards, so function keys with preprogrammed sequences are essential operator interface tools. The alphanumeric keyboard is then used only for configuration and other special programs. For some small batch applications a QWERTY keyboard may be necessary for operator entry of recipe parameters, batch identification, and comments about any abnormal conditions that occurred during the execution of the batch.

Because the communications ports of the PC are inherently slow and tie up PC resources, they are not recommended as the interface to the SSDC, PLC, and operator keyboard. A more effective approach might be to use a coprocessor board as a secure interface between the PC and the rest of the control process. The coprocessor provides such functions as (Ref. 14):

- a high-speed communications link to the SSDCs, PLC, and operator keyboard;
- tasks to automatically get SSDC and PLC data for viewing and operation;
- running a real-time, supervisory control program separate from the PC tasks; and
- battery backup of data and supervisory program for security against power interruptions.

The PC/PLC/SSDC combination can be implemented using either serial communications or a data highway. The system in Figure 16-4 uses serial communications along with a coprocessor. The coprocessor provides the communications with the PLC and the SSDCs. This system represents an approach to batch

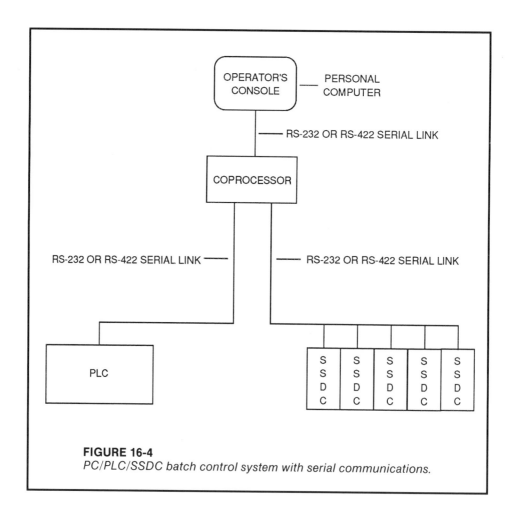

FIGURE 16-4
PC/PLC/SSDC batch control system with serial communications.

control that is becoming more and more accepted in batch applications. Some of the advantages to this approach include the following (Ref. 15):

1. Regulatory control can be implemented with single-loop integrity. A failure of an SSDC, the coprocessor, or the PLC will not affect the other devices.

2. The system is truly distributed. Control takes place at the lowest level possible in the system.

3. The system cost should be lower when compared with dedicated system architectures for small batch applications.

4. The PC, PLC, and SSDCs each perform the functions they are best designed to do.

5. The system is flexible and can be expanded later.

A disadvantage of this system is that there is no peer-to-peer communication between the PLC and the SSDCs; all communications must take place through the coprocessor.

The system in Figure 16-5 connects the SSDCs, PLC, and PC via a high-performance proprietary data highway (Ref. 16). The computer interface on the PLC calls the ASCII/BASIC module in the PLC to read data from the distributed SSDCs, contribute data to the global database, change set points on the loop controllers, and accept commands from the operator's local workstation. A connection is also provided to the same manufacturer's large DCS.

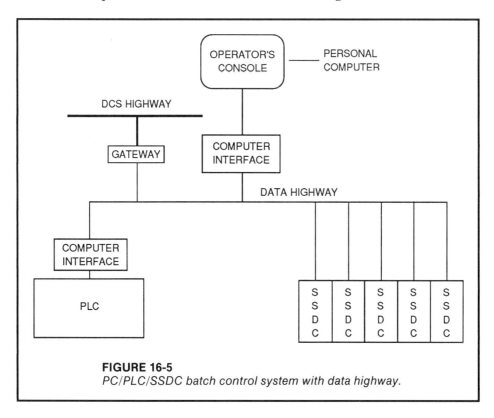

FIGURE 16-5
PC/PLC/SSDC batch control system with data highway.

Downsized DCSs (Batch Controllers) An example of a downsized DCS is shown in Figure 16-6. It consists of one multiloop controller, a PLC, and an operator's console. Both the multiloop controller and the PLC may not be needed in some small batch applications.

Reasons that favor DCSs for small batch applications include the following (Ref. 17):

1. Distributed control systems have grown smaller and are much more cost-competitive with PLCs than before.

2. Newer DCSs include an increased amount of flexibility and logic-handling capabilities.

3. Except for programming done in ladder diagrams, PLCs are much harder to program and use than DCSs.

4. Lack of applications expertise on the part of PLC distributors and some PLC vendors has hindered PLCs. Instrument companies, on the other hand, are known for applications expertise.

5. Users interested in performing supervisory control complain that some PLC companies don't offer a variety of application software packages or interface capability for different brands of computers. Instrument companies, on the other hand, are starting to offer more and more software for batch processes. They are also more willing to develop interfaces with common brands of computers.

The DCS together with the PLC integrated into the architecture can satisfy the entire spectrum of control requirements for small batch applications.

Medium Batch Applications

Medium batch applications tend to be implemented either with DCSs or by DCSs in conjunction with PLCs. Some applications may be served by the PC/PLC/SSDC system. In the future, the medium batch application will fit very nicely into the realm of the cell controller (train/line supervisor) combined with PLCs and SSDCs (see "Cell Controllers (Train/Line Supervisors)"), where the cell controller is probably a super microcomputer rather than a PC.

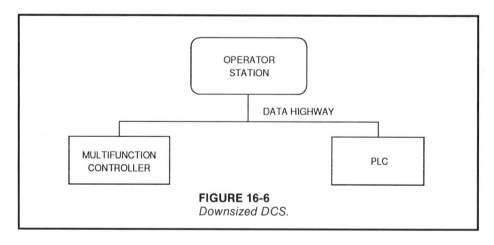

FIGURE 16-6
Downsized DCS.

Large Batch Applications

Distributed control systems (DCS) that are manufactured specifically to handle process systems with large numbers of I/O points provide a viable solution for most large batch applications.

The following are advantages of distributed control for large systems (Ref. 1):

1. Improved operator interface, allowing the operator to better understand and react to process problems.

2. Improved computer interface, particularly in eliminating dual reduction of data, i.e., data can be transmitted in its reduced form (trends, etc.) from operator station to computer.

3. Reduced control room size. Conventional control panels are not required.

4. Wiring cost savings. Instead of multipairs between field and control room, two coaxial or fiber optic cables are looped around the plant.

5. Flexible control implementation. Changes in control strategy are implemented by software instead of hardware changes.

6. Complex control modes are easily performed by the microprocessor; digital calculations are precise and do not require the recalibration required of analog components.

An example of a large DCS is shown in Figure 16-7. Manufacturers who make SSDCs generally provide an interface to allow the SSDCs to sit on the data highway. Not all of these components are required in all batch applications. Additional items can be added as needed. The batch operator's console is usually a microcomputer- or minicomputer-based CRT station. Some of the devices on the highway are dedicated to specific tasks, e.g., the data historian.

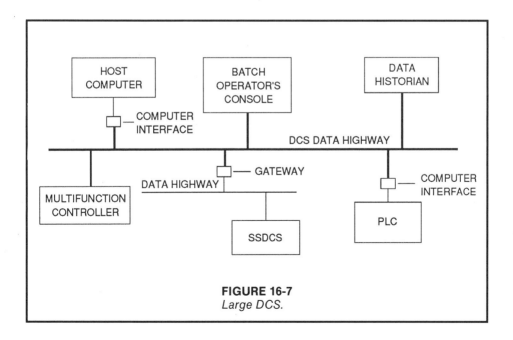

FIGURE 16-7
Large DCS.

Future Trends in Batch Control Systems   The trend in batch control is towards an architecture designed for the integration of loop, logic, and sequential control. New systems should satisfy key criteria such as easy-to-use loop control, fast logic control, easy-to-use sequential control, and extensive control integration. Recent control systems designed for large batch processes satisfy these requirements except that they have a high entry-level cost and are based on proprietary architectures. The challenge is to provide similar functionality at a much lower cost and with an "open systems" architecture.

Most control companies have been selling proprietary communications networks for many years. In the future, the move is going to be to MAP networks. They are likely to purchase these interfaces from a communications company because only a select few major control companies are expected to develop MAP networks in-house.

The cell controller (train/line supervisor) is making major inroads in the discrete parts industry. The same effect will eventually be seen in the batch process industry. Since these cell controllers in the future are likely to be based on general-purpose computers, e.g., super microcomputers and PCs, control companies will continue to purchase computers from the computer companies. This means that control companies will be purchasing an increasing number of products from other firms, specifically the computer and communication companies, so that they can assemble a complete control system. Therefore, they will become much more like systems integrators, since an increasing amount of their revenues will be from services.

Advances in technology will continue to provide control systems with reduced costs and increased functionality. New features for PLCs are expected to revolve around providing better integrated solutions, easier-to-use PID algorithms, and improved operator interfaces. Communication is the key to achieving better integrated solutions. MAP is one of the "open systems" standards that will enable this integration to take place.

PCs are proliferating in manufacturing, and they will significantly change the role of control companies involved in batch control. PC-based operator interfaces will start to include traditional DCS features such as supervisory control tasks, additional control algorithms, and data historians.

SSDCs will also continue to decrease in price and increase in functionality. Alphanumeric prompts will make SSDCs even easier to use, and expensive options, such as communications, will become standard features. Communications will be used to improve the control integration between a PLC and SSDCs.

Two primary areas of improvement are seen for the DCS. The first is in providing a competitive, low-cost entry system that is completely upward compatible with their total offering. This will enable the DCS to compete in process applications such as the small batch applications. The second area of improvement is in providing a true single-window system, which encompasses the entire array of tasks and tools involved with batch control.

Loop control and interlock logic have different processing requirements. Loop control requires consistent, predictable update times to optimize the PID algorithm. Typically, these update times are 1 second or less. Interlock logic often requires a faster update time, possibly from 10 to 50 milliseconds. Because of the different requirements, it makes sense to have separate loop and interlock logic processors so that each can be optimized independently. This provides an additional advantage in that the interlock logic processor is physically separate from the loop processor. Ideally, the loop processor should have the loop control capability of a small distributed control system, and the logic processor should have the logic control capability of a programmable controller. However, the interlock logic processor requires a higher level of reliability than is typically required in a loop processor. Sequential logic does not require the fast update times needed by the interlock logic processor. Therefore, sequential logic could be implemented in the same processor as the control loops or in a general-purpose computer that is handling supervisory activities.

Batch Control in the MAP Environment

There are many ways to configure a batch control system. The ideal system will allow the user to combine PLCs, the multifunction controllers from DCSs, microprocessor-based single-loop controllers, fault tolerant PLCs for safety interlock systems, and minicomputers as shown in Figure 16-8. At the present time, this system is realizable only on a limited basis, because the MAP specification is not complete at the process control level. That will change in the near future because many PLC and DCS manufacturers have committed to supporting MAP.

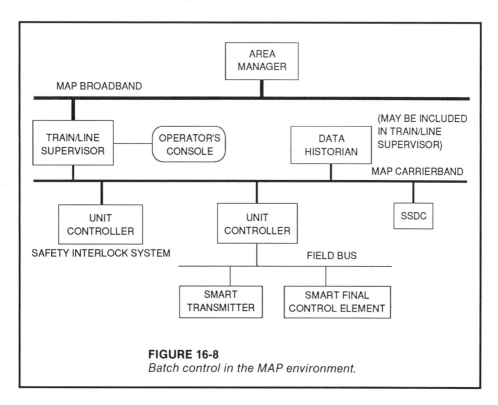

FIGURE 16-8
Batch control in the MAP environment.

The following are some features of this system:

1. The MAP carrierband network is used at the train/line level.

2. All equipment needed to directly control the batch process is connected to the carrierband network.

3. With a fully realizable MAP system, the batch control system is very flexible. Additional equipment, of basically any manufacturer, can be connected to the data highway at any time.

4. There is peer-to-peer communication between all devices on the network because of MAP.

EXERCISES

16.1 Functionally, PLCs, SSDCs, and PCs do many of the same tasks that a DCS does. Discuss why, even though the functional distinctions between these different types of batch control hardware are diminishing, these systems don't all offer the same capabilities to the user.

16.2 Why don't many process industry companies want to use PCs for direct control of I/O?

16.3 Why don't most PLCs have the capability to function as a cell controller?

16.4 How can the user solve the integration problem when using a PC/PLC or PC/PLC/SSDC combination for batch control?

16.5 Why is the conventional typewriter style keyboard not the best interface for the operator in a batch control system?

16.6 What things will distinguish one vendor from another once the industry moves to open systems based on standards?

16.7 Why doesn't sequential control require the same speed as discrete control?

REFERENCES

1. Querido, J. C., "Distributed Control," *SCMA Journal, M&C*, April 1985.

2. Lim, V. C., and R. M. Ray, "Small Batch Reactor Control System Integration," ISA/88, Paper #88-1581.

3. Kendricks, L. E., "An Approach to Using Personal Computers and Programmable Controllers for Flexible Cost-Effective Control Systems," Proceedings of the Sixth Annual Control Engineering Conference, May 19–21, 1987.

4. Holman, J., "Computing Batch Control Choices," *InTech*, April 1989.

5. Chatha, A. S., "Role of PCs in Manufacturing," ISA/87, Paper #87-1135.

6. Bartos, F. J., "Cell and Area Controls Make Automation Building Blocks," *Control Engineering*, April 1988.

7. "Cell Controllers Target Batch Applications," Industry News, *InTech*, November 1987.

8. "Minimum Functionality for a Cell Controller," National Electrical Manufacturers Association, 1988.

9. Malone, R., "Cell Controls Need Definition," *Managing Automation*, September 1987.

10. Cole, D., and F. Stewart, "The Benefits of the Cell Controller in a MAP Network," Enterprise Conference Proceedings, The Society of Manufacturing Engineers, 1988.

11. Jasany, L. C., "Controls for Cells," *Production Engineering*, April 1987.

12. Blanchar, D., S. Israni, and J. Kniskern, "Cell Controllers—An Emerging Technology," *Control Engineering*, November 1986.

13. Pinto, J. J., "Personal Computers Bridge the Gap for Programmable Controllers in the Industrial Environment," Proceedings of the Sixth Annual Control Engineering Conference, May 19–21, 1987.

14. Yingst, J. C., "PC-Based Architecture Guides Process Control," *InTech*, September 1988.

15. Yingst, J. C., "Integrating Personal Computers and Programmable Controllers into Process Control," *CONTROL*, October 1988.

16. Arnold, J. N., "Practical Techniques for Linking Foreign Devices to a Distributed System," ISA/87, Paper #87-1162.

17. "DCSs and PLCs Battle for Batch Applications," *I&CS News, I&CS*, May 1988.

17

Reliability/ Availability

Introduction   If a control system fails in a batch process and no process data base can be accessed, recovery may be impossible. Batches in progress during a computer failure are likely to be lost as saleable product.

Another aspect that must be considered when looking at control system failure is safety. Unsafe conditions may arise simply because control has been lost, e.g., a reactor no longer has temperature control. Safety systems protect plant equipment, personnel, and the surrounding community from damage and injury and should be provided external to the regulatory controllers. These safety systems do not substitute for the regulatory controllers and, therefore, do not allow continued operation when these controllers fail.

Reliability   Control system failures often shut down processes, because many plants are too complex to run manually and high cost often rules out backup systems. To avoid danger to personnel or property as well as to prevent loss of product or production time, manufacturers need to supply quantitative reliability estimates for instruments and other items that comprise the monitoring and control systems.

Reliability is a statistical parameter used to evaluate equipment on the basis of failure probabilities. Reliability is defined as the probability of equipment performing its required function for a specified time interval under stated conditions (Ref. 1). If malfunctions are random, rates of failure will be uniform during this period and the probability will be an exponential function of time (Ref. 2):

$$R(t) = e^{-\lambda t}$$

where: $R(t)$ = reliability
λ = failure rate (failures/hr)
t = time (hr)

Equipment typically goes through three distinct failure rate regions during its lifetime (see Figure 17-1) (Ref. 3). Improper handling or use can also cause failures, but these are not usually considered in reliability studies.

There is commonly an early failure period (also called infant mortality) when failure rates are high. This may be caused by inadequate quality control or poor manufacturing practices. Most manufacturers conduct burn-in tests, during which devices are operated for specific periods under simulated conditions to eliminate early failures before shipment. Burn-in is the operation of the component, module, or system under some increased stress, e.g., increased temperature. The increased stress is intended to cause most of the early failures to occur in the manufacturer's shop rather than in the user's plant.

Problems such as faulty connections that might occur during shipment of the equipment can also cause systems to fail early, so users should conduct burn-in tests of their own on complete systems before final start-up. Some early failures will be detected during the commissioning phase of the project when the equipment is powered up and connected to real-world inputs and outputs.

The second stage is a normal operating interval in which random operating stresses cause failures. Although these stresses cannot be predicted in a deterministic fashion, data for large numbers of similar products typically show constant

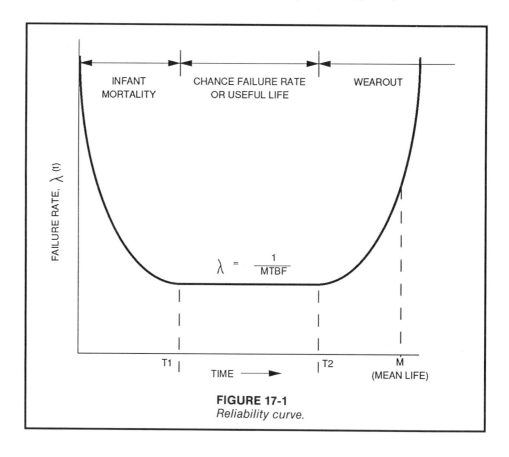

FIGURE 17-1
Reliability curve.

failure rates during this period. These give the frequency at which the devices can be expected to fail (failure rate); the reciprocal of the failure rate is the MTBF (mean time between failures), usually given in hours. Note that this applies only during the constant failure rate period.

The final stage is the wear-out period, during which aging is the dominant failure mechanism. Wear-out is a relatively minor problem with solid-state devices since normal operating lives are extremely long.

If burn-in eliminates early failure and if replacement is scheduled in accordance with mean wear-out life, random failures become the only reliability problem. To compensate, instruments and other components can be selected and configurations can be specified that will maximize overall system MTBF during the normal operating period.

If equipment is properly selected, installed, and maintained and if the system software is reliable, the main variable affecting the chance of system shutdown is the failure rate of the system components. This failure rate is normally measured by the control system's mean time between failures (MTBF).

When equipment has been in service for long periods of time, MTBF, a measure of reliability, can be determined from the historical data. MTBF is defined as the average time between failures for repairable modules. Sometimes data is not available. However, techniques were developed for predicting reliability for the space program. These same techniques are now being applied on industrial equipment that is used for process control and for safety systems.

The reliability of any module is a function of time and the module failure rate. Reliability can be increased by (Ref. 4):

- the use of high quality components, e.g., mil spec;
- low stress on components;
- a minimum number of components;
- burn-in at board level;
- environmental protection; and
- heat soak of the final assembly, including cabinet and cables.

Availability
Reliability does not take into consideration that equipment can be repaired and put back on line. Another reliability parameter, availability, considers both MTBF and the mean deadtime (MTD), which includes the mean time to repair (MTTR). A useful definition of system availability was given in Chapter 8:

$$A = \text{Uptime/Total Time}$$

where A = availability.

The availability of a series string of modules is simply the product of the availability of the individual modules:

$$A_s = A_a \times A_b \times A_c \times \ldots A_m$$

where: A_s = the overall series system availability

A_a = the availability of module a (A_b is the availability of module b, etc.)

Because of the definition of availability, the availability of each module will be a number less than one and, at best, can be exactly equal to one. So the multiplication of a series of numbers less than one will result in a product that is less than any of its factors. The more modules in a system, the smaller the system availability.

The availability of the parallel combination of two modules would be:

$$A_p = A_a + A_b - A_a A_b$$

where: A_p = the overall parallel system availability

A_a = the availability of module a (A_b is the availability of module b, etc.)

Using the parallel formula, most complex system configurations can be reduced to a series connection of availability blocks. The final product of the multiplication of all the availability blocks together will produce the system availability.

Availability can also be defined in terms of the mean time between failures (MTBF) and the mean downtime (MDT):

$$A = MTBF/(MTBF + MDT)$$

MDT is really a summation of the mean time to diagnose the presence of a system fault (MTDF) and the mean time to repair (MTTR)

$$MDT = MTDF + MTTR$$

Heron (Ref. 5) points out that the MTTR can be broken down into:

$$MTTR = MTDL + MTRF + MTRO$$

where: MTDL = mean time to determine a fault location

MTRF = mean time to replace a faulted component

MTRO = mean time to return the system to operable condition

The MTD values can be developed from considerations of (1) the location of repair personnel, (2) the average repairman's skill level, (3) the ease of diagnosis of the system fault, and (4) the accessibility of spares. MTD values can then be combined with the vendor's quoted MTBF numerics to produce availability values for a module.

For FTS faults, MTDF = 0, because the fault is self-revealing.

$$A = MTBF/(MTBF + MTTR)$$

For FTD faults, MTDF is most important and often determines the overall availability, because this term is usually much larger than the MTTR. Therefore:

$$A = MTBF/(MTBF + MTDF + MTTR)$$

The MTDF is a function of how often the system is tested, or the test interval, TI. The test interval is the time interval between two successive tests. An FTD fault can occur any time during the test interval. On the average, it can be assumed that it will occur about the middle of the test interval or 1/2 TI. Therefore (Ref. 6),

$$A = MTBF/(MTBF + 1/2TI + MTTR)$$

If the system is tested manually, the test interval tends to be much longer than MTTR, and

$$A = MTBF/(MTBF + 1/2TI) = MTBF/(MTBF + MTDF)$$

What does high availability mean? Is an availability of 99.88% good?

EXAMPLE 17-1

Problem: If a control system failed ten times per year, it would have a MTBF of 876 hours (8760 hours per year/10). If the MTTR was 1 hour, what would the availability be (Ref. 7)?

Solution: A = 876/877 = 0.9988 (99.88%).

EXAMPLE 17-2

Problem: If a control system failed only once in two years, it would have an MTBF of 17520 hours. With the same MTTR of 1 hour, what would the availability be (Ref. 7)?

Solution: A = 17520/17521 = 0.99994 (99.994%).

Several nines after the decimal point are required for good performance.

Safety, profit, and ease of maintenance should be considered when determining how much availability is required (Ref. 1).

1. Safety. Safety should be the first priority in all control systems. In extremely hazardous processes, e.g., nuclear power plants, this may require redundancy not only of control, but also of methods. In a nuclear power plant, a particular valve may be controllable by both an electronic system and a backup pneumatic control system. In addition, the valve may also have to be controllable by manual means, e.g., a handwheel. The availability of the function of control by that valve must be 100 percent despite the failure of both the electronic and the pneumatic systems.

2. Profit. The amount of money lost when a process line is shut down is usually known or can be calculated. The value of the materials, cost of reprocessing or disposal, lost time in cleanup, and the dollar value of lost production in the

event of a control system failure will define approximately the maximum value of the backup system.

When the availability of a control system is known, the unavailability, U, is automatically known because unavailability and availability are complementary:

$$U = 1 - A$$

where: U = unavailability
       A = availability

The time lost due to system unavailability in, for example, 1 year, can be found by multiplying the total time by the unavailability:

$$\text{Downtime} = \text{Total Time} \times U$$

The downtime can then be multiplied by the amount of money lost per unit time to determine the dollars lost.

EXAMPLE 17-3

Problem: If a plant loses \$50,000 of production an hour when the plant cannot produce product, how much money would be lost in one year if the unavailability were 0.0012 (availability equals 99.88%)? How much money would be lost in one year if the unavailability were 0.00006 (availability equals 99.994%)?

Solution: For an unavailability of 0.0012, the downtime equals 0.0012 × 8760 hours/yr or 10.512 hours/year. The amount of money lost/yr is equal to 10.512 hours/yr × \$50,000/hour or \$525,600.

For an unavailability of 0.00006, the downtime equals 0.00006 × 8760 hours/yr or 0.526 hours/year. The amount of money lost/yr is equal to 0.526 hours/yr × \$50,000/hour or \$26,300.

3. Ease of Maintenance. A certain number of failures can be expected in any control system. After safety and profit requirements have been satisfied, then ease of maintenance should be considered. Detection and correction of failures can be operator-controlled or performed automatically with built-in hardware and diagnostic routines. If there is time to discover a failure and correct it by replacement or switching in a spare, initial equipment capital costs can be traded off against maintenance costs over the life cycle of the equipment.

Availability depends on a number of factors, such as whether single-loop controllers or multiloop controllers are used, how much backup is provided, and whether redundant and/or fault tolerant systems are used.

Single-Loop Integrity   If the process can tolerate the failure of any one controller, then a non-redundant, single-output architecture can offer excellent

system reliability. Analog installations (both pneumatic and electronic) have single-loop integrity because each loop is independent of the others. If a loop fails, control might be degraded in one part of the process, but the whole batch system will not be shut down.

This is different from computer control where all the control is done in one computing device; here, a failure in the computer can shut down the whole system.

Distributed control systems (DCSs) have replaced analog control systems and computer control systems in many applications. The integrity of these systems tends to be somewhere between that of analog control systems and computer control systems (Ref. 9). Because the control devices are distributed, a failure in one of the controllers will probably not shut down the whole batch system. How much of the system is shut down is a function of the design of the system. Some controllers may allow the user to implement only eight PID controllers in one of these devices; another supplier's equipment may allow sixty-four PID controllers to be implemented in one device.

Backup Systems
Backup systems are used to allow the system to be safely shut down, to allow for limited production when the control system fails, or to allow for continued plant operation. Each system must be evaluated to determine what level of backup is justified.

The simplest and least expensive backup consists of local process indication and manual override switches or handwheels for valves (Ref. 10). If the process is not hazardous, if the plant is small, and if the unit will be shut down when the control system fails, this approach is adequate.

A higher level of backup uses computer-auto-manual stations for throttling control and manual switches for sequencing and interlocking (Ref. 10). The intent of this type of backup is to allow continued plant operation at reduced throughput. This could be very important in a batch process, because it could allow the operator to take the batch to a safe stopping point. However, a considerable amount of interfacing hardware is required between the computing devices and the backup stations. It is also necessary to synchronize the backup device with the process, because the backup system will not have control of the process when the computing device is operating properly. This type of backup system generally provides no information on the current state of the process. Backup systems can get very costly and complex if all these requirements are met.

Redundant and Fault Tolerant Systems
The current approach to ensuring integrity is with redundant and fault tolerant systems. Redundant and fault tolerant systems can be used to make systems more fail-safe and to increase the availability.

Baur (Ref. 11) points out that the primary distinction between redundancy and fault tolerance is whether the implementation is static or dynamic. Redundancy is normally static in that the backup device does nothing until it is automatically switched in because of a failure in the primary device. Fault tolerance implies continuous redundancy, where failures are typically handled by voting procedures that are internal to the computing device.

Fault tolerant and redundant systems are used when:

- system availability is critical,
- bad outputs cannot be tolerated,
- continuous operation is required, or
- the system is installed in a remote location where maintenance is a problem.

A variety of different process controllers are currently available to the user. These controllers differ in level of redundancy and size (number of outputs). Using these controllers to achieve the optimal level of reliability depends on understanding different controller architectures and matching these to real process needs.

Areas of the batch control system in which redundancy or fault tolerance may be necessary are:

- operators' consoles (including the electronics that drive the consoles),
- data highways (including the transmission medium, the device interfaces to the highway, and any controlling master on the data highway),
- power supplies, and
- single-loop controllers, multiloop controllers, programmable controllers, data historians, etc.

The following are some advantages to be gained with a properly designed system (Ref. 12):

1. Control of the process continues in the event of a failure in one of the systems.

2. The second system will not be affected by the failure of a module in the other system.

3. Maintenance can be performed on one system while the other system is still in operation.

4. Each system can be used to monitor the other for hardware errors.

5. An independent system (i.e., a host computer) can be used to monitor both systems and report system errors.

Redundant Systems

There is no substitute for a system that has been designed with high-quality parts. This tends to provide higher MTBF. A second way to increase MTBF is with a redundant system. This can take the form of redundant processors, redundant I/O, or redundant systems. A redundant system, although the most costly of these three, has the capability of providing the longest MTBF.

Redundancy is generally incorporated in one of two ways: either by supplying additional elements in parallel on a one-for-one basis or by a one-for-many system in which one controller box is used to take the place of any one of a small group that may have failed (Ref. 13). One-for-one redundancy provides a greater increase in MTBF than a one-for-many system as shown in Table 17-1 (Ref. 9).

The simplest type of redundancy is an uninstalled spare processor that can be installed if the main processor fails. This type of system is applicable only for noncritical applications that can stand some downtime.

In most redundant systems, two processors are installed, and each processor performs the same logic. Each processor is monitored to make sure it is functioning properly. If the main processor fails, control is switched over to the backup processor, as long as it is operating correctly.

An example of static redundancy (redundant processors but only single I/O) is shown in Figure 17-2. The watchdog determines if the running controller has

TABLE 17-1
The Effect of Redundancy on System MTBF

Number of Backup Units/Number of Controllers	Predicted MTBF (Years)
No backup	3.2
1 backup per 8 controllers	36
1 backup per 6 controllers	59
1 backup per 4 controllers	118
1 backup per 2 controllers	349
1 backup per 1 controller	939

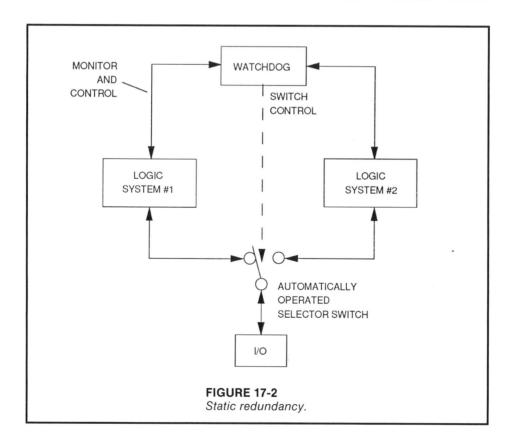

FIGURE 17-2
Static redundancy.

failed and makes an automatic switchover. The watchdog could be a PLC, a computer, or a separate piece of equipment. In this case, the backup controller makes a cold start after failure of the first controller, so some data will probably be lost during the transfer. Bumpless transfer probably can't be expected unless the internal data storage of the backup machine is updated each scan. Some systems are now using high-speed communications via direct memory access to reduce the update time. These are often called "hot backup" systems.

Although this system appears to be safe, its availability can actually be less than using two separate controllers without the automatic switchover (Ref. 4). When redundant components are used, it is often more appropriate to talk about unavailability, U, where

$$U = 1-A$$

Some people call this the fractional deadtime, or the fraction of the time that the system is inactive. The unavailability of two systems in series, U_s, and two systems in parallel, U_p, is (Ref. 14):

$$U_s = U_a + U_b - U_a U_b$$

$$U_p = U_a \times U_b$$

where: U_a = unavailability of system A
       U_b = unavailability of system B

Assume that the availability of each item in this system is 99% (see Figure 17-3). Therefore, the unavailability is 1% because of failure, functional testing, or repair. The unavailability of the two parallel units is $1\% \times 1\%$ or 0.01% (availability is 99.99%). But the watchdog and the switch are in series. The unavailability of the series combination is $1\% + 1\% - (1\% \times 1\%)$ or 1.99% (availability is 98.01%). However, the availability of the watchdog and switch would have to be near perfect if the overall system availability is to be maintained at 99.99%.

Failures in the watchdog and switch can affect both the other PLCs. They are called common mode failures. Any kind of interconnection between two PLCs may allow a single failure to disrupt the whole system (Ref. 15). This is also true with "hot backup" systems. And there is no guarantee that, when the transfer is made, good information is available in the primary controller. If not, then the system will still go down, or worse—the backup controller will try to operate using bad data.

Figure 17-4 shows a redundant system with redundant I/O. This type of redundant system can be set up as either static or dynamic. If the system is set up as a statically redundant system, both controllers read the inputs and run the same application program, but only one set of outputs is connected to the field devices. A watchdog is needed to detect a failure in the primary controller and switch in the backup controller. This system is applied more in DCS systems and with analog output devices.

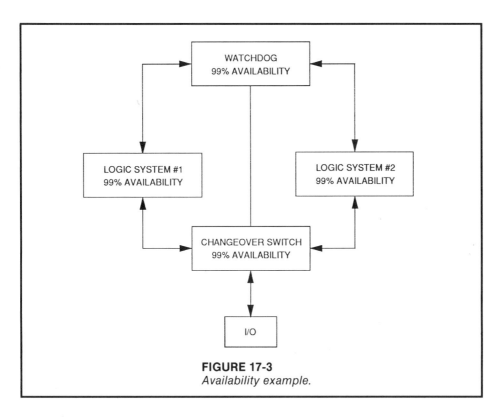

FIGURE 17-3
Availability example.

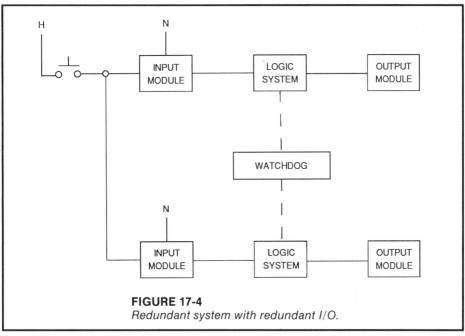

FIGURE 17-4
Redundant system with redundant I/O.

This system can also be set up to run as dynamic redundancy. Then both systems are active, and both are scanning inputs, solving logic, and directing outputs. This system can be configured with or without the watchdog. Without the watchdog, the two systems operate independently. With the watchdog, a comparison can be made of what is happening in each system. This system can provide better diagnostics of input and output problems, such as:

- individual input or output module failure,
- field input signal miscomparison between the redundant systems (the same input signal detected differently by the two systems), or
- field output signal miscomparison.

There are two ways to wire the outputs in the dynamically redundant system: in series or in parallel (digital outputs). The series hookup shown in Figure 17-5 minimizes the danger of a triac failing on and affecting the output, since both triacs would have to fail to cause a problem. But it does increase the possibility of nuisance shutdowns if the triac fails open. The parallel hookup shown in Figure 17-6 minimizes the nuisance shutdowns from the triac failing open, since the other controller can still energize the output. But it does increase the possibility of an unsafe condition if the triac fails on. Frequent testing is required with this type of system. This type of redundant system is used more often with discrete devices, e.g., in a safety interlock system.

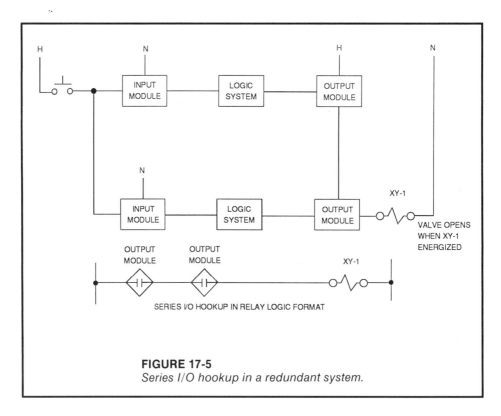

FIGURE 17-5
Series I/O hookup in a redundant system.

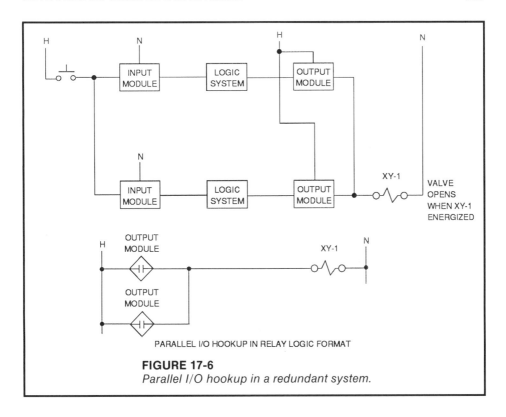

FIGURE 17-6
Parallel I/O hookup in a redundant system.

Coverage and Common Mode Failure
Having redundant systems is useless unless the systems have excellent built-in fault diagnostics to detect errors in the systems. Each system must be able to (Ref. 16):

- sense hardware failures, annunciate the fault, and shut down the system in an orderly manner;
- sense noncritical failures, annunciate the fault, and provide for user logic intervention; and
- maintain highly reliable communication with the I/O and annunciate communication failures.

Any part in common with both sides of a redundant controller can cause the entire system to fail, including non-redundant parts and parts that cannot be replaced on-line. Another factor is the undetected failures of redundant parts. If a component fails in a redundant unit and the diagnostics do not detect the failure, switchover will not occur, and the redundant system will fail. Special diagnostic hardware is required to achieve a high fault detection rate within a controller.

The biggest problem with most redundant systems is that they were not originally designed to be used in a redundant system, and they have a hard time achieving a failure detection rate of even 70%. This means that 30% of all failures in these systems contribute to the "common" failure rate. In a well designed system, the fault detection can achieve a much better rate. In a study of field returns on a commercial multiloop controller, current diagnostic software was capable of detecting greater than 90% of actual field faults (Ref. 6).This percentage is called "coverage" and represents the single most important parameter in high reliability controllers. Three types of parts can be logically classed as a "common part" (Ref. 17):

1. Any part physically in common with both sides of a redundant controller
2. Any part that requires shutdown to replace the part
3. Any part that fails and is not detected by diagnostics

When a "common part" is added to the system, the failure rate of the "common part" is simply added to the failure rate of the redundant components.

Fault Tolerant Systems

Considerable emphasis is now being given to *fault tolerant* computer systems. If a system is fault tolerant, it can withstand an internal failure and still function. Some commercially available systems have three identical microprocessors. If one unit fails, the other two will continue to operate. Each module within the system performs critical functions simultaneously, and the results are compared to the results of the other units using a majority voting system (best two out of three). Normally, all three outputs will be identical. If one unit fails, the results will be determined by the other two units because the two of them are the same and they outvote the failed unit. Fault tolerant systems are applied more often to safety shutdown systems than to process control systems.

Examples of fault tolerant systems are shown in Figure 17-7 (Ref. 18) and Figure 17-8 (Ref. 19). Faults in these systems can be identified and bypassed by rejecting one value if it doesn't agree with the other two. The fault tolerant system allows first faults to be bypassed without introducing switching transients and helps eliminate nuisance trips. Separate voting modules are used to compare the outputs before passing commands to the process. These fault tolerant systems are called triple modular redundant (TMR) systems.

The system in Figure 17-7 uses three independent channels, each running the same logic and each having its own input and output modules. The outputs from these three channel go to a voting network where they are voted 2 out of 3 using hard-wired electromechanical relays. Watchdogs and automatic testing are incorporated in this system.

The system in Figure 17-8 does the voting at two points. The outputs of the three controllers are voted 2 out of 3 before they go to the output modules. If one controller does not agree with the other two, it is voted out. This allows the system to identify failures as early as possible. There are two methods for doing this voting at this point in the system: by software or by hardware. Using software voting schemes allows standard computers to be used in the system. But the overhead required to handle the voting tasks tends to slow down the system. It is also difficult to achieve high reliability in the software for this type of system. The hardware voting scheme has the disadvantage of needing custom hardware. But

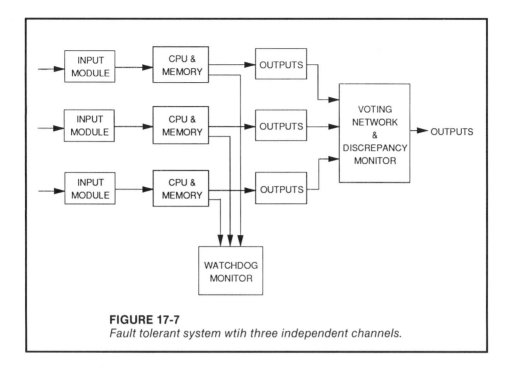

FIGURE 17-7
Fault tolerant system wtih three independent channels.

the hardware voting system executes faster and is not plagued by the software problems.

For process operations that cannot tolerate control loop failures, or where repairs cannot be guaranteed before the process has been affected, the redundant multiple output architecture or the TMR multiple output architecture offers the best system availability. The implementation of the redundant controller is critical. It must offer "low common area" and high diagnostic "coverage."

Sensors and Final Control Elements   On critical applications, multiple sensors and/or multiple final control devices may be necessary. When multiple sensors are used, it is important that they have individual process connections, since this is a potential common mode failure point. If two sensors are used, a comparison must be made between the two. When there is a miscompare, it is often difficult to determine which of the two sensors is correct. This problem can be solved by using three sensors. If the three sensors are digital, they can be voted two-out-of-three to determine a bad sensor. If the three sensors are analog, then circuitry in the controllers is used to detect the median of the three, and this is used for control. In all cases, an alarm should be activated when a deviation is detected in any of the sensors.

Output devices are usually not duplicated because of the cost. However, in critical applications, duplicate final control devices may be used, as shown in Figure 17-9. If the valves are supplying energy to the process, e.g., steam supply valves, they are normally piped in series using fail-closed valves, so energy can be

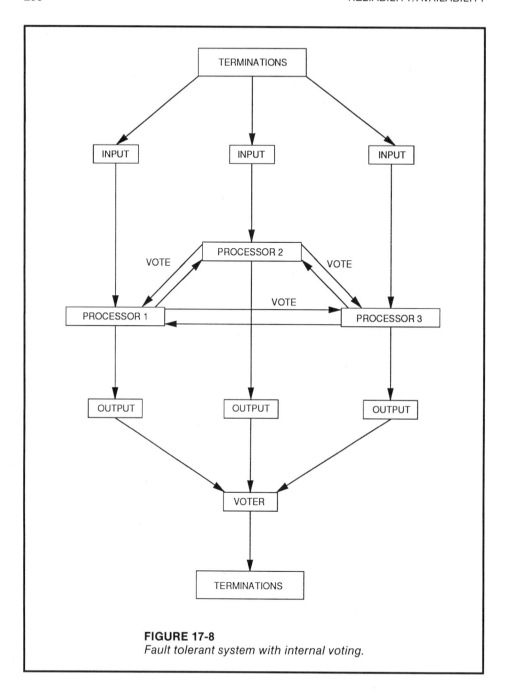

FIGURE 17-8
Fault tolerant system with internal voting.

removed from the process when one device fails (see Figure 17-9(a)). When energy is being removed from the process, e.g., cooling water supply valves, the valves are typically piped in parallel using fail-open valves. Then cooling water can still be applied to the process if one of the valves fails (see Figure 17-9(b)).

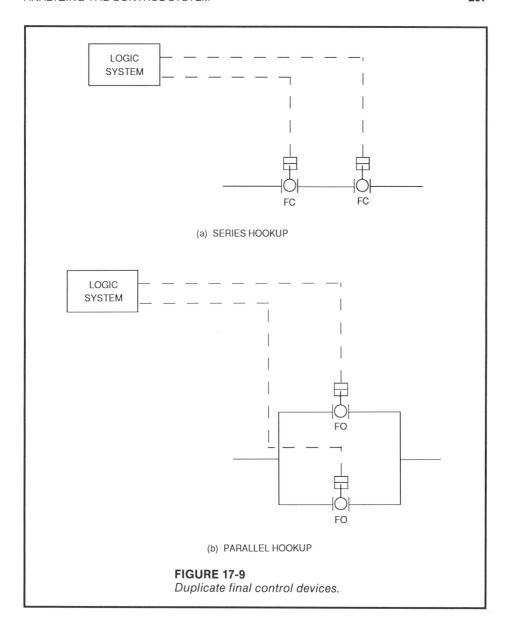

(a) SERIES HOOKUP

(b) PARALLEL HOOKUP

FIGURE 17-9
Duplicate final control devices.

Analyzing the Control System   A number of steps are necessary to carry out an analysis of a control system to make sure it provides the necessary level of availability (Ref. 20):

1. Acquire a thorough understanding of the process and the goals to be achieved.

2. Understand how computer systems function.

3. Understand the hardware functions of each component within the control system.

4. Understand the software functions operating within the hardware architecture.

5. Coordinate the needs and goals of the process, along with proper selection of hardware and software. Then write this in the form of a suitable specification.

6. Evaluate vendors' proposals carefully.

7. Implement the selected vendor's system in the way that meets the specified needs.

Cocheo (Ref. 20) recommends looking at the hardware and asking some questions about the consequences of a failure before deciding on how much backup is necessary, e.g.:

1. Can the operator always know the status of functional portions of the process?

2. Can any essential functions be lost, and how can you avoid or reduce the chances of this happening?

3. What functions can you afford to lose rather than incur excessive costs to avoid the loss?

It is also worthwhile looking at how a redundant system has evolved with a particular manufacturer. In general, many DCS vendors have done a better job of implementing redundancy than most PLC vendors have. This is because many DCS vendors designed redundancy into their systems from the beginning. As a result, the necessary diagnostics to provide a high coverage factor were built into the system. In contrast, most PLCs were designed as stand-alone controllers. When redundancy was needed, two PLCs were connected in parallel along with some means of detecting failures and causing a switchover. Many of these systems do not provide the high coverage factors needed to assure the high availability needed in many batch control applications.

EXERCISES

17.1 Why is it important to consider both reliability and availability when comparing batch control systems?

17.2 Why is it more important to look at availability based on fail-to-danger faults in safety interlock systems than with regulatory and discrete controls?

17.3 An SSDC has an availability of 0.9988. What would be the system availability if two of these SSDCs were used in parallel?

17.4 Develop a voting circuit for discrete inputs using AND and OR logic gates, where the output of the voting circuit will remain ON unless at least two of the input signals are lost.

17.5 Develop a circuit using high and low selectors that will select the median of three analog input signals.

17.6 Assume that a controller rack for a DCS has the capability of holding eight controller cards. If one of the controller cards can act as a backup for the other seven and the predicted MTBF for a single controller with no backup is 5.7 years, what will be the approximate MTBF in this one-for-seven redundancy?

REFERENCES

1. Rooney, J. P., "Availability Used as a Criterion for Control System Reliability," *Control Engineering*, December 1981.

2. Deuschle, R., and J. Goldberg, "A Reliability Primer," *Instruments & Control Systems*, February and March, 1974.

3. Rooney, J. P., "Predict Reliability of Instrumentation," *Hydrocarbon Processing*, January 1983.

4. Wilkinson, J. A., and B. W. Balls, "Microprocessor-Based Safety Systems Designed for Fire and Gas and Emergency Shutdown Applications," ISA/85, Paper #85-0841.

5. Heron, R. L., "Critical Fault Control Systems," Presented at Florida Municipal Utilities Association 21st Annual Engineering & Operations Workshop, Ft. Pierce, Florida, November 4-6, 1986.

6. Balls, B. W., G. R. Creech, and A. B. Rentcome, "Automatic On-Line Testing—An Essential for High Availability Safety Systems," ISA/87, Paper #87-1176.

7. Goble, W. M., and T. W. Tucker, "High Availability Controller for Safety Systems within a Distributed Control Environment," Moore Products Company.

8. Balls, B. W., "Safe Operation of Process Plants, Part 2," *IN CONTROL*, September–October 1988.

9. Moore, J. A., and S. M. Herb, *Understanding Distributed Process Control*, Instrument Society of America, Research Triangle Park, NC, 1983.

10. Brodgesell, A., "Design Considerations for Batch Plant Computer Control," ISBN 87664-469-8, ISA 1980.

11. Baur, P. S., "Ensuring Instrument Reliability without Overkill: Where Users Draw the Line," *InTech*, October 1986.

12. Sykora, M. R., "The Design and Application of Redundant Programmable Controllers," *Control Engineering*, July 1982.

13. Williams, T. J., and F. J. Mowle, "Industrial Software Requirements in Terms of Overall Plant Control Systems," Proceedings of the Fourteenth Annual Advanced Control Conference, West Lafayette, IN, September 19–21, 1988.

14. Kletz, T. A., "Eliminating Potential Process Hazards," *Chemical Engineering*, April 1, 1985.

15. Finkel, V. S., and L. S. Filho, "Use of Programmable Controllers and Personal Computers in Safety Shutdown, Fire and Gas, HVAC Systems on Offshore Oil and Gas Production Platforms," ISA/86, Paper #86-0408.

16. Cherba, D. M., "Redundancy in Programmable Controller Systems," *Instruments & Control Systems*, April 1983.

17. Goble, W. M., "Redundancy or Not—Matching Process Controller Architectures to Your Process," ISA/88, Paper #88-1543.

18. ICS-MESD2000, "Microprocessor-Based Emergency Shutdown," Industrial Control Services, Houston, 1984.

19. Machulda, J., "Fault Tolerant Control: You Can Afford It," *In Tech*, September 1985.

20. Cocheo, S., "Avoid Vulnerable Distributed Control System Architectures," *Hydrocarbon Processing*, June 1983.

18

Information/Display Requirements

Introduction   Information is a very critical part of a batch control system. Many aspects of this topic relate to the operator's use of the information, the engineer's use of the information, and storage of information for access at a later date.

The Operator's Role   The operator plays at least two major roles in the success or failure of a batch process, whether it is controlled manually or automatically. First, he is the local expert responsible for the hour-to-hour or minute-to-minute operation of the batch system. The experience gained from running hundreds of similar batches makes it possible for an operator to respond intuitively to variations that would otherwise ruin a batch. Second, the operator acts as a complex sensor to determine when a batch is completed. The operator may judge the look, feel, smell, or taste of a product before deciding that the process is complete. Replacing some human senses, such as vision, with automated versions can be prohibitively expensive. In other cases, the necessary technology is not available.

The Operator's Information Needs   The first issue to be resolved for batch process control interfaces is the data the operator needs to make decisions. This question is easy to answer for a continuous plant; the operator needs to know present values of process variables and set points, along with the current on/off status of pumps, compressors, and similar devices. But in a batch process, the operator needs much more information, such as the following (Ref. 1):

   1. The values of process variables such as temperature, pressure, or chemical composition, which include alarm, limit, and other status indications.
   2. Information about pending changes, which includes the consequences of predetermined operations, usually with fixed time constraints, such as temperature ramps or termination of cooking periods. But this information could also

include possible changes based on reactions or other conditions where rates and endpoints are uncertain and must be determined by measurements.

3. The states of discrete elements, e.g., the positions of automatic block valves. Complete information would include present states and indications of what they should be.

4. Status of equipment, which would include present and projected availability of units for use in the batch sequence. The operator should also know the conditions that govern when or whether access will be possible.

5. Location in the recipe. Of interest are the present control step or phase being implemented, how long the process has been at this phase, how much longer it should continue, and options for shortening or lengthening the durations. Expected, alternative, or modified next phases are other key items.

6. The product or grade mix within the train/line. Information should cover present, scheduled, and alternative permissible future mixes.

Assuming the operator can be given all this information, there remains the question of how to present it in a meaningful way. Graphics appear to be more desirable than tabulation or textual messages, because they give a visual representation of the process. This makes complicated processes easier to monitor and understand, which means that large amounts of information can be assimilated when presented in this form.

Fetterly and Fihn (Ref. 2) point out that the use of process graphics to represent a process unit is more useful in batch processing than in continuous processing because of the following:

1. The dynamic nature of the batch process demands more attention to device state changes. The process graphic can show the contacts, valves, solenoids, and so on that apply to the unit, along with the states of each of these devices.

2. Text and variable data (real-time and trend) can be included in the graphic.

3. Sequence data and status can be shown on the graphic.

4. Alarm data can be included in the graphic.

Krigman (Ref. 1) offers the following comments on graphic displays:

In principle, graphic screens can be devised showing any specified amount of the information in predetermined formats. But there are still unanswered questions about numbers of possible graphic displays, the complexity of each display, and the likelihood that an operator might be interested in a combination of elements that cannot be brought together on a single screen. And how do you integrate the present process state with the effects of projected changes? A resolution to the batch operator interface issue can probably be found in systems that simulate the process and show future states of the plant in graphic form. This would avoid forcing operators to view present and pending conditions separately and trying to predict what will happen. The computer is good at analyzing this type of information and predicting where the plant is heading.

The Operator's Console

Batch automation systems must be planned with the proper recognition of the roles played by human operators, because the best systems work with the operator. Operators must be provided with efficiently displayed information to support their decisions.

One of the most important characteristics of a good control system is simplicity of the operator interface. The success of an installation may depend on how easy it is for the operator to learn how to use the system.

The following are some guidelines for laying out screens on CRTs (Ref. 3):

1. Know the user of the display and design the display for that user. Don't design it for yourself.

2. Make things self-explanatory to the user. Make things consistent, clear, and obvious to the operator.

3. Avoid unnecessary detail and background clutter, e.g., excessive tick marks and numbers on the axes of graphs.

4. In numerical tables, align decimal points; in word tables, justify left.

5. Group associated items. Humans can mentally grasp a limited number of things at one time (about seven). But they can remember more by grouping things into chunks.

6. Locate things logically for the user.

7. Make the display balanced.

8. Do not use more than seven colors. Humans don't easily receive information from more than about seven different values in any single alternative coding.

9. Use a dark color for the background, but not black. This is true as long as the refresh rate on the CRT screen is greater than 50 Hz. A dark color, such as dark blue or dark gray, requires less adaptation of the eyes to brightness differences between the CRT and the room and between the CRT foreground and background.

10. Watch out for colors that look bad in combination.

11. Use color effectively. Avoid using just the eight basic colors (red, green, blue, magenta, cyan, yellow, white, and black) because they tend to lead to garish-looking displays. Try using shades of brown (or yellow or blue or green) for two or three of the eight colors.

Odom (Ref. 4) advises that the five most commonly used colors are red, yellow, green, white, and blue. Red is generally used to alert an operator that an incompatible or dangerous condition exists, and that corrective action needs to be taken. Yellow advises an operator that a marginal condition exists, e.g., PRESSURE BELOW NORMAL. Green indicates that the monitored equipment is in tolerance or that the condition is satisfactory (such as VALVE OPEN or MOTOR ON), and it is all right to proceed. White is used to show information, such as POWER ON, where that information does not imply success or failure. Blue is sometimes used as an advisory light, although the preferential use of blue should be avoided.

12. When coding by size and shape, do not use more than about seven different sizes or seven different shapes.

13. Avoid blinking the display except for important highlighting. Blinking a portion of the display is a powerful visual technique that catches the eye so strongly that it is hard to read anything else on the screen.

14. Use a font that is easily read on the CRT. Spacing is an important element that has a large impact on the readability of alphanumeric messages. Character spacing of 40 percent of character width, word spacing of one full character, and line spacing of 50 percent of character height are minimum. Use all uppercase letters unless the CRT resolution is 640 by 480 pixels or more. Labels on a CRT are generally more readable if they are all capital letters.

The following are some ways to make the operator interface more useful to the operator:

1. Make sure the operator can respond as quickly as possible to an alarm condition and with as few keystrokes as possible (preferably one).
2. Provide adequate speed for process graphics (two seconds or less) because (Ref. 5):

- alarms for critical situations must be displayed as quickly as possible;
- if operators wait longer than two seconds for a screen drawing, they will grow impatient and become less efficient in their work; and
- screens must be drawn as quickly as possible to reflect process activity, which enables operators to fine tune and maximize production.

3. Provide predefined displays for the operator to view the process. These usually include overview displays that show the whole plant and allow the operator to quickly determine if loops are out of control. Group displays are provided for different sections of the plant (e.g., a reactor system) and give the operator more detail than he/she gets from an overview display. Single-loop displays quite often simulate the faceplate of an actual controller.
4. Provide the operator with a trending package that is user-definable. Ideally, the system should allow a trend to be configured into any display. The ability to overlay one trend on top of another trend is highly desirable.
5. Provide the operator with a historical trend package with features similar to those in item 4 above.
6. Provide configurable keys on the operator keyboard so that the operator can define a key to a group of functions that are often repeated (Ref. 6).
7. Provide a configurable process display hierarchy that allows the operator to tailor the hierarchy to fit the application (Ref. 6). A display hierarchy is a collection of displays arranged in successive order or classes, each of which is dependent upon the one above it. This hierarchy usually starts with the most detailed display, the *point* display, e.g., a controller faceplate, and proceeds upward to the *overview* display, where a major subsystem or an entire plant may be shown on one display. In between, there are usually *group* displays, which show a smaller section of a plant or unit, and *graphics* (custom).

The hierarchy of displays must be structured to mimic the operation of the plant and the process so that the operator can interact effectively with the control system. A logical organization of displays makes it easier for the operator to make rapid decisions under process upsets and multiple alarm conditions.

Some operator interfaces used in batch control systems utilize a fixed hierarchy of operator displays. A typical relationship between the four types of displays is shown in Figure 18-1 (Ref. 7). Push buttons on the keyboard typically would allow the operator to move rapidly between related displays with a minimum of effort. In this case, however, the number of levels in the hierarchy is limited to three. The user must then divide and subdivide the plant to match the vendor's hierarchy.

A configurable display hierarchy will allow the user to assign the relationship between displays. The lowest level in the hierarchy would still be the *point* display. All the other displays are custom designed and assigned a unique position in the hierarchy. Although the displays can be made to emulate the traditional *group*, *graphic*, and *overview* displays, the freedom is available for the user to define his/her own *standard* formats. This may be combination displays, e.g., *group/graphics*, or displays that mimic existing hardware such as alarm annunciator panels.

In one example (Ref. 6), each operator display has an associated set of display numbers that can be assigned for each of seven keys on the operator's keyboard: PLANT, AREA, GROUP, GRAPHIC, LEFT, RIGHT, and UP. This gives the user almost complete flexibility concerning which display the operator can access from a given display. This flexibility is needed with processes such as batch, where flexibility in graphic layout and content is very necessary. These types of processes tend to defy the standard OVERVIEW-GROUP-POINT hierarchy.

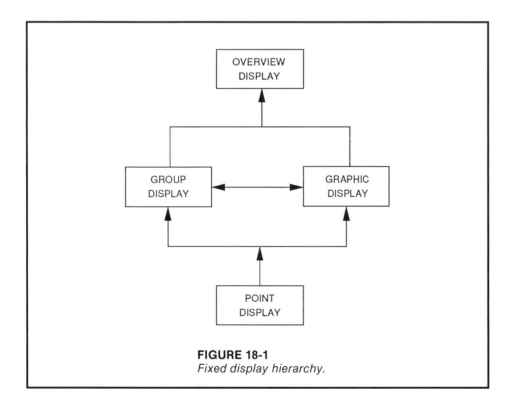

FIGURE 18-1
Fixed display hierarchy.

Having a configurable display hierarchy can provide the following advantages (Ref. 6):

- The user can define the display hierarchy to more closely match the actual operation of the plant or unit.
- If the number of levels in the hierarchy is not limited, the process can be subdivided into as many levels of detail as are necessary to allow the operator to move smoothly and logically through the process.
- If two (or more) operator's consoles within the same BPCS can be configured with different display hierarchies, one console could mimic the entire plant, another console might display a specific process area, and so on.
- If uneven distribution of display types is allowed, the user can then define the number of displays at each level. This allows him/her to achieve the balance of display types required for the particular application.
- A more intuitive operator interface is provided, because the hierarchy is constructed based on the relationship between displays. This eliminates the need for the operator to recall operator display numbers or descriptors.

8. Provide automatic configuration to the operator's needs, e.g., 6 above, when the operator signs onto the system with his/her password.

Whitmer (Ref. 8) provides these additional guidelines for building graphic displays for the operator:

1. The graphic displays of most impact in a demonstration are not useful to the plant operator because they are too colorful, contain too much static light (minimum information), and must convey understanding beyond what an operator who sees it every day needs.

2. Live information captioned by a minimum of recognition background is of most value to the operator. The position of the information on the display relative to the picture and engineering units usually will tell the operator what the data is. This diminishes the need to fill the graphic with tag names.

3. The static function on a graphic should "caption" or "label" the live information. This suggests using a low-emotion calm color of half intensity to show a piece of equipment and using a brighter color with higher intensity to show the information (live updates).

4. Blink is very attention-getting, but it can be too distracting at a 0.5–3 Hz rate. It should be used very selectively and only in small amounts because blinking data is harder to read than static data.

5. Reverse background is occasionally useful to highlight information. It works well to call attention to a single item in a table of values. If it is used too much, however, it can become irritating.

6. Low intensity static pictures are usually sufficient for the background of the schematic.

7. Color can be a very powerful medium to convey information when it is used effectively and consistently.

8. Bar graphs can convey a real "sight-glass feel" of level or magnitude to the operator. However, it is good to remember that a one-character-wide bar

conveys the same information as a ten-wide and is just as visible. Wide bar graphs can dramatically increase the light load to the operator when near full scale. Scale or reference marks are also needed with bar graphs.

9. Touch targets on the screen have become available (on displays that utilize touchscreens) that provide single-touch access through a hierarchy of related displays or that select a loop or data item for further manipulation. User-built macros or programmed functions can also be built into touch targets. These targets can also be used to ensure identical operator action-sets while leaving the operator the ability to choose which set of actions to take.

10. Some systems are capable of showing data in a parts-of-a-whole style using segmented pie diagrams (pie charts). This can be useful when the component relative magnitudes, e.g., a stream analysis, need to be shown.

11. Interface concepts popularized by personal computer, such as windows and menus, are now being offered. This is a good way to zoom in on selected data. An example would be to show a sequential function chart diagram (operations and phases) in a window on the same display as the process graphic.

The Engineer's Interface

The engineer's interface is used for program development, graphic development, controller tuning, and for viewing and analyzing the historical data base (Ref. 9). Some desirable features for this interface are (Refs. 9 and 10):

- keys and software for easy viewing, changing, and testing of programs;
- special keys and devices for easy graphic development;
- the ability to trend and view all tuning values associated with tuning;
- the ability to quickly move through the historical data base, utilizing the CRT as the window into the data base;
- the ability to display all the functions that are displayed on the operator's interface device;
- the ability to test the control strategy via simulation before start-up; and
- a self-documenting control system so that the process configuration is always up to date.

The engineer's interface should be a separate device from the operator's interface. Ideally, it should be located in the engineer's office and not in the control room. This is quite easy to do if the engineer's interface can be directly connected to the data highway. A number of distributed systems now allow a personal computer to be used for this interface device. This has advantages in that standard programs, e.g., Lotus 1-2-3, can be used to analyze and manipulate data.

Cursor Movement/Data Selection Techniques

Many different methods allow the operator or engineer to interact with the CRT console.

Keyboards Although attempts have been made to replace the keyboard with such devices as the mouse, trackballs, and voice-actuated units, the keyboard has developed an efficient coexistence with these devices (Ref. 11). Some questions should be asked when evaluating the use of a keyboard so that the technology will not be misapplied (Ref. 11):

1. Does the keyboard have to be sealed?
2. Is the operating force of a key important?
3. Should a standard "QWERTY" key arrangement be used?
4. Is audible feedback a requirement?
5. Should a touch panel (interactive keypad) be considered?

The type of keyboard may be critical to user satisfaction. In general, a keyboard with a "QWERTY" key arrangement should not be used for the operator, although they may be necessary in some small batch systems. The operator needs a custom keyboard that is designed to allow him/her to easily move around the display. However, the "QWERTY"-style keyboard is probably the preferred type for the engineer's use. In a harsh, damp environment, a sealed keyboard may be required.

Touchscreens Touchscreens are most widely used with CRT displays. They detect a touch aimed at some part of the display, determine where the touch is made, and send that data to a computer. Shirley (Ref. 12) points out the following advantages of touchscreens:

1. They are very versatile, since software controls the display to show any response area on the touchscreen surface.
2. The hand and the eye work together, so that "what you see is what you touch" is what you get.
3. They lead to transparency of operation, where the human can concentrate on the task with no need to invoke an intermediate command.
4. For menu selection, touchscreens are the fastest input device available.
5. They require no extra objects other than the display and no wire dragging on the console.

However, there are also some disadvantages (Refs. 12 and 13):

1. They are not precise for positioning a cursor to the nearest pixel or for inputting more than a few alphanumerics.
2. Parallax can cause the human to miss a displayed target unless the display and touchscreen are carefully designed.
3. It is so natural for humans to point at and touch displays that inadvertent touches sometimes occur.
4. Touchscreens typically cost more than other input devices, such as joysticks and keyboards.
5. A touchscreen requires tiring arm movements; these can also block portions of the display.
6. The display can become smudged with continued use, so spectrally coated glass used for glare reduction cannot be used.

Trackballs, Joysticks, Mice, and Light Pens Nelson (Ref. 13) points out that the trackball and joystick provide speed but are not reliable in a process environment, have limited accuracy, require deskspace, and cause problems with some operators who experience eye-hand coordination difficulties. Similar problems can be experienced with mice and light pens (Ref. 14). In addition, they are prone to contamination and breakage in a control room environment.

Interactive Keypads This is a flat panel display, typically a part of the keyboard, that has a touch-sensitive surface (Ref. 13). Moving a finger or some other object over the keypad causes the cursor to move on the CRT screen. They can also be used to perform functions through the selection of only one button, which can minimize reaction time and improve the efficiency of responding to upset or abnormal conditions.

Data Logging/Batch Reporting   Although data logging and reporting techniques for batch processes are similar to those for continuous systems, some methods are unique to batch control systems. Some typical logs and reports are discussed below (Ref. 15).

1. Current data report. This report usually consists of measured, computed, and operator-entered variables. It may also include such things as operator-entered data, data from analytical instruments or from the laboratory, etc. This data can be accessed and printed on demand or periodically. This report describes the operation of the batch plant at a given time, so it provides information that the engineer or technician can use to detect equipment performance problems, to determine where the batch is in relation to the schedule, and so on.

2. Historical report. Because the batch system is not a steady-state operation, the current data report cannot characterize the quality of the final product. Quality depends on the processing that takes place from the start of the batch to its completion, so data must be accumulated over the entire batch. This data is provided in the historical record, which provides a way to go back in time to investigate what happened in the batch. This may be necessary for government reporting, to try to figure out why one batch was better than another, and so on.

The historical record includes measured, computed, and operator-entered variables; these values may be retained for several months. Although real-time data is normally recorded based on a high sample frequency, this data is usually averaged as time proceeds. For example, twelve 15-second measurements become a 3-minute average, five 3-minute averages become a 15-minute average, etc. Data may also be stored based on maximum values, minimum values, totals, etc.

3. Alarm log. The alarm log is simply a record of off-normal conditions and how they are resolved.

4. Batch end report. A batch end report provides a record of what occurred during the course of the batch processing in a concise format. This report is very useful to both production and engineering personnel. They can often identify recurring problems, the potential for future problems, the reason for a bad batch,

etc., from this report. Then, if they need more detailed information, they can go back to the historical record.

Batch end reports typically include the following:

- A copy of the working recipe that was used to make the batch. This may not be identical to the original recipe because of operator changes, equipment problems, and so on. It may be desirable to record both the original recipe and the actual recipe. Within a batch facility, several recipes may be in some stage of processing at a given point in time. The recipe expresses the desired approach by which a batch is to be made; the batch report provides a record of how a batch was actually made.
- Batch identification data that was entered as part of the batch start-up sequence. This may be data that was entered by the operator or entered automatically. This data is used to distinguish multiple batches made with the same recipe; this may be necessary to meet government regulations.
- Recipe-specified data. This is data that corresponds exactly to the recipe, e.g., the amount and type of material charged. This can then be compared to the original recipe.
- Recipe-generated data. This is data that does not correspond directly to the recipe. It may be data that was generated in response to recipe-directed operations, e.g., the time a sample was taken and the results of the analysis.
- Summary batch data. This is data such as utilities consumption, equipment run times, temperatures, etc., for the entire batch.
- Operator scratchpad. This is free-format text storage where the operator can enter remarks (usually via the CRT) concerning such matters as equipment problems, instructions to the next shift, and so on.
- Event log. This records occurrence times of events such as alarms, operator instructions followed or ignored, and equipment status changes. This log must be able to retain the total operational sequence chronologically with date and time such as, for example, all actions by operating personnel, all changes and system problems detected through monitoring the process sequence, custody transfer data (this is an end-of-batch accounting record containing storage tank number, shipping method, etc.), and a trend chart showing important data during the batch (e.g., reactor temperature and reactor pressure).

The batch report is a statutory requirement in some applications. However, the information in the batch report is so valuable that it is being demanded in almost all batch applications.

Batch Tracking   It is increasingly common, not only in pharmaceutical products, that regulatory authorities require evidence of proper production procedures for each individual batch (for purity, safety, utility, environmental protection, and so forth). For this reason, a batch log must be produced at the conclusion of every batch. This log contains the complete process history of the batch from insertion through transfer to the product tanks or completed product manufacture.

The batch log usually contains information such as (Ref. 16):

- identification data from the recipe header,
- order number/batch number,
- effective production data (quantities, temperatures, pressures),
- equipment used,
- chronological sequence of the phases,
- analysis values,
- failure and trouble indications,
- location of the finished product,
- identification of the finished product, and
- identification of the system operator.

The task of keeping track of each batch in a simple batch system is not difficult, because only one batch is in existence at a given time, and one set of computer files is all that is necessary. In a more complex system, the job is more difficult because many batches are in existence at one time. Separate log files must be maintained with each batch. This log must move with the batch. As the batch moves along from one piece of equipment to another, it may come under the control of a different control system, so the log file must move along with the batch.

This problem is simplified if one global data base is associated with the batch control system. Then a pointer can be associated with each batch, and the batch logic writes to the file identified by the pointer. If there is no global data base, that data must somehow be identified as belonging to the particular batch. That data must then be collected and combined at the end of the batch.

Data that should be tracked on a given batch includes which units the batch passes through, what time it entered and left that unit, how long it was in each unit, and what operations it went through in the unit. A history of important data is kept on the batch as the batch is tracked throughout its processing, and a report is printed at the end of the batch cycle.

Batch Historians

The batch history integrity can be as critical to ultimate product quality in a batch system as are the control functions because a perfect batch may be undeliverable without batch records. The ability to control the process during outages of higher-level functions is desirable from a safety viewpoint, but it may result in an unusable batch unless the record-keeping functions are as robust as the control functions.

Batch history has the following characteristics (Ref. 18):

1. Many batch processes have continuous history components. However, the capture of a batch history data set is typically time- or event- triggered. The trigger function may be completion of a phase, completion of a batch, process alarm, process downtime, operator input, etc.

2. The captured batch history is typically maintained and managed as a related data set as contrasted to a rolling history of variables.

3. The batch data is specifically characterized by time and a phase, batch, or lot identification.

4. Although not unique to batch history, one class of historical data is inserted after the fact, such as lab analyses or visual quality results. Ideally, this data is merged with the related batch history data based on time of sampling rather than time of insertion, which can be minutes to hours after sampling.

A good batch historian must collect and maintain integrated, identifiable sets of dissimilar data in order to provide an easily usable batch history. This event-triggered data set will typically contain the following related data associated with a batch or product (Ref. 17):

1. Continuous process data (flows, pressures, temperatures)
2. Event data (operator actions, alarms, notes)
3. Quality data (lab analysis, inspection data)
4. Recipe data (set points,.........)
5. Calculated data (totals, material usage, accounting data)
6. Manual entries with audit trail
7. Stage, batch, lot identification
8. Time/date of collection

At the process control and process supervision levels of the batch architecture, today's systems are capable of locally controlling both continuous and batch operations with only periodic direction from higher levels. This allows safe and complete termination of a batch operation even in the event of loss of the higher-level functions. But a level of history must also be maintained by the system to ensure complete batch reporting after the upper-level functions are restored. These devices must have reporting capability. Ideally, they will also retain history on critical parameters so that the required history for higher-level reports can be reconstructed following a temporary outage.

Higher levels of the batch architecture will contain a complete batch history capability with archiving/replay to ensure infinite recall of the history. Also at this level, the batch history data is compressed into a complete integrated batch history record. These filtered batch records, with SQL-like query capabilities, provide applications a wide view of the process, either at this level or by exporting the data to personal computers (Ref. 17). A key application is the area of statistical control. Many software packages are available to apply statistical control techniques that, combined with relational queries, provide a tool for determining special (assignable) causes. Another obvious application is a report-writing capability for producing customized batch reports at various locations in the plant or corporate offices.

Advances in relational data base management system performance and capability allow the bridging of data between the process control and higher-level systems. This is especially useful in the case of batch history where the history is presented as a series of transaction records. The ability to use SQL-like queries to access these records adds a new dimension to batch history in terms of analysis, statistical process control, and reporting (Ref. 17).

Goldford (Ref. 18) describes some functional requirements for a data historian:

1. It should have direct memory access (DMA) to ensure that a high data transfer rate will not lose any data.

2. It should have a separate multitasking microprocessor to off-load the main processor.

3. It must have an efficient data compression function that minimizes the mass storage requirements.

4. It must store both digital and analog data.

5. It must have a data file structure that will allow selected data portions to be conveniently selected for analysis and/or removed from the mass storage device.

6. The reporting task must have the capability to have flexible axes on the trend chart that can be modified interactively.

7. Several types of preprogrammed plots should be available, e.g., pie charts.

8. Any graphical display should be printable on a variety of hard copy devices.

9. A simple English-like query language should be available that can be used to generate an ad hoc report.

10. An editor should be provided that interactively allows data files to be selectively updated or specific data points to be deleted. It should also keep a record of all data modifications to a file for audit purposes.

11. A set of statistical process control (SPC) routines should be included that can interactively access the stored data.

Alarm Management Systems

An alarm is an event caused by the erratic, strange, or unexpected behavior of the basic elements (objects or tags) contained within a control system (Ref. 19). A basic element or tag in a control system (such as a PID loop, a device, etc.) can generate a number of different alarms. Most of these alarm types have been identified historically and are well known for the basic objects. Figure 18-2 shows typical alarm types for a loop tag (Ref. 19). Since tags are associated (at least in the operator's perspective) with physical objects, the alarm system should support this association and reinforce it if possible.

Alarm management systems can enhance the safety of an operation by ensuring that trouble is presented to operators in an understandable fashion. Response choices can be automatically displayed or given priorities. Alarm summaries or equipment histories can be reviewed quickly as an aid in selecting the best response to a new alarm. A system could even monitor the status of plant equipment and emergency systems and modify its recommendations accordingly, e.g., by incorporating expert system technology.

LOOP TAG ALARM TYPES	
ABSOLUTE	RELATIVE
HIGH-HIGH ALARM HIGH ALARM LOW ALARM LOW-LOW ALARM BAD TRANSMITTER	HIGH DEVIATION ALARM LOW DEVIATION ALARM RATE OF CHANGE ALARM

FIGURE 18-2
Typical loop tag alarm types.

Arnold and Darius (Ref. 19) indicate that alarms have three primary filter criteria—importance, grouping, and context—which closely reflect the early questions an operator would ask when confronted with an alarm:

1. How important is the alarm? Should I devote any of my time to it? How will it affect production, etc.? Not every alarm has the same importance, so the operator needs to know how important an alarm is relative to the presence of another alarm. This categorization provides the most natural (and important) filtering of alarms.

2. From where is the alarm coming (geographical location)? The logical grouping of alarms has always been one of the tools available to the engineer when providing alarm management for the operator. The first implementations used the physical grouping of flashing lights (annunciators). Later generations of basic process control systems offer a much more configurable grouping capability.

3. What was the process doing when the alarm occurred? What was the context information? The process state, typically the batch phase, provides important context information. Depending on the process state, an event may or may not be important to an operator. The process state as an alarm management tool is very significant, because it allows the operator to quickly identify the importance of an alarm because he knows how it relates to the current operation of the process.

Integrating alarms into advanced programmable electronic control systems can expand the capabilities available to operators for detecting and acting on emergency situations. These systems offer the ability to implement large numbers of alarms at low cost, but they also can enhance the effectiveness of alarms by alerting the operators to situations that require special action. For example, the use of computerized voice messages and artificial intelligence can give the operator detailed alarm information and full diagnosis.

Because alarms are easy to configure and cost virtually nothing with a PES (programmable electronic system), there is a tendency to add too many alarms. However, too many alarms can be as dangerous as too few. Nuisance alarms, for example, can be generated when alarm set points are very close to the normal operating point. If an operator is overwhelmed by too many alarms, their significance is quickly diminished — a situation that could possibly lead to indifference and a safety incident.

Inferred Alarms PES-based control systems can be used to generate inferred alarms. These are alarms based on calculated variables or combinational logic rather than direct measurement or contact sensing, but they can be indicated to the operator in the same way as a normal alarm.

EXAMPLE 18-1

Problem: How could the rate of reaction in a batch reactor be inferred and used to generate an alarm for the operator?

Solution: The rate of reaction could be inferred by measuring the flow of cooling fluid through the jacket of the batch reactor and the temperature differential across it and then calculating the amount of heat removed. An alarm can be generated if the calculated value is above or below some predetermined value.

EXAMPLE 18-2

Problem: How could an inferred alarm be generated to tell the operator that a vessel is not properly sealed?

Solution: This could be done based on indications that a locking mechanism has been activated and a block valve is closed but the internal pressure is below a minimum value after a predetermined interval.

Alarm Diagnosis Advanced control systems can be used to help the operator diagnose problems. The objective is to determine and tell the operator not only the symptoms but also the cause of the problems. A chemical reactor may have alarms on several temperatures, pressures, and flows. A combination of alarms on these points would indicate that something is wrong, but the situation could arise from a number of problems, both internal and external to the reactor.

Process models have been suggested as one basis for alarm diagnosis (Ref. 20). A computer model, operating in a simulation mode, could determine how the process differs from its baseline behavior. Another proposed method for alarm diagnosis involves expert system technology (Ref. 20). In this case, a knowledge base would be built using a set of rules provided by process engineers, based on the way they would normally interpret alarm and other conditions to determine faults.

Advisory Information The alarm management system can also be used to provide the operator with suggestions about actions that might be taken in response to alarm situations. This advisory information would probably be reported in the form of text. It would usually be provided in response to operator requests. The advisory information may be important enough in some cases that its presence could be indicated to the operator with the same urgency as an alarm. For example, if the system detects that a valve is stuck open, the advisory information might be a message to tell the operator to have it closed by hand immediately.

Alarm Management Techniques Good alarm management must provide methods for interpretation of the important alarms and suppression of the nuisance alarms. Alarm management techniques deal with the following main areas (Ref. 21):

1. Suppression of alarms for non-operating equipment
2. Suppression of alarms generated during shutdown of a plant or portions of a plant
3. Suppression of all but the most important alarms in cases where one alarm is the direct cause of several others
4. Segregation of alarms into priorities, ensuring that the most important alarms will receive first attention

These objectives can usually be achieved through alarm prioritizing, alarm suppression, and alarm reduction (Ref. 21).

Alarm Prioritizing

An alarm severity or priority level should be assigned to each data point within the batch control system. This should correlate to the severity of a process alarm condition on that point with respect to similar conditions on other data points within the system. The alarm priority is a user-configurable parameter that is assigned on a point basis. The selection and prioritization of process limits and alarm points are process-unit specific.

Each plant should have standards or guidelines for selecting and prioritizing alarms for its specific processing operations. For example, the alarm management system might provide four different priority levels: CRITICAL, WARNING, ATTENTION, and INFORMATION, one of which can be assigned to each alarm. The alarm priority determines how alarm information should be presented to the operator and how the operator should be required to acknowledge the alarm. A single process variable may be assigned more than one priority, depending on the state of the process.

Based on the assigned priority, the operator may be required to acknowledge the presence of some alarms. Two of the alarm priorities require operator acknowledgment and the remaining two require no acknowledgment action. Alarms that require acknowledgment are latched by the system until they are acknowledged.

1. CRITICAL. Alarm conditions of great importance should be assigned the CRITICAL priority. For example, several high-high alarms in the process could be considered CRITICAL. These alarms require prompt operator action to

maintain the unit onstream and to protect major equipment or personnel. These alarms should be displayed in a distinctive color, e.g., red. CRITICAL alarms require the operator to acknowledge them on a one-by-one basis. This provides for a guarantee that the operator has seen the alarm and will take the appropriate action to correct the condition. Audible signaling devices should be used to alert the operator to the actuation of a CRITICAL alarm. Different audible tones may also be necessary to allow the operator to distinguish CRITICAL alarms from other, less important, alarms.

2. WARNING. Alarm conditions that are important but not CRITICAL should be assigned this priority. High, low, high-deviation and low-deviation alarms would probably be assigned this priority. Prompt operator attention is required to maintain the unit production rate or to protect equipment. These alarms would be displayed in another distinctive color, e.g., white. These alarms must still be acknowledged by an operator, but more than one WARNING alarm can be acknowledged at the same time. Another distinctive audible signaling device tone may be required to allow the operator to distinguish WARNING alarms from other types of alarms.

3. ATTENTION. These are alarm conditions that the operator needs to be aware of but that are not detrimental to the process. The first stage of the normal annunciator sequence, i.e., flashing displays and audible signaling devices, should be suppressed for ATTENTION alarms. If audible signaling devices are actuated, they should be automatically silenced after a specified period of time. Corrective action is required but not directly by the operator. Time is available so that other personnel can be sent to investigate the problem. This priority requires no acknowledgment from the operator. However, ATTENTION priority alarms are presented to the operator on the operator console. They should be presented as a steadily illuminated light that indicates to the operator that an ATTENTION alarm has actuated; the light may be set up to be self-clearing after a specified period of time.

4. INFORMATION. Alarm conditions that require some kind of correction in the near future but will not affect the process at present should be assigned the INFORMATION priority. This priority requires no acknowledgment. Furthermore, alarms assigned the INFORMATION priority should be recorded only in the alarm log and should not be presented to the operator on the console.

In addition to the above alarms, the operator needs status information that shows whether a pump is running or not running, whether a valve is open or closed, and so on. These do not require corrective action by the operator, and the operator console is probably the ideal place for this information. Operators also need trip analysis information that is related to, or leading up to, a shutdown of the unit. This information should be recorded so that a permanent record is available.

Color coding may be desirable. Critical alarms should be designed to facilitate on-line testing and should be so tested on a routine basis. For more fail-safe operation, consideration should be given to using contacts that are closed during normal operation for critical alarms. The documentation and identification of critical alarms on process and instrumentation diagrams (P&IDs) and in operating manuals are essential. The documentation should include a separate listing of alarms, their associated shutdown systems (if any), methods for testing, and so forth. The addition, deletion, or modification of critical and warning alarms must be done only according to formal plant procedures.

Provisions to inhibit nuisance alarms and to show which one of simultaneous alarms indicated first (i.e., first-out, or first-alert, capability) should also be included. Sequence of events recording capability may be needed in some critical applications.

In a PES-based control system, each alarm indication (at least in the alarm summary) should contain a time-stamped message giving a clear description of the alarm event, the current value of the process variable, the limit that was violated, the priority or seriousness of the alarm, and the status (e.g., unacknowledged and active). A single (perhaps dedicated) keystroke or action is desirable for accessing the controller action display associated with the most recent alarm event.

A means for summarizing and logging each alarm event (triggering, acknowledging, and clearing) dynamically in order of occurrence is desirable. Unfortunately, all batch control system vendors do not offer the capability of recording alarm acknowledgment.

Audible alarms should be part of a PES-based control system to indicate a malfunction in all redundant or backup system components. These alarms should be designated as either warning or critical, depending on the consequences of a failure in the redundant or backup components. Operations should have a procedure to notify maintenance personnel of the problem even though it is not causing an immediate process shutdown. Similar malfunction alarms should also be used wherever possible to monitor operating and backup processors. In the case of redundant processors, it is expected that the backup processor will bumplessly take over in the event of a primary processor failure. An audible alarm should report this malfunction as well as any problems with redundant processors. If not, an undetected backup processor malfunction could occur, and the backup processor would be totally ineffective when needed.

Warning and critical alarms must have an audible indication as well as a visual sign. If the batch control system has an automatic acknowledge feature, it should not be used indiscriminately. Critical alarms must be acknowledged by an operator. Alarm presentations should readily alert the operator of unsafe conditions no matter what display screen is being viewed.

Alarm Suppression

This technique suppresses excessive alarms that tend to confuse the operator. As an example, assume that the occurrence of one main alarm (level A) triggers multiple alarms (level B), which activates more lower-level alarms (level C). Alarms are propagated to lower levels and, at the same time, increase in quantity and become a nuisance for the operators. This problem is addressed by reducing the number of alarms as close to the source of the alarm as possible.

PES-based control systems are now versatile enough that they can implement alarm reduction techniques using the logic blocks available in the controller. The advantage is that the alarm reduction can be done at the source (instrument level). Where programmable controllers are used for the safety shutdown system, much of the alarm reduction can be done in the programmable controller. A typical situation might be where a number of alarms are linked together in the sense that failure of one unit causes an alarm and triggers all other alarms in the group.

EXAMPLE 18-3

Problem: A series of conveyer belts feed into each other and must be alarmed in the event of stoppage of any belt. They are also interlocked so that the stopping of one belt for any reason shuts down the entire series of belts to prevent material pileup. How could alarm suppression be used here?

Solution: In this case, when one unit goes into alarm, it can be used to inhibit the alarm of any of the other units, using the logic block capability of the controller. This will minimize the nuisance alarms for the operator.

Shaw (Ref. 20) gives two types of suppression techniques that can reduce the burden on the operator without eliminating valuable information or increasing the hazard level in the plant.

1. In conditional suppression, an alarm is totally prevented from occurring. Conditions leading to the suppression may be sensed or inferred states or variables, including the results of measurements, the presence of other alarms, or even the acknowledgment of a problem by the operator. Conditional suppression is appropriate when an alarm does not represent a dangerous situation and is a symptom of a problem that can be more readily deduced from the remaining active alarms.

2. In flash suppression, the first step of the alarm sequence is bypassed. The message is shown directly in its steadily illuminated form with no audible warning (as if a standard alarm had been presented and acknowledged). This minimizes distractions to the operator but still reminds him of problems. It may also be of value in analyzing process conditions. This type of suppression is appropriate when an operator would expect the condition based on other alarms occurring, but the point still represents a potential hazard or some form of malfunction.

Alarms may be suppressed separately or in groups, and summaries of suppressed alarms maintained by the batch control system for reference by the operator are also desirable. Suppressed alarms and alarm set point changes should be recorded or logged in the same way as process alarm events.

EXAMPLE 18-4

Problem: When an operator stops a pump, low discharge pressure and low flow alarms may be actuated, even though the operator expects these conditions. How could suppression techniques be used here?

Solution: It might be good to suppress those alarms if they occur when the pump is stopped. If the only purpose of the alarm is as a symptom of pump failure, conditional suppression might be appropriate. If the low pressure and flow indicate process hazards, e.g., if the fluid were emergency cooling water, flash suppression might be the better choice.

Another technique that lends itself to the solution of alarm management in the batch environment is the ability to enable and disable alarms according to a process state. A process state is defined as a normal state of a process, e.g., a START-UP, RUN, or FLUSH state. In the alarm management system, each alarm group in the system could be assigned several different process states. Each individual alarm (High-High, High, Low, etc.) for each tag in the alarm group could then be enabled or disabled selectively for each process state of the alarm or alarm group.

Alarm Reduction

Batch processes must be properly monitored, and all process upsets and equipment malfunctions must be adequately reported. However, the danger is that there will be so many alarms that the system can be overloaded or the operator can be totally confused. Advanced systems have tended to aggravate this problem because it is so easy and inexpensive to add alarm points. An analysis of several applications indicates that many of the alarm conditions generated during a process disturbance are (Ref. 21):

- interrelated and result in nuisance reporting at the incidence of any one going into alarm;
- generated by digital inputs that cycle in and out of alarm; or
- nuisance alarms that are generated by process equipment that is known to be not operating.

It is difficult during a process upset for operators to detect and differentiate the critical alarms from the less serious alarms. Because this overabundance of information is provided to the operator in a short period of time, a considerable amount of interpretation and attention is required by the operator, so misinterpretation is a possibility.

The overall performance of the system may also be drastically affected because of the excessive alarm load being placed on the alarm processing devices. This probably won't affect the data highway, but it could affect the supervisory computer that handles the alarms. As a result, the console response time could increase (Ref. 21). This could pose a problem for the operator who is trying to deal with the situation.

The reduction or elimination of nuisance alarms is addressed by the alarm management system via several techniques for enabling and disabling alarms during a process. When an alarm is disabled in the system, the operator is not notified of the alarm condition. Selectively enabling or disabling a particular alarm is normally accomplished by alarm grouping.

Group status alarms check to ensure that the states of various process variables are combined properly for a particular mode of operation. They typically apply to batch operations and to the start-up and shutdown of continuous processes. Group status alarms usually involve some combinational logic and calculations.

> ### EXAMPLE 18-5
>
> **Problem:** A batch process has three pumps on the feed to a reactor; each of the pumps has the capability of supplying the necessary feed rate. One of three pumps must be running, with its associated block valve open and discharge pressure between some limits, or an alarm must be generated. How could group status alarms be implemented here?
>
> **Solution:** These alarms will most likely be in one of three states: correct, incorrect, and not required (Ref. 20). The alarms would be conditionally suppressed in the "not required" state. And, in most cases, a single alarm would be sufficient to indicate the entire group status. Details, including the various inputs to the group and the criteria for the alarm, can be provided elsewhere. They can be accessed when they are needed to determine what action must be taken to clear the alarm.

EXERCISES

18.1 Figure 18-3 shows a batch reactor system where material A is converted to material C in an exothermic reaction. Diluent B is added to the reactant feed under temperature control to control reactor temperature. If reactant A feed stops, the reaction ends; this is a safe condition. If diluent flow B stops while the reaction is continuing, overheating and a dangerous situation could occur.

There are several alarms in this system to warn of either pump tripping, high or low reactor temperature, low diluent feed flow, and low discharge pressure on either pump. If the reactant pump is shut off, the operator will receive immediate alarms for pump stop, low discharge pressure, and low flow. As the reaction ends, a low temperature alarm will be received.

What alarm reduction strategies could be applied here (Ref. 20)?

18.2 In the batch reactor system of Figure 18-4, feed is charged through either of two pumps and a recirculating header. Before the charge begins, the operator or system checks that one of the pumps is running, the associated block valve is open, the feed header pressure is above some minimum, and sufficient material is in the feed tank (Ref. 21). Describe how group status alarms could be used in this situation.

18.3 Why are graphic displays so important for the operator of a batch process?

18.4 Why is it desirable for the operator to be able to respond to an alarm condition with a single keystroke?

18.5 Why should the engineer's console be a separate device from the operator's console and installed in a separate room?

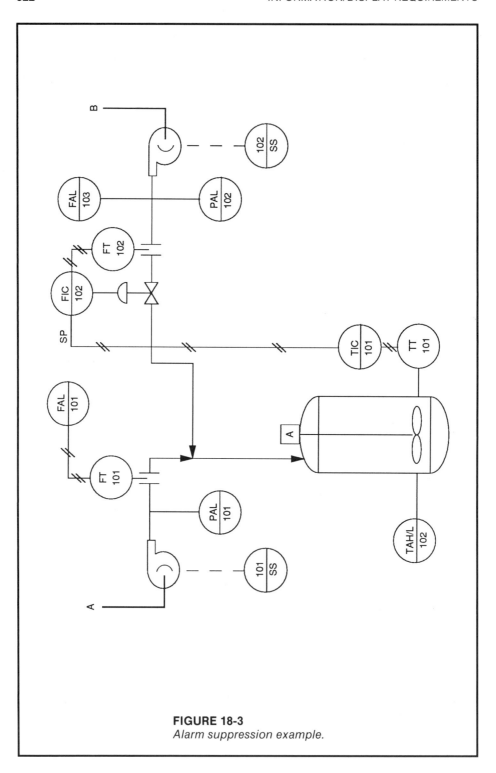

FIGURE 18-3
Alarm suppression example.

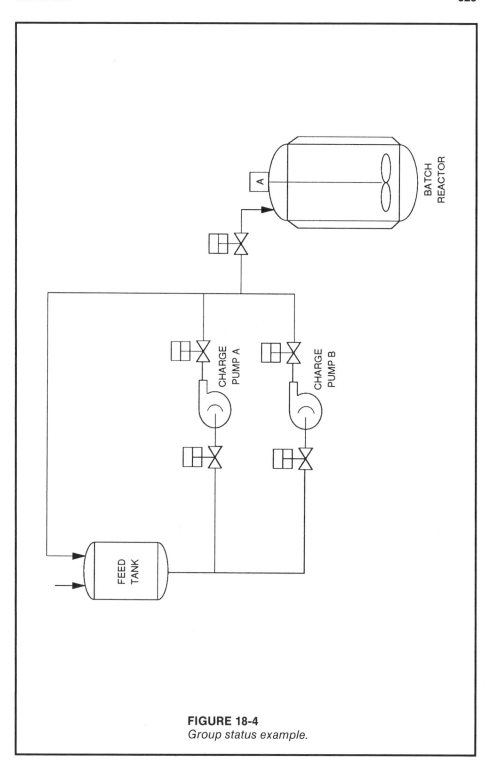

FIGURE 18-4
Group status example.

18.6 What are the disadvantages of a standard typewriter-style keyboard for operating a batch process?

REFERENCES

1. Krigman, A., "Batch Process Interfaces: Static Tools for Dynamic Jobs,"*InTech*, November 1984.

2. Fetterly, L., and S. Fihn, "Batch Control Operations," ISA/87, Paper #87-1167.

3. Shirley, R. S., "A Fog Index for CRT Displays," ISA/85, Paper #85-0764.

4. Odom, J., "Selecting Color for Visual Displays,"*EC&M*, January 1986.

5. Fleming, B., "Selecting Terminals for Industrial Applications,"*I&CS*, July 1988.

6. Goble, W. M.; D. J. Frantz; D. A. Johnson; and L. C. Lewis, "User-Configurable Operator's Console Fits a Variety of Specific Control Needs," ISA/85, Paper #85-0762.

7. Tucker, T. W., "Guidelines for Organizing Displays of Process Information on CRT Monitors," ISA/81, Paper #81-562.

8. Whitmer, E., "A New Look at Interactive Batch Displays," ISA/88, Paper #88-1470.

9. Sharp, R. N., and J. D. Williams, "One Utility's View of the Ideal CRT-Based Control Interface," ISA/85, Paper #85-0601.

10. Wegelin, V., "Benefits of the Modern Distributed Control Systems Hierarchy," ISA/84, Paper #84-772.

11. Turner, G., "Designing Man-Machine Interfaces for Effective Operator Use,"*I&CS*, July 1988.

12. Shirley, R. S., "Human Factors Features of Touchscreens, Hardware, and Software," ISA/86, Paper #86-2741.

13. Nelson, J. D., "Design Considerations for a Human Interface in the Process Control Industries," ISA/87, Paper #87-1166.

14. Off, P. P., "Human Interface Techniques for Real-Time Global Data Base Access," ISA/87, Paper #87-1165.

15. Rosenof, H. P., "Data Logging and Reporting for Effective Batch Control,"*I&CS*, July 1985.

16. "Development of Sequence Controls for Charge Processes with Variable Formulation from Pretailored Functional Models," NAMUR Recommendations, July 1985.

17. Morris, M., and N. Sumrall, "Batch History in Distributed Systems," ISA/88, Paper #88-1472.

18. Goldford, A. I., "The Functional Requirements for a Process Control System Data Historian," Proceedings of the Seventh Annual Control Engineering Conference, May 23–25, 1988.

19. Arnold, M. W., and I. H. Darius, "Alarm Management in Batch Process Control," ISA/88, Paper #88-1473.

20. Schellekens, P. L., "Alarm Managemnt in Distributed Control Systems,"*Control Engineering*, December 1984.

21. Shaw, J. A., "Smart Alarm Systems: Where Do We Go from Here?" *InTech*, December 1985.

19

Batch Control System Specification/ Implementation

Introduction   Defining and implementing a complete batch control system is a complicated task and merits a team approach, as discussed in Chapter 15. Once the top down design approach discussed in Chapter 15 has been completed, the following requirements should be known:

1. The control requirements of the batch process, e.g., the type and number of inputs (digital, analog, pulse, etc.), the type and number of outputs (analog, digital, pulse, etc.), modes of operation (e.g., manual or automatic), process start-up and shutdown procedures, and so on

2. Other important needs of the system, such as those relating to safety, quality control, and the like

3. The sequence and logic of controlling the process

4. The functional requirements of the control system, e.g., the safety interlocking functions needed, regulatory and discrete control algorithms needed, sequence control capabilities, scheduling requirements, recipe management requirements, batch management requirements, communications and display requirements, and so on

5. A general architecture of the batch control system

Overall Project Scheme (Refs. 1 and 2)   Once all the above information is known, a functional specification should be developed that can be reviewed and approved by all interested parties. This specification is then used to obtain bids from a number of suppliers. This document describes the process and system requirements and has enough detail that it can be used for requesting bids, purchasing the hardware and software, and testing the system prior to start-up. The format of the functional specification is discussed below under the heading, "Functional Specification."

Procurement can begin by sending out requests for quotations based on this functional specification. Plan to meet face to face with the bidders to discuss the contents of the functional specification. If possible, an on-site visit to the location where the system will be installed is desirable.

Once the bids have been received, they can be evaluated. Some evaluation criteria to be kept in mind when reviewing the bids are discussed under the heading, "Evaluation Criteria." However, remember that there will probably be no system that can exactly match the requirements in the functional specification. It will be necessary to drop some of the nonessential items. Select the system and supplier, but make sure that this is a team decision. At this time, the bid from the selected supplier can be evaluated further to see if there are any additional items they proposed that would be desirable in the system.

When the details of the system are known, conduct a detailed hazard analysis to see if any additional changes are required; then write a purchase specification that is specific to the manufacturer's equipment you have selected. This specification should include all the items in the functional specification (you can now use terms that are specific to the supplier) and specify the performance requirements. This document then becomes part of the performance contract between you and the supplier.

Have the supplier issue another firm quote if changes have been made to the system. The system can then be purchased, and detailed system design can begin.

The design usually starts with the hardware and the software applications. During this phase of the project, some changes in scope or in the desired system philosophy usually are needed. These changes should all be reviewed and approved by the project team.

Once the system is complete, test it at the supplier's factory before it is shipped to the site. This test at the supplier's factory should be very detailed and well thought out. It is much easier to correct mistakes while the system is still at the supplier's factory than when it is at your site.

Next, install the system at the site. Check out the system and perform dry runs, followed by wet testing using oil, water, or some other suitable material. Once this checkout is complete, make a final inspection of the system to make sure the system is ready for start-up.

Start up the system and debug as necessary. The purchase specification and the remaining documentation for the system should then be updated. This is a very important step so that the system can be easily maintained and so that future modifications to the system are easily made.

Functional Specification The purpose of the functional specification is to allow a number of different manufacturers the opportunity to propose a solution to your batch project. The terminology in the specification should be kept as generic as possible. Try to avoid terminology that is specific to a given manufacturer. Also try to write the specification so that the supplier has some flexibility in proposing the solution. The supplier is probably going to be able to propose solutions that have not occurred to you.

Typical information included in a functional specification is shown below (Refs. 1 and 2).

1. Introduction
   a. General description: describes the location where the system will be installed, the type of process, whether a new plant or retrofit, etc.
   b. Process description: describes the process being controlled and the boundaries of the system, how the control system should respond to abnormal conditions (e.g., utility outages or disturbances, abnormal maintenance modes, special start-up or shutdown procedures, equipment or control failures, etc.), unusual environmental conditions that will affect the control system (e.g., weather conditions, highly corrosive process materials, vibration, electrical noise, etc.), what federal, state, or local regulations the control system must comply with, etc.
   c. System philosophy: discusses how the system will function, whether it is a distributed system (may need a drawing of the architecture to make sure the supplier knows what your definition of a distributed system is), how many operator stations, etc.
   d. Project background: e.g., schedule (when bids are due, when delivery is expected, etc.)
   e. Scope of work for both supplier and buyer: defines who is responsible for each part of the system. For example, the buyer may decide to do the programming. The supplier must know this so that those costs won't be included in the bid.
   f. Criteria to be used for selection: lets the supplier know what portions of the specification are most important to you and areas where he will have some flexibility in the solution he proposes.
   g. Terms and conditions of purchase: gives the supplier a chance to note any exceptions.

2. System Requirements
   a. Overall design: further amplifies the information in Item 1c, e.g., how the regulatory/discrete control subsystem is to interface with the sequential control subsystem, how the process will be split up into various units, description of shared resources, how this system will interface with Production Planning (e.g., format of the data, the type of data that must be exchanged, frequency of the exchange, etc.) and so on.
   b. Safety interlocking subsystem: how this interfaces with the rest of the control system, whether fault tolerance is required, etc.
   c. Regulatory/discrete control subsystem: discusses where controls for the various units will be located (i.e., in which part of this subsystem), the types of regulatory control and discrete control functions required, advanced control and optimization requirements, etc.
   d. Sequential control subsystem: where the batch sequencing will be done, what the language requirements are, etc.
   e. Batch management subsystem: the tracking and reporting require-

ments, recipe editing requirements, methods of allocating resources to batches, etc.

f. Recipe management subsystem: the format of the recipes, the number of recipes, special operator access tools required, etc.

g. Production scheduling subsystem: where scheduling will be done, whether it is automated or manual, frequency of schedule updates, etc.

h. Supervisory control subsystem: details the requirements for the supervisory station, e.g., whether a cell controller is required and what its requirements are, special alarm management needs, etc.

i. Man/machine interface subsystem: how the operator will interface with the system, how many consoles, whether there is a regular panelboard, what kind of keyboard, security requirements, graphics required, reporting requirements, etc.

j. Communications subsystem: type of network, whether easy migration to MAP is a necessity, the types of systems to be networked together, etc.

k. Database management subsystem: what foreign devices must access the database, whether a global database is required, specific access requirements (e.g., SQL), etc.

l. System redundancy requirements: where redundancy is necessary, what kind of backup devices, etc.

m. Batch historian requirements: what data must be stored, frequency of data collection, special access requirements, statistical quality control (SQC) needs, etc.

3. Project Management, Testing, Installation, and Training

a. Project organization: identifying the contacts at the buyer, the seller, etc.

b. Factory testing and staging: how much time is allotted for this function, how much support is expected from the supplier, etc.

c. Project documentation: what type of documentation, timing of documentation, etc.

d. Classroom and on-site training: how much training is provided, for how many people, where it will be conducted, cost for additional training.

e. Installation supervision: specify if the supplier will have any involvement and how much.

f. Start-up assistance: specify amount.

g. Maintenance support: whether there is free maintenance for a certain time period, cost and conditions of maintenance contract, how much hardware is stocked by the local representative, etc.

4. Supporting Documents

a. P&IDs: as detailed as possible

b. I/O list: including types and quantities of inputs and outputs, special input requirements, etc.

c. Sequence description: provided in the form of time sequence diagrams, flowcharts, etc.

    d. Recipe description: format, method of operator selection, etc.

    e. Report formats: provide samples of both batch and historical reports.

Evaluation Criteria   Listed below are some items that should be kept in mind when reviewing the quotations from the suppliers:

1. General System Requirements
   a. Is there a common database or is the database distributed among all the various components in the system? A common (global) database is highly desirable.
   b. How rugged is the hardware? How long has it been on the market? How many systems have been installed? Can they provide a list of users in your industry that you can talk to?
   c. What are the environmental requirements for installing the equipment? Is it suitable for field mounting? Are portions of the system available intrinsically safe?
   d. Does the system use state-of-the-art components? If so, does the system have field operating experience? On what microprocessor is the system based? (This can often be a clue to how field-proven the system is.)
   e. How many point tags are available in the system? Where are point tags required? For example, is a point tag needed for the results of an intermediate calculation? This can use up point tags very quickly.
   f. Is floating point math available? What types of math functions?
   g. How expandable is the system? For example, what if more digital inputs are needed, more point tags, etc.?
   h. Can the regulatory controls communicate directly with the sequential controls?
   i. What is the scan rate for I/O, software routines, console updates, etc.? Is it a fixed rate for all items? Can the user vary the scan rates for different items? Does the scan rate vary with the load on the system (not a very desirable condition)? Does the system use exception reporting?
   j. How many copies of software are included with the system hardware? What form is it in? Are updates provided and for what time frame? Are software and hardware updates compatible with existing systems? Will the vendor supply software, installation, and checkout to allow your system to function within any upgraded system that the vendor may presently be designing?
   k. What are the grounding requirements? Will a new grounding grid be required?
   l. What voltage and frequency fluctuations in the power to the system are allowed? How many sources of power are recommended and what type of filtration or capacitance is recommended? What happens to configuration on a loss of power for as little as one cycle of the 60-Hz power and for intervals up to twenty-four hours? What options are available for automatic restart after a power failure? Does the system have capability for battery backup?

2. I/O System
   a. How many discrete input and outputs are available? What are their voltage and current levels? How fast can they be scanned? Is there a specific failure mode for solid-state outputs, and how does the system accomplish this?
   b. How many analog inputs and outputs are available? What is the resolution of the analog inputs (the resolution of the analog outputs is not usually as important since they are mostly used to drive control valves), e.g., 8-bit, 10-bit, 12-bit, or 14-bit? This determines the resolution. An 8-bit converter has a resolution of 0.4% (1/256), a 10-bit converter has a resolution of 0.1% (1/1024), a 12-bit converter has a resolution of 0.025% (1/4096), and a 14-bit converter has a resolution of 0.0006% (1/16384). How is data for analog inputs and outputs entered into the system, e.g., by a fill-in-the-form menu? Can inputs be scaled into engineering units?
   c. What special purpose input cards are available? Is there a pulse input card for flowmeter inputs? What is the maximum count rate? What are the signal characteristics required for this input? Does this input card produce a flow rate signal in addition to the pulse signal?
   d. Can thermocouples and RTDs be taken directly into the system without transmitters? Are BCD inputs and outputs available? Are special cards available for items such as scale interfaces (i.e., from a load cell system), gas chromatographs, etc.?

3. Regulatory/Discrete Controls
   a. How are these functions implemented, e.g., function blocks, ladder logic, etc.?
   b. What functions are available? How many of each?
   c. How is reset windup handled?
   d. Are advanced control schemes available, such as feedforward, cascade, and override?
   e. Are logic functions available? What types?

4. Sequential Controls
   a. How are the sequences programmed, e.g., function blocks, sequential function charts, procedural languages, etc.? How many sequences can be programmed in? How many can run at the same time? Does running additional sequences slow the system down? Does the programming language enforce the hierarchy of operations, phases, and control steps? In what language are the control instructions programmed?
   b. How easily can the sequence be modified? Can it be done on line?
   c. Where does the phase logic reside?
   d. Can a partial download of a recipe be made? Does this shut the system down?

5. Batch Management, Recipe Management, and Production Scheduling
   a. Does the system have any scheduling capability?
   b. How does it handle recipes? How many recipes can be stored? How easy are they to modify?

    c. Can recipes be downloaded from a host computer?

    d. What types of reports can be generated? Are free formatted report capabilities included? Are preformatted reports built in to the software? What kind of information can be put into a batch report? Can a trend chart be included in the batch report? Can the report be printed on demand, once per shift, etc.?

    e. What are the batch tracking capabilities?

6. Man/Machine Interface (Operator's and Engineer's Displays)

    a. How does the operator input data into the system, e.g., standard typewriter-style keyboard, a custom keyboard, trackball, mouse, etc.? Can manually entered data be time- and date-stamped?

    b. How are graphics configured? How many graphics pages are allowed? How fast are the screens updated with data?

    c. Are preformatted graphics pages available, e.g., overviews, points, etc.? How many?

    d. How many operator's consoles can be attached to the system? Can a separate engineer's console be used? Can it access the database over the data highway?

    e. Can data be password protected? How many levels of passwords?

    f. How many levels of alarms are available? Are there any built-in alarm management capabilities? How many keystrokes are required for the operator to get to the source of an alarm?

    g. Can messages (prompts) be displayed for the operator? How long can the message be? How many messages can be stored?

7. Communications

    a. Is a proprietary network used? What is its architecture? What access scheme is used? What is its throughput rate (actual throughput rate, not the stated speed of the highway)? Does the throughput rate go down as more devices are attached to the highway? How many devices can be attached to the highway? Is peer-to-peer communication available?

    b. If the highway is proprietary, can other manufacturers' devices be attached to the highway? Is there a MODBUS (Modicon) interface? Is there a Data Highway (Allen-Bradley) interface? If a foreign device is attached to the highway, what other devices on the highway can it communicate with? Is this true for both analog and digital data? Is a MAP gateway available or planned? If so, is a migration path available?

    c. If it is a MAP highway, is it broadband or carrierband? What version of MAP is it, 2.1, 2.2, or 3.0?

8. Logging and Reporting Capabilities

    a. Are trends available? How many variables can be trended at one time and for what length of time? How many can be displayed at one time?

    b. Is data archiving available? How is it handled? How many points can be archived and at what frequency? How is this archived data accessed?

    c. How many printers can be attached to the system? Can a separate printer be used for event logging? Can a graphics page be copied to the printer?

9.   Maintenance and Reliability
    a. Is reliability data available?
    b. Is maintenance history available? Is maintenance of the system easy? Are the various components accessible? What quality of technician is required? How much training does he need? What kinds of diagnostics are provided?
    c. Are spare parts readily accessible locally?
    d. What kind of redundancy is available (e.g., only the CPU)? Are redundant highways available? Are redundant inputs and outputs, multiple operator's consoles with separate electronics, etc. available?
    e. What diagnostic capabilities are provided? Where is the information presented? Do the built-in diagnostics isolate problems to the board level to allow a maintenance technician to bring the proper replacement parts on the first trip?

10.   System Documentation Capabilities
    a. Does the system offer personal computer software that allows both system configuration and drawings to be accomplished through a personal computer and a plotter or printer?
    b. Will it update the drawings with current tuning parameters?
    c. Does it match system configuration with current configuration and update the drawings?
    d. Does the system require a plotter or will it generate drawings on a printer?
    e. What is the speed of drawing generation?

11.   Supplier Qualifications
    a. How much batch control experience does the company have?
    b. Is a hotline available for programming and maintenance support?
    c. How close is the nearest service person?
    d. Do they provide both maintenance and configuration training? Where is that training held? How long are the courses?

EXERCISES

19.1 Why should the user be concerned about a batch control system that is advertised as state-of-the-art?

19.2 Why is it important for the bidders to actually visit the plant site where the batch control system will be installed?

19.3 Why should the detailed hazard analysis be conducted after the bids are received but before detailed design is started?

19.4 Why is it best to test the batch control system at the supplier's factory instead of waiting until it arrives at the plant site?

19.5 What are the advantages of a batch control system where the phase logic is downloaded to the unit controllers as part of the recipe versus a system where all the phase logic resides in the unit controllers and the recipe merely specifies the order in which they will be executed?

19.6 Where would partial downloads of recipes be desirable?

19.7 What problems might be encountered when downloading recipes from a host computer?

19.8 Give reasons why it might be desirable to incorporate a trend display of a critical process variable in the middle of a batch end report.

REFERENCES

1. Leach, D. B., "Specifying a Batch-Process Control System," *Chemical Engineering*, December 8, 1986.

2. Dunbar, R. D., "Bid & Purchase Specifications for Process Control Systems," Texas Instruments, Inc., June 12, 1986.

20

Cost Justification/ Benefits

Introduction   Batch processing often involves labor-intensive operational steps, so there is potential for cost savings through increased automation. But it is often difficult to estimate projected cost savings based on proposed control system improvements. Roerk (Ref. 1) points out that the effectiveness of the design, total project cost, potential for process downtime, and control equipment complexity are all issues that contribute to the difficulty of estimating the return on investment.

Many types of available hardware can be used to automate batch processes. This technology is rapidly changing, and that compounds the complexity of engineering and designing a batch control system. The many input and output signals required for batch process automation also contribute to the complexity and cost of the system. Not only are final control elements and instrumentation more expensive, but the engineering design and installation effort is much larger than for a manually operated system.

However, tremendous improvements in operational efficiency have been reported (Refs. 2, 3, and 4). Mehta (Ref. 4) points out that many of these projects have a payback period of between 4 and 24 months. This represents a very attractive capital investment.

Many operations in a batch process are typically performed manually, e.g., addition of materials, sample extraction, and vessel discharge; these are the primary reasons for the intensive labor requirements in many batch processes. In many batch processes, the process steps are manually executed by operators who follow written instructions in a batch sheet. These written procedures describe in detail the raw material additions, valve sequencing instructions, set point changes, and instructions for recording process variables. But the interpretation of these instructions will inevitably vary from operator to operator. In a complex batch process, equipment coordination can also be a problem because of shared equipment. If the operator must pay attention to other processes being executed simultaneously, it can distract him from important observations.

335

These inconsistencies in the way operations are carried out means there will be variations in the yield and quality of the product. The degree of fluctuation may vary from process to process, but it will still be there. These variations can cause problems with materials and equipment planning in addition to their effect on productivity. If an operator makes a mistake in the proper execution of one of these steps and if the mistake is not recognized and action taken to correct the mistake, off-specification product will most likely result. This further reduces production efficiency, because this material must be scrapped, recycled for re-processing, or blended with good product. This reworking ties up production equipment. All of these problems ultimately contribute to the manufacturing cost of the product.

Benefits of Batch Automation

Automation offers many benefits to batch manufacturers, but they differ from the benefits that drive discrete or continuous manufacturers to automation. The competitive pressures in discrete manufacturing and the small profit margins in continuous manufacturing tend to focus their efforts on cost reduction. A singular focus on cost reduction blinds a user to many opportunities for profitability improvements through automation.

Batch processes lend themselves to a higher degree of automation and control than commonly found in process applications today. Significant benefits can be gained from control in almost all batch processes. The following sections discuss batch process improvements reported as a direct result of automation (Refs. 1, 2, 3, 4, 5, and 6).

Higher and More Consistent Product Quality

The ability to make good product the first time through the system means that productivity will be higher. There will be less waste and scrap, so yields and production rates will be higher.

Actively controlling quality can substantially reduce manufacturing costs. But this means that quality control data must be processed rapidly and presented to operators in an appropriate and efficient manner.

The batch process industry has relied almost exclusively on process data and trends to produce quality products. It is generally assumed that if the right raw materials are used, and if the correct quantities of these materials are charged, and if the same temperature profile is followed, good material will be produced. However, this approach alone is not sufficient; many batch process manufacturers are using SPC techniques, e.g., Shewhart control charts to improve quality and productivity and to reduce waste.

Improved acquisition of process data and the removal of human variables from the control of a system allow powerful statistical methods to be applied to processes. Besides aiding in process optimization, these methods can drastically reduce the time required to bring a process on line. And if the process is being controlled automatically, the operator can spend more time focusing on improving the process. Data acquisition, SPC, and process simulation can all make significant contributions to reducing process commissioning times.

Improving product quality can't be a one-time-only program; it must be an ongoing process. It is difficult to characterize process variations between batches when they are hidden by batch-to-batch or shift-to-shift variations caused by human operators. The repeatable performance of an automated control system helps significantly.

Batch automation provides the ability to add ingredients consistently, which contributes to making a more uniform product. It also minimizes the possibility of adding improper ingredient quantities or wrong ingredients, thus eliminating bad batches. The batch control system can also prevent the expensive but not so common occurrence of mixing products by incorporating cross checks in the control programs.

Having repeatable batches also allows the production runs to be used as controlled laboratory experiments. The process can then be optimized by changing variables slightly from batch to batch and noting the effect on product yields and time cycles. This is usually not possible in a manually controlled plant.

Higher Production Rates Economic savings for batch control systems result from increased production due to improved scheduling, reduced batch cycle time, and higher yields. This results from more efficient use of processing equipment, e.g., by reducing the delays between events in a sequence or optimizing deployment of vessels to minimize time between consecutive batches.

The throughput of a batch production system depends not only on the rate of conversion of product and the feed rate, but also on the batch cycle time and the percent utilization of the major equipment, such as reactors and recovery systems. Scheduling of shared systems, such as weigh tanks that service multiple reactors, involves estimating times of various process events. The objective is to reduce batch cycle time, for example, by minimizing waiting time for a reactor to be charged.

Some of the production rate improvement is provided by the ability of the batch control system to operate in different modes under program control. For instance, alternate control strategies and tuning parameters can be employed during start-up, shutdown, and various reactions and other processing operations.

Reducing batch processing time can affect energy and labor costs, but the most significant benefit usually occurs when additional batches can be produced because of time savings. This allows a greater return on the investment in production equipment but may also mean that the manufacturer can offer more varieties or grades of products without major investments in equipment.

More Flexible Systems This means that the process can be configured in a number of ways to make multiple products where material and product flows, as well as processing steps, are controlled by the computer. This offers several advantages:

1. New products can be introduced more quickly.
2. The changeover from one product to another can be made in less time.
3. Product can continue to be made even when something doesn't operate as expected, e.g., a reactor fails.
4. There are fewer constraints from economy of scale; smaller plants can produce more economically.

5. Product modifications and improvements can be made quickly and economically.

More than ever before, companies need to be adaptable to changing market conditions. Changes in raw material availabilities and prices, as well as significant shifts in product demand, sometimes happen overnight. As a result, operating flexibility is a must.

A measure of flexibility is the company's ability to quickly change operating instructions to both machine and operator. Supervisory controllers in some batch control systems are now capable of downloading recipe information (including temperatures, pressures, cooking times, set points, tuning constants, and so on) directly to the controllers.

Smaller Inventory Requirements Because products can be scheduled better and good material can be made on each batch, smaller inventories are required. This includes raw materials, in-process materials, and final products. Productivity is also better on an automated plant, so smaller equipment can be used for a given capacity rate, and less space is required for the plant.

Better Delivery Response and Delivery Reliability Improved quality, system flexibility, and better scheduling capabilities result in better delivery response and delivery reliability.

Small errors in a batch process can sometimes be rectified by operator intervention, typically by making modifications to procedures or ingredients. Failures frequently take one of three forms: overproduction caused by the addition of more ingredients to restore recipe proportions after a measuring error, substandard grade of product caused by missed recipe targets, or total batch failure. A properly specified batch control system can minimize the number of completely failed batches or eliminate them entirely.

Lower Product Costs Lower product costs are achieved by reduced labor requirements, by improved raw material usage, by more efficient consumption and demand for energy and other utilities, by reduced final product inventories, and by lower maintenance costs.

Automated systems frequently reduce utility costs by reducing production cycles, allowing coordinated staging of equipment for load shedding schemes, and regulating process heating or cooling for optimal efficiency. Reduced production times also may translate into labor savings and may decrease the possibility that maintenance operations will affect production schedules.

Increased Safety for Personnel, Plant Equipment, and Users Because the system has the ability to detect and respond quickly, precisely, and predictably to abnormal conditions, safety for personnel, equipment, and users is enhanced. Instrumentation also can be used to protect the environment, personnel, and neighboring plants and communities by reducing emissions.

Batch processes rely heavily on the skill and attention of their operators. But batch operations are largely repetitive tasks. Operators may also be required to inspect or operate devices that are remote from their control consoles. Both of these factors can mean that the operator is slow to respond to alarm conditions. Automation can improve safety in many applications by assuring prompt response to alarms.

In processes that have the potential for uncontrolled (or runaway) reactions, the impact of automation on safety can be enough to justify automation enhancements. Many uncontrolled chemical reactions hold the potential for equipment damage, environmental pollution, and, in the worst cases, human casualties within a plant or a community. Such processes should be primary candidates for automation.

Preservation of the Company's Production Expertise The basic knowledge of how to make a product or operate equipment rests with the people in the plant. This expertise is a critically important asset of any manufacturing company. In a manually operated plant, this expertise may be lost when these valuable employees retire.

Automated systems can protect a company from this loss of knowledge in two ways:

1. By capturing details of operation when the information is used to generate software for control systems.

2. By using developments in artificial intelligence technologies, e.g., expert systems, to capture human expertise so that it can be used in future systems.

Justification of Batch Control Systems   The benefits of improved batch process automation are easy to describe but hard to justify. Cost justification is possible, but it may take a change in the way management thinks about how these projects should be justified (Refs. 7, 8, 9, and 10).

Some of the benefits discussed above can be evaluated and converted into tangible economic gains to justify a batch control automation project. Fewer operators will be required in an automated batch process, but the labor requirements in other areas will probably increase, at least in the early stages of the project. For example, more control system engineers will be needed during the design and construction phases of the project. More and higher quality instrument technicians may be necessary to support the more sophisticated control equipment. Yield and quality improvements are more difficult to use for justification if the batch process is making a completely new product. As a result, not only the projection of forecasted benefits but also post-installation audits will probably be necessary until management accepts batch process automation as a way of life.

The traditional cost-accounting criteria used by industry—direct labor, materials, and indirect overhead—cannot place fair dollar values on benefits such as quality and responsiveness. Corporations need to look less at justifying individual pieces of automation and look more at how they fit into the overall profit picture. For example, direct labor at one time accounted for up to a third of a product's cost. Today it has dropped to 10% for many industries, while materials and overhead have climbed to 55% and 35%, respectively (Ref. 7).

Some reasons that an improved approach to cost management and economic justification for automation projects is needed are listed below (Ref. 11):

1. Many cost-accounting systems no longer reflect the manufacturing process. Direct labor may no longer be the appropriate basis for allocating or assigning fixed indirect costs (overhead) to products. Some systems also ignore certain process and product costs, e.g., material handling and expenses associated with maintaining inventory levels.

2. Cost patterns have changed. Manufacturing overhead continues to grow; for some companies it is now 400 to 500 percent of direct labor. But the assumption that reducing direct labor will reduce indirect labor is often wrong. Cost control efforts need to be redirected with some additional focus on indirect costs. However, costs such as maintenance, quality control, and material handling can still be evaluated on a direct basis.

3. Direct labor is no longer the driver for production costs, so many cost management systems fail to identify the true components of product cost.

4. Traditional financial techniques are inappropriate for technology planning. Payback and return on investment calculations only evaluate previously identified projects; they don't identify potential improvements.

Higher quality products can open up new markets. Faster cycle times can deliver new products ahead of the competition. The databases that are created offer an opportunity to improve communications within the company. This immediate access to process and engineering information can lead to less rework and faster identification of yield and time cycle problems. These benefits can be translated into reduced manufacturing cost. With improved product tracking and scheduling, on-hand inventory can be reduced.

A batch process automation project should not be justified only by how it may or may not pay for itself in strict accounting terms over the short term. It should also be viewed as a way of allowing the company as a whole to make more money in the long run.

EXERCISES

20.1 If the operators have a written procedure to follow in a manual batch system, why are there inconsistencies from operator to operator?

20.2 When an operator makes an execution mistake in a manual batch system, how is that mistake usually discovered?

20.3 Assuming that using the correct raw materials, charging the right amounts of ingredients, and processing the batch properly doesn't guarantee good quality product, what other technologies besides SPC might be used?

20.4 How do automated batch systems allow the company to respond quickly to changing market conditions?

20.5 What kinds of intangible benefits should be looked at when justifying a batch automation project?

REFERENCES

1. Roerk, P. E., "Control, Scheduling and Optimization of Batch Processing, Batch Process Automation Difficult but Cost Effective," AIChE Paper, Date of Presentation and Origin Unknown.

2. Clifton, D. M., "Batch Computer Control of a Bulk Pharmaceutical Chemical Process," ISA/83, Paper #83-913.

3. Barsamian, J. A., "Process Control Computer Systems: Spend Money, Make Money," *InTech*, March 1986.

4. Mehta, G. A., "The Benefits of Batch Process Control," *CEP*, October 1983.

5. Donovan, J., "Batch Process Automation," *Plant Engineering*, September 24, 1987.

6. Conroy, R. C., "Batch Control—Part 1, Discrete vs. Process Batch Control," *I&CS*, October 1987.

7. Baer, T., "Cost Justification Is Possible," *Managing Automation*, August 1986.

8. Inglesby, T., "All It Takes Is Money," *Manufacturing Systems*, June 1986.

9. Cullinane, T. P., "Justifying Expenditures Is the Tough Part," *Modern Materials Handling*, June 1986.

10. Major, M. J., "The Bottom Line in Manufacturing," *Business Software Review*, August 1986.

11. "Integrated Manufacturing," appeared in *Material Handling Engineering*, *Computer-Aided Engineering*, and *Production Engineering* during 1986.

Appendix A
Communications

Introduction   Communications between various devices is an important part of any control system. This is especially true now with the new and sophisticated control equipment available such as programmable controllers (PLCs), microcomputers, and distributed control systems (DCSs). With distributed control a number of programmable controllers and/or microprocessors each handle a small part of the total control system and communicate with each other over a data highway. This distributed philosophy improves reliability of the control system, since a failure of one part does not shut down the entire system.

Many different digital control components are necessary to control a batch process. Unfortunately, they seldom are able to communicate within the same distributed control system. Although it is desirable to interface components from different vendors to a distributed control system, most often a standard interface is not available.

Three different means of communicating between these hardware devices are:

- serial interfaces,
- parallel interfaces, and
- data highways.

Serial Interfaces   The Electronics Industries Association's RS-232 (now in the D version) is the most common serial interface standard in use today. Serial transmission means that data are transmitted one bit at a time. This interface has been around for about 20 years under EIA Standard RS-232-C (Ref. 1). Although a 25-pin connector is normally used, EIA standard RS-232-C defines only 20 of these signals. Not all signals are used by all devices, so not all RS-232-C devices will work together without modification. The original RS-232-C standard did not specify the mechanical connector, so the standard was updated in 1986 to include a mechanical (connector) specification. In addition, a few new signals were added, one signal was redefined, and some terminology was changed. This new standard was released as EIA: RS-232-D, 1987 (Ref. 2).

The RS-232 interface does have some serious limitations:

1. The major drawback is its limited transmission distance of 50 feet. In practice, longer distances can be used but some risk is involved. RS-232 is often used to connect PLCs to computers, computers to other peripheral equipment, and so on. This is where the 50-foot limit becomes restrictive. Devices are available from some manufacturers (e.g., fiber optics) that can significantly extend the maximum transmission distance.

2. A second disadvantage is its maximum transmission speed. While RS-232 can operate at speeds up to 19,200 bps, the data rate between various devices is usually 9600 at best.

3. A third problem is the physical plug-to-plug incompatibility. Not all manufacturers implement the RS-232 standard in the same manner. This can make the interconnection between devices a problem. When manufacturers claim that a product is RS-232 compatible, they usually mean that the equipment accepts and generates only a small fraction of the RS-232 signals and also that it does not violate any other parts of the standard.

Regardless of the above problems, RS-232 is probably the most widely used communications interface. The main reason for choosing RS-232 is the wide range of equipment available with the interface. Figure A-1 shows how the RS-232 interface might be used to link control equipment in a batch process. With this type of system, there is no peer-to-peer communication between the single-station digital controllers (SSDCs) and the programmable controller (PLC). All communications must go through the minicomputer.

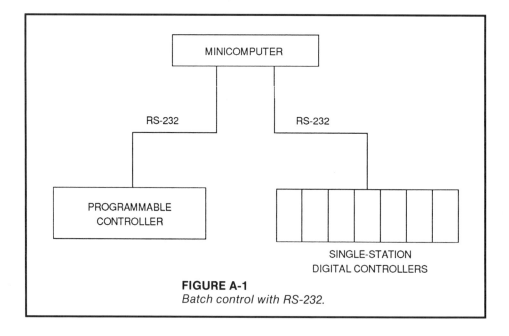

FIGURE A-1
Batch control with RS-232.

Because of the inherent problems with the RS-232 interface, three new standards were introduced in the late 1970s with the intention that they would gradually replace RS-232. These standards were RS-449, RS-422, and RS-423. They were developed to permit higher data rates and longer distances and to solve some of the other problems with the RS-232 interface. Although a number of manufacturers offer their equipment with these interfaces, their adoption by both vendors and end users has been minimal (Ref. 3).

Parallel Interfaces

The simplest example of parallel transmission is the direct connection of inputs/outputs (I/O) from one device (e.g., a programmable controller) with the inputs/outputs of another device (e.g., a distributed control system). Discrete I/O are used to transmit digital data. Separate modules must be dedicated to inputs and outputs since the I/O devices are capable of transfer in only one direction.

BCD (binary coded decimal) I/O are used to transmit numerical (analog data) information to and from devices such as thumbwheel switches, digital displays, and other like peripheral devices. Parallel BCD interfaces require four digital inputs (or outputs) for each digit of information. A large number of digital input and output modules may be required if many digits of information have to be interfaced.

These types of schemes are normally used when not too much data needs to be transferred or when a more sophisticated interface device is not available. When a great deal of data must be transmitted between devices, this type of parallel interface can use up a significant portion of the input/output capacity of a device.

The IEEE-488 Bus (IEEE Standard 488-1978) is one of the most widely used parallel interface standards. It is also called the General Purpose Interface Bus (GPIB), the Hewlett-Packard Interface Bus (HPIB), or the ANSI Bus (ANSI MCI-1975). This interface bus was developed by Hewlett-Packard for connecting its own instruments to each other. Although the IEEE-488 Bus is widely used to connect laboratory and test instruments together, it is not widely used in the process control industry.

The IEEE-488 Bus consists of a 24-wire cable that contains sixteen signals. Eight of the signals are parallel data lines; eight signals are control lines. Three of the eight control lines are handshake lines that control the flow of information over the data bus. The remaining five lines carry control signals for and status information about all devices attached to the bus. Devices can be separated by as much as 20 meters. For maximum speed, separation distances should be limited to about one meter per device. Up to 15 peripheral devices can be connected to the bus.

Extremely high data transfer rates can be achieved with the IEEE-488 Bus. Data are transmitted on the bus in a byte-serial, bit-parallel manner, which means that the 8 bits (1 byte) of data are transmitted in parallel, while successive bytes of data are transmitted serially.

Data Highways

Data Highways   Data highways, sometimes called local area networks (LANs), are used to provide a communications network between distributed components. Data highways can also be used as a means of integrating components from a variety of manufacturers into a combined control system.

The main function of the data highway is to move data between the various devices in the system such as computers, PLCs, or other microprocessor-based devices. These devices gain access to the data highway via an interface unit that performs data buffering, data transmission or receiving on the highway, error checking, and error recovery (Ref. 4).

Data buffering is one of the most important jobs for the interface unit. It is not uncommon for a data highway to run at 5-10 Mbits/sec (million bits/second). But data transmission between the interface units and the local devices may take place over an RS-232 interface at 9600 bps. Without data buffering in the interface unit, the data highway would be tied up while the local device was transmitting. Because of the buffering, the interface unit can accumulate data from the local device at the slow transmission rate and transmit it to the data highway at the high transmission rate.

Some factors that must be considered before selecting a data highway are (Refs. 5 and 6):

- the communications medium,
- the network topology,
- bandwidth, and
- the access (priority) method.

Communications Mediums   The selection of the best cable medium for a given network application is determined by several variables (Ref. 7). The speed (data transmission rate) is one, the actual topology used in the network is another. Other important factors are the layout and size of the network. The most common types of mediums are twisted-pair wiring, coaxial cable, and fiber optics.

Twisted-pair cable is the lowest in cost and can be easily expanded to include new equipment and locations. Since the two insulated wires are wrapped around each other, they provide some immunity to electrical noise. However, the data transmission rate is limited because of its susceptibility to noise. Speeds over 1-2 million bits/second (Mbits/sec) are not possible on this cable; most run at much lower speeds (300-9600 bits/sec) to ensure reliable transmission (Ref. 7). Shielded twisted-pair wiring does increase noise immunity and allow higher data rates than ordinary twisted-pair wiring.

Coaxial cable is the most common communications medium. It consists of a single center conductor surrounded by an insulator and a shield. This provides protection from outside interference and allows for the transmission of high-frequency signals. This cable has a high data-carrying capability, from 1 to 15 Mbits/sec (Ref. 7). Coax has much better noise-rejection characteristics than twisted pair cable.

Fiber optic cables are also being used for data highways. They are hair-thin strands of highly transparent glass fiber made into a bundle of glass rods. Data signals are converted to light pulses and transmitted over the cable. The light pulses are converted back to electrical signals at the receiving end of the cable.

Fiber optic cables have the greatest data-carrying capacity of all the communications media discussed, with data transmission rates up to 200 Mbits/sec commercially available at the time of this writing (Ref. 7). They can also be used for transmission distances of 10 kilometers or more and are immune to electromagnetic noise (Ref. 8). They are also not troubled by electric ground potential problems as the other communications media are. Their main disadvantages at this time are high cost (both initial and maintenance), difficult terminations, and the problem with tying additional devices into the highway without using repeaters.

Network Topologies The simplest configuration is a star network (see Figure A-2) in which each device interacts directly with the central control unit (host) through a dedicated communication channel. A failure in one remote device does not affect another remote device since the various devices do not interact directly with each other. But all communications between individual remote devices must take place through the central control unit. Reasonably high speed can be

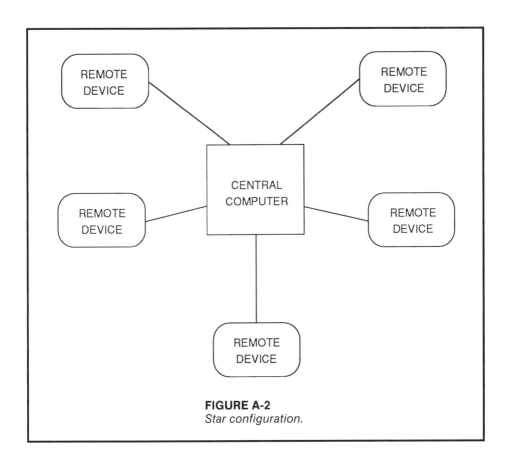

FIGURE A-2
Star configuration.

achieved in the star network even with a slow-speed interface such as RS-232. The advantage of the star network is that the network devices can be relatively unsophisticated. However, the central control unit must be fast and sophisticated, and a failure in the central control unit can disable the entire network. A redundant central control unit may be required when high availability is required. Most industrial control systems use either ring or bus configurations.

In the ring network (see Figure A-3) point-to-point connections are made between the various remote devices and there is no controlling master. Messages are passed around the loop; each remote device reads the message and retransmits it to the next. However, a failure of a remote device can break the loop, so means must be provided to bypass a failed unit. Although this network works well for small systems, it can become very complex as the number of devices increases.

Most newer systems use a multi-drop data highway (bus) (see Figure A-4) with a number of remote units interfaced to the highway. The interface to the highway may be as simple as an RS-232 interface or as complicated as a high-speed direct-memory-access device. All devices on the highway receive all messages, but they do not retransmit them. Redundant highways can be provided to improve availability. Since this single highway must communicate to all the remote units, higher transmission speed is required.

Bandwidth Information is transmitted over a communications network in either digital or analog form. Baseband networks transmit only digital signals. Signals are put onto the cable as voltage pulses that represent the binary bits 0

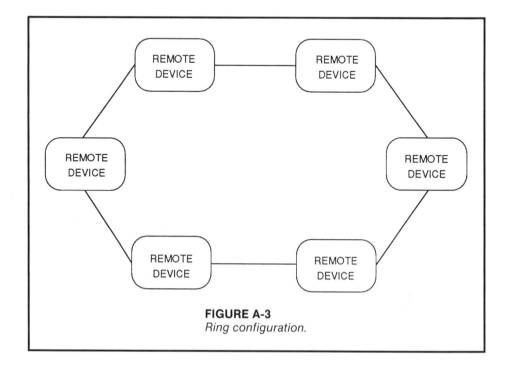

FIGURE A-3
Ring configuration.

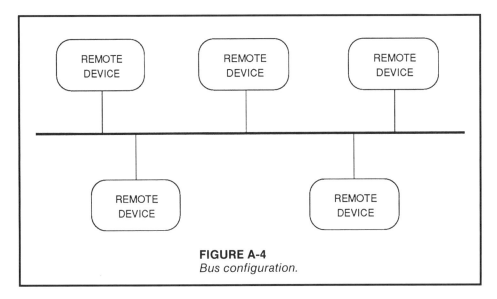

FIGURE A-4
Bus configuration.

and 1. During transmission, the signals travel at one frequency and consume the entire bandwidth of the cable. The transmission rate capability then depends on the physical medium being used, with twisted-pair wiring the slowest and fiber optics the fastest.

Broadband networks transmit the information as analog signals that travel over the network in a continuous wave-like motion. The information transmitted is represented by varying either the signal frequency (the number of waves, or cycles/second) or its amplitude (the height of the wave). Digital signals, e.g., from an RS-232 interface, can be converted to analog and back to digital again.

Bandwidth is usually defined in terms of the frequency range, i.e, the number of bits/second. Because the data stream on a baseband network, e.g., Ethernet, is digital, the medium is forced to be utilized as a single-channel medium. Therefore, baseband does not support multiple services, e.g., data and video simultaneously. Baseband is more often used in an office environment.

Broadband, however, is a versatile communication technique that supports multiple services across a single cable. To transmit video, voice, or data signals on a broadband network, the signal is modulated up to the required channel frequency by means of a high-frequency modem and is impressed onto a continuous carrier signal. It then travels piggyback to its destination, where it is demodulated back to its normal frequency.

Broadband divides the available transmission capacity into separate communication channels by *frequency division multiplexing (FDM)* (see Figure A-5) (Ref. 6). Each channel is adjusted to give the frequency range required to cope with the particular type of information to be transmitted. The available bandwidth on a broadband cable is 300–400 MHz (millions of hertz). A bandwidth of 300 MHz could be divided into 50 TV channels (each one 6 MHz higher in frequency than the one below it), or into a greater number of data channels, or into any desired combination of voice, video, or data.

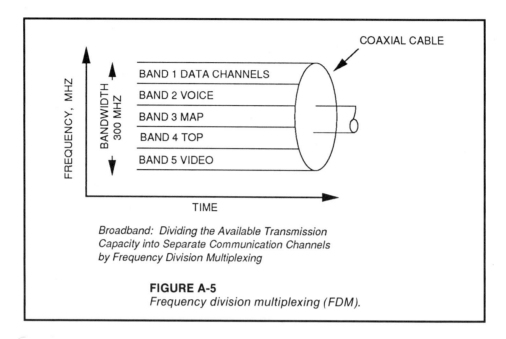

*Broadband: Dividing the Available Transmission
Capacity into Separate Communication Channels
by Frequency Division Multiplexing*

FIGURE A-5
Frequency division multiplexing (FDM).

In a broadband network, the signals can be transmitted in only one direction along the cable. This problem can be overcome by using two separate cables, one for "send" and one for "receive." However, this results in higher cable costs.

The most common approach to solving the one-way-only communication problem is to use two separate channels (one a "send" and one a "receive") using frequency division multiplexing and then controlling these by using a head end remodulator, as shown in Figure A-6 (Ref. 6). In this case, the data is sent up the cable, usually on the lower frequency channel, to the head end remodulator. The head end then amplifies the signal, modulates it to the higher frequency of the other channel, and retransmits it down the cable to the addressee node. All signals put on the network travel towards the head end; all signals taken off the network travel away from the head end.

Broadband communications technology is an obvious selection as a communications utility for the industrial environment for several reasons. The ability to support data, video, and audio communications over a single wire is a major feature. The fact that broadband is a stable technology that has been proven in the cable TV (CATV) environment is another factor. Finally, the shielding on coaxial cable provides protection from electromagnetic or radio frequency interference and gives it the ability to survive in harsh environments. Some of the applications that have been used on broadband are:

- energy management systems,
- fire alarm systems,
- manufacturing data communications,
- controlled access systems,
- time and attendance,

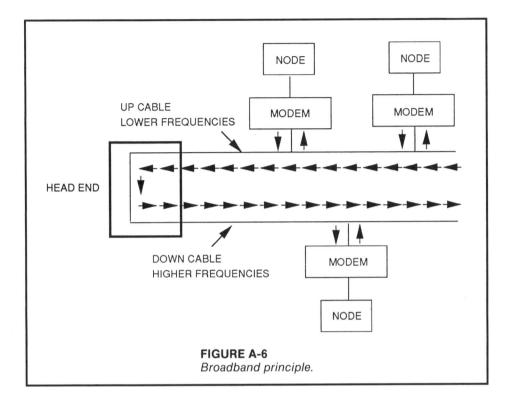

FIGURE A-6
Broadband principle.

- security (two-way video),
- audio paging,
- engineering data communications,
- broadcast television signal distribution, and
- business data communications.

Carrierband is basically a single-channel version of broadband. In the most common type, signals are modulated onto a single carrier frequency. The whole bandwidth of the cable is treated as one channel. Since the cable taps are non-directional, the signals can be transferred in both directions along the cable. Therefore, a head end is not needed; modems are used to modulate the digital signals.

Access (Priority) Schemes Two types of access schemes are currently used (Ref. 9): the active bus master system and the passive bus system. Ring networks use only the passive system, while bus networks use either active or passive systems.

Active Bus Master System
This system requires a third device, e.g., a traffic director to direct the communications between the various remote units (see Figure A-7). This system works well when the majority of the system intelligence is located in one central location. The

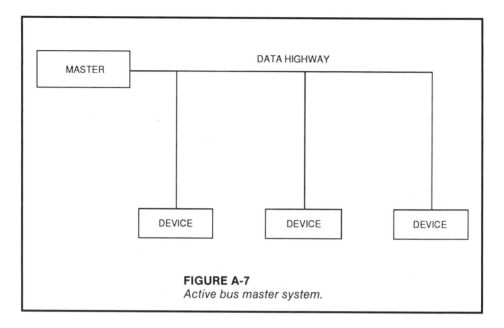

FIGURE A-7
Active bus master system.

response time tends to go down, however, as the number of slave units increases. The major disadvantage with this system is that all communications must be passed through the master. Therefore, there is no peer-to-peer communications capability.

Passive Bus System

This system eliminates the master and provides the devices attached to the bus with the intelligence necessary for communications. Most ring and bus networks use this system. Two types of passive buses are used.

1. *Carrier sense multiple access with collision detection* (CSMA/CD) is a generic name for a line-sharing system that allows a number of devices to share a data highway. CSMA/CD is normally used with bus networks and is a contention system. A station wishing to transmit first listens to find out if another device is transmitting. If not, it transmits immediately. If the line is busy, the device waits and does not interrupt an ongoing transmission. The station continues to listen periodically to see when the highway is free, and then it transmits its message. If two stations try to transmit a message at the same time, a *collision* occurs. Then the stations stop their transmission and wait for a period of time before attempting a retransmission. This is the collision detection feature of CSMA/CD.

An example is shown in Figure A-8 (Ref. 6). In Figure A-8a, node 3 is currently transmitting. Nodes 1 and 6 want to transmit. They sense that the channel is in use, so they wait and continue to monitor the network. In Figure A-8b, node 3 has finished transmitting. Nodes 1 and 6 sense that the channel is free and begin to transmit at virtually the same time. The two signals collide. However, the nodes detect this and stop transmitting. After waiting for a random time, and having assured that the channel is carrying no traffic, nodes 1 and 6 try again (see Figure A-8c). Since node 6's random waiting time is shorter than node 1's, node 6 starts transmitting and assumes control of the channel. Node 1 waits until the channel is free of traffic and then tries again.

This type of system is very efficient, particularly for longer messages. The disadvantage is that there is some uncertainty of data delivery as traffic on the data highway increases. For this reason, CSMA/CD is called a probabilistic

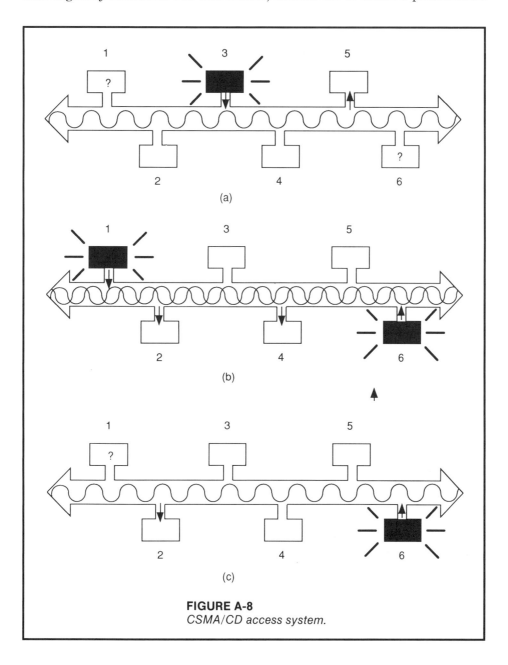

FIGURE A-8
CSMA/CD access system.

system, because there is a chance that a device will always sense a collision and never be able to send its message. However, the CSMA/CD system does treat all devices equally, and a station cannot take over control of the highway if another station is using it. The CSMA/CD access system is most applicable to communications networks where large amounts of data must be transferred but where timing is not extremely critical.

The most common example of the CSMA/CD system is Ethernet.

2. In a *token-passing* system the right to access the highway is distributed among all the devices attached to the network. Only one device has the right to transmit—the device holding the "token" (see Figure A-9) (Ref. 6).

A token is a special control "packet" that is passed around the network from node to node in a pre-ordained sequence, i.e., every node knows the address of its predecessor and successor in the sequence. The token confers an exclusive right to the network, and no node can transmit without it.

Each node constantly monitors the network to detect any packet addressed to it. This might be a message from another node, or it might be the token. If the token presents itself and the node has nothing to transmit, it is passed on immediately to the next node in the sequence. If the token is accepted, it is passed on after the node has finished transmitting.

Since the token has to be surrendered within a specific time, it is impossible for any node to hog the network. The sequence by which the token is offered to the nodes is set by network management and might not be physically sequential, e.g., A-C-F-B-D-E-A, as shown in Figure A-9. It may be further modified by the priority assigned to a particular message.

The logic required to perform the token-passing system is considerably more complex than that required for the CSMA/CD system. The token-passing system is used with both ring and bus networks.

One advantage of this system is that it guarantees that a critical message will be transmitted within a certain period of time. The token-passing system is called a deterministic system because of the ability to precisely determine the maximum time that a device will wait without being able to transmit messages. However, the system is complicated because recovery circuits have to be built into each device so that the "token" gets started again after a power loss. Another major advantage of the token bus access system is that it allows peer-to-peer communication (as CSMA/CD does).

The token-passing system is more suitable for real-time control than CSMA/CD because transmission of a critical message can be guaranteed and because the sequence by which stations gain access to the highway can be predetermined. In a standard token-passing system the token is passed sequentially from one device to the next device. It is possible to configure the system so that critical devices get the token more frequently.

RS-485 Networks   The RS-485 interface was introduced by the Electronic Industries Association (EIA) in 1983, several years after the RS-422A interface was introduced (Ref. 10). The characteristics of RS-485 are essentially an

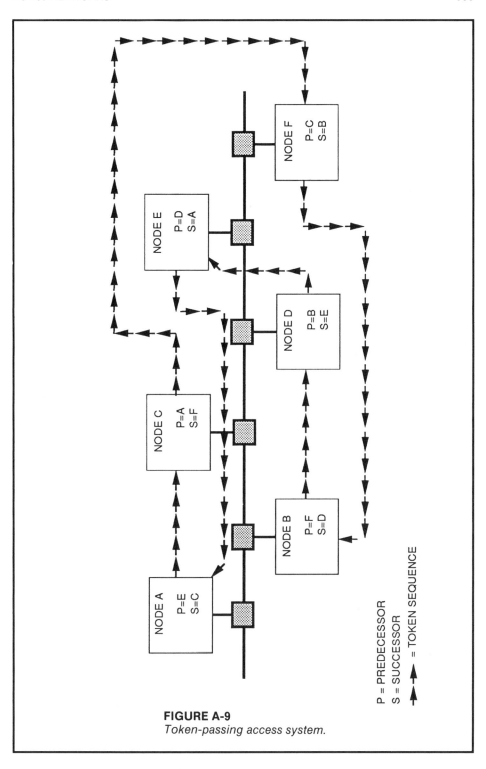

FIGURE A-9
Token-passing access system.

extension of those of RS-422, and properly designed RS-485 interface ports can also be used as RS-422 ports.

RS-422, along with RS-232 and RS-423, are point-to-point communications. RS-485 goes beyond these simple serial communications interfaces by supporting multidrop operation, allowing up to 32 devices to communicate with each other over a common pair of wires. This is accomplished by using drivers with tri-state outputs, which can go into a high-impedance mode when they are not driving the communication line. This effectively removes them from the line.

Both RS-422-A and RS-485 offer a balanced design that incorporates differential drivers and receivers that provide greater noise immunity. This allows them to communicate at higher speeds over longer distances. RS-485 allows communication distances of up to 4000 feet and transmission speeds of up to 10 Mbits/second. However, the allowable communication distance is a function of the transmission speed. The maximum allowable cable length is reduced as the transmission speed increases beyond 90 kbits/second (Ref. 10).

The RS-485 communications network uses the bus topology and twisted-pair wiring. The access method can be either multiple master or master/slave (active bus).

The RS-485 interface is being offered by a number of manufacturers that are supplying control systems based on personal computers.

Manufacturing Automation Protocol (MAP)

Batch control systems have historically been implemented in distributed control systems (DCSs). DCSs are used because the DCS manufacturers have extensive application expertise and can provide an integrated process control system. These systems are integrated from the standpoint that they are built from a set of system components, all available from the same manufacturer. They are designed for easy assembly into a complete arrangement that tends to have a uniform, modular appearance from one application to another.

The problem with this type of system is that it tends to be very proprietary, i.e., the network is unique to that particular manufacturer. Trying to connect a piece of equipment from another manufacturer into this system can be very difficult and expensive. Even when this connection is accomplished, it doesn't always integrate well into the overall control scheme.

Programmable controller manufacturers are breaking into the batch control market with their own versions of proprietary networks. Again, this doesn't provide the user the ability to connect equipment from different vendors into one batch control system.

Manufacturing Automation Protocol (MAP) is the largest and most significant force behind the integrated automation movement. A MAP architecture allows equipment from many vendors to communicate over network levels reaching from the factory floor to top management. Vendor involvement in the MAP structure is substantial, with a representation in every level of its widely accepted ISO/OSI architecture.

In the late 1970s, General Motors (GM) realized a need for communications standards. So, in 1980 GM decided to push for standardization in factory communications by announcing that all their suppliers would have to communicate over a broadband network scheme called the Manufacturing Automation Protocol. By 1984 GM had about 40,000 programmable devices installed in its plants, but only about 15% were able to communicate with each other. When this communication did occur, the cost was about 50% of the total automation expense because of the special wiring and the custom hardware and software interfaces required (Ref. 11). GM expected to have 200,000 such devices installed by 1990.

MAP, in its original form, is a broadband network using the token bus accessing scheme with a data rate of 10 Mbits/sec. When MAP was first introduced by GM, plans called for only the broadband network, because the time response on the MAP broadband network is sufficient for the discrete control industry in which GM is involved. But when the process industries began looking at using MAP for real-time control, they realized that the speed of response was not sufficient for their applications. Now there is a second MAP specification based on a carrierband network operating at 5 Mbits/sec.

Broadband is a multiple-channel system. Carrierband, a single-channel system, is simpler than broadband and is cheaper to install. Since data is transmitted and received on the same channel, no head end is required on the network. The physical cost of the carrierband system is also less than for a broadband system. The MAP carrierband network uses a modulation technique called phase-coherent modulation, which is a form of frequency shift keying where the two signals are integrally related to the data rate. It is called phase-coherent because the zero crossing points are in phase at the beginning and end of each bit time. A data one (1) is represented by one full cycle of the lower signaling frequency per bit time (see Figure A-10, Ref. 12). A data zero (0) is represented by two full cycles of the higher signaling frequency per bit time. A third symbol, known as nondata, is used in frame delimiters and occurs only in pairs. A pair of nondata symbols is represented by one full cycle of the higher frequency, followed by one full cycle of the lower frequency, followed by one full cycle of the higher frequency. The higher signaling frequency is always twice the data rate. The lower signaling frequency is always the same as the data rate.

Carrierband should not be confused with baseband. Baseband is also a single-channel system, but no carrier modulation takes place in a baseband system. Carrierband has more noise immunity and higher data rates than baseband.

The OSI Model MAP is based on the 7-layer ISO (International Organization for Standardization) Open Systems Interconnection (OSI) model. The seven layers of the standard, shown in Figure A-11, are: Physical, Data Link, Network, Transport, Session, Presentation, and Application. The first two layers, Physical and Data Link, are responsible for getting the message from one node to the next. The third layer, Network, finds the best route for sending messages between two or more nodes separated by intermediate nodes. The fourth layer, Transport, is responsible for getting the message there correctly and in the right order. These are the layers that deal with the actual routing of the information through the network. However, the data format and exchange must be compatible before the

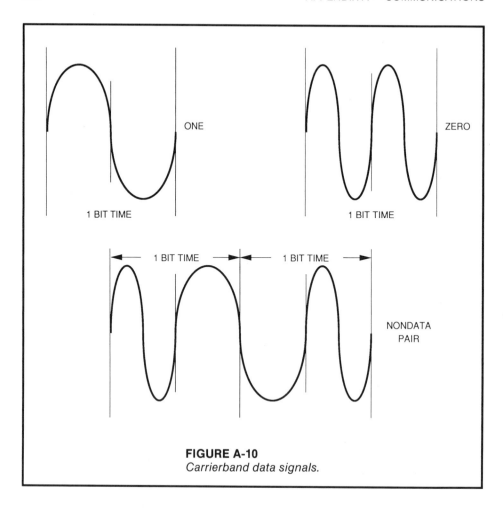

FIGURE A-10
Carrierband data signals.

two computer systems can understand each other. This is the function of the upper three layers, Session, Presentation, and Application, and they are the most difficult. They provide the protocols that will make one end user's data understandable to other end users.

The Physical Layer (Layer 1) provides a physical connection to the communications medium for transmission of data. It is responsible for encoding the data for transmission over a cable and regulates access to the physical medium.

The Data Link Layer (Layer 2) describes the procedure for transferring blocks of data over the network and ensuring that data gets from one device to another. This protocol identifies a five-step procedure for communicating within a network: (1) format a message into packets, (2) access the network with a token, (3) put the error-checking flag on the message, (4) send the message across the network, and (5) check the error flag to verify that the correct message was received.

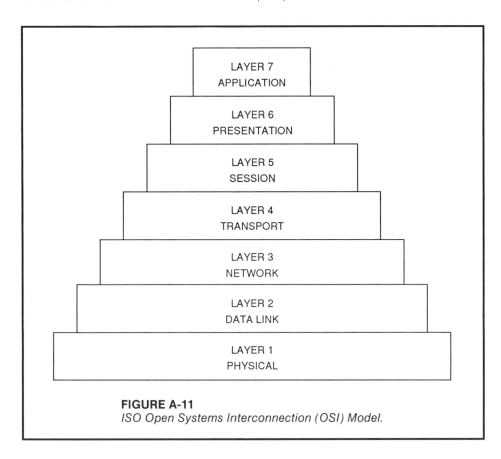

FIGURE A-11
ISO Open Systems Interconnection (OSI) Model.

The Network Layer (Layer 3) controls the switching and routing of messages between stations. The data exchange takes place independently of the transfer technology. Protocols under this layer handle addressing of packets of data and the routing of these packets to their final destinations. They define all possible routes that a packet could travel to get to its final destination.

The Transport Layer (Layer 4) describes message transfers between interface units and the network. This layer contains a set of functions that make sure the receiving end is ready to receive, that the transmitting end is ready to transmit, and that the connection is established between the two. Using routes provided by Layer 3, it chooses the best path for information from one node to another.

The Session Layer (Layer 5) provides a structured or logical exchange of messages between points on the network. It governs the process of setting up or terminating a communications session. It also checks to determine if proper communication is taking place. If not, it must restore the session without data loss or terminate the session under the prescribed rules.

The Presentation Layer (Layer 6) handles the transfer of messages between various computer, data terminal, and data base formats; codes; and languages. It defines the form of data at its source, during transfer, and at its destination. This ensures that each network has a common format into which the data can be translated so it can be exchanged with other devices.

The Application Layer (Layer 7) is the highest in the OSI architecture. This layer applies end-user information to the network. It provides communication services (such as file transfer, access, and management; directory services; remote terminal access; network management; message handling; etc.) to the particular application. The other layers exist only to support this layer.

Each layer in the stack communicates with the layers above and below it. Figure A-12 shows the flow of information in the MAP system when a message is sent (Ref. 13). Information flows down through the sender's protocol stack, across the physical link, and up through the receiving stack. As the data moves down through each layer, information is added by each layer, as shown in Figure A-13 (Ref. 6). As that packet of information moves up through the stack on the receiving end, each layer strips away the information applicable to that layer. By the time the packet of information reaches the end user, the end user application sees the original data.

Time Critical Applications Sending information down through the seven layers on the sending end and up through the seven layers on the receiving end does take time. In addition, even though MAP broadband transmits at 10 Mbits/sec over the physical medium, that is not the actual throughput rate. Throughput

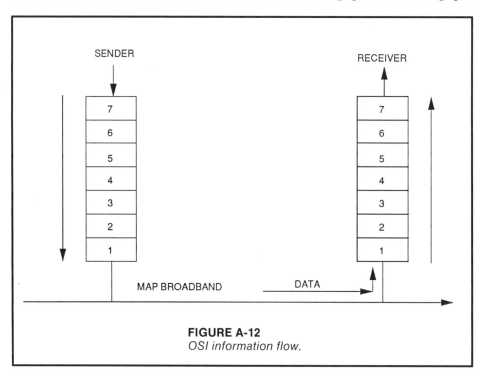

FIGURE A-12
OSI information flow.

rate is measured by the actual amount of data transmitted in a given time. As Figure A-13 shows, a significant amount of overhead is involved in the information transmission, so the actual throughput will be considerably less than 10 Mbits/sec.

For time critical applications using a carrierband network, two new architectures have been added. The first is the enhanced performance architecture (EPA) system (see Figure A-14). It is a dual architecture device that supports the full set of MAP protocols. But it also has a mechanism to bypass upper layer protocols to create a collapsed architecture for time critical applications.

The second architecture is the Mini-MAP system (see Figure A-15). This architecture has only layers 1, 2, and 7 of the OSI model. It is a low-cost version intended for time critical applications. Figure A-16 (Ref. 14) shows how these new architectures can interface with the broadband MAP network (backbone). Since the MAP/EPA node has a full 7-layer implementation on one side, it can communicate with devices on the backbone, but the Mini-MAP node cannot. However, the Mini-MAP node has full communication capability with any device on the carrierband network.

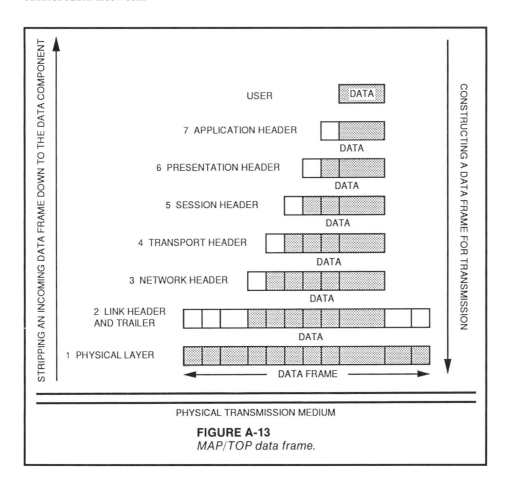

FIGURE A-13
MAP/TOP data frame.

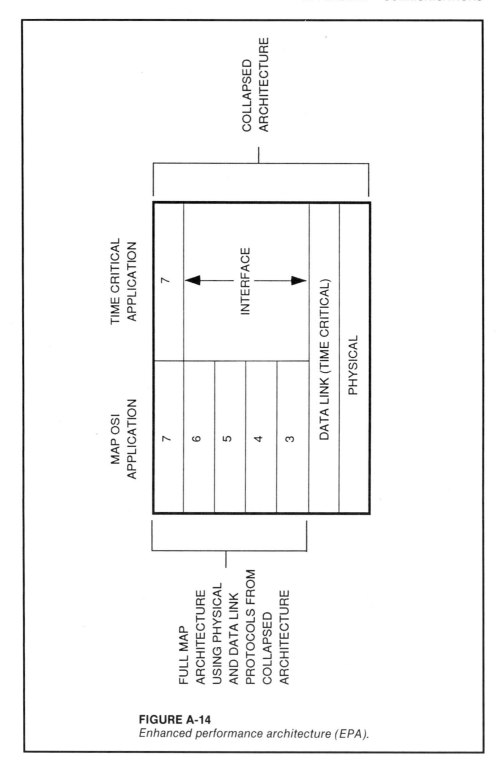

FIGURE A-14
Enhanced performance architecture (EPA).

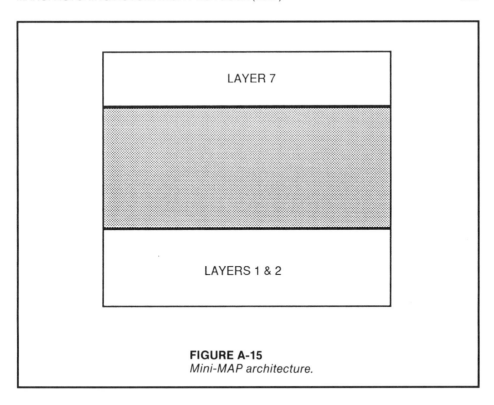

FIGURE A-15
Mini-MAP architecture.

Manufacturing Message Specification (MMS) The manufacturing message specification (MMS) is a standard that specifies a method for communicating with intelligent plant floor devices (e.g., PLCs, robots, cell controllers, etc.). However, many of the services provided by MMS are applicable to a wide variety of applications other than manufacturing (Ref. 15). MMS has been accepted as an ISO recognized international standard (ISO 9506).

MMS is an application layer protocol that fits into the OSI reference model at Layer 7, the application layer, but it is not an application program. It fits into the application layer because it contains a set of communication types called "services" that define methods of sending and receiving data; these services are used by the real application programs (e.g., operator stations, supervisory control workstations, historians, etc.) to communicate with other devices on the network. MMS is a generic message specification that applies to all manufacturing devices for: control, monitoring, upload, and download.

The MMS services are implemented by the supplier, so it is usually not necessary for the user to become intimately familiar with the MMS standard. However, the supplier must define which MMS services are being supported, what nested elements of the services have been implemented, and what are any service side effects (Ref. 16). This information is essential so that different supplier equipment and systems can communicate with each other over MAP.

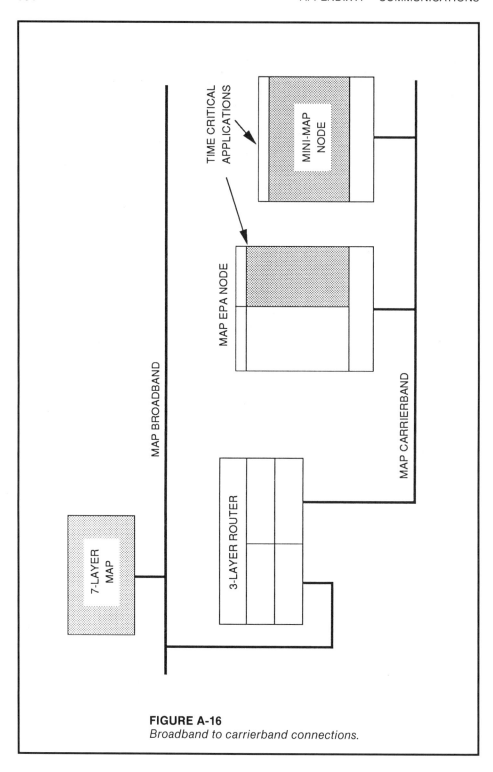

FIGURE A-16
Broadband to carrierband connections.

An MMS companion standard can also reside in the application layer. These companion standards are alternatives to plain MMS that offer increased functionality in the application-specific direction. They define the communication over MAP at a higher or more user-friendly level. Companion standards are needed because different classes of devices behave differently, so MMS has to be extended to suit the particular behavior of these classes of devices. For example, a "Request to read loop data" may be defined in a companion standard as a request to read, in order, the process variable, set point, valve position, mode status, alarm status, high alarm setting, low alarm setting, and deviation alarm setting (Ref. 16). Companion standards for robots, numerical controls, programmable controllers, and process control are either developed or under development at this time. The companion standard for process control is being developed by ISA's SP72.02 Committee.

Companion standards are not essential to create an interoperable, multivendor environment in MAP. However, without the companion standards, it is necessary to establish the MMS communication context in advance by knowing more about the intended association between two products.

The Field Bus The field bus is being defined by ISA's SP50 Committee. The charter of this committee is to establish a standard for digital, serial, bidirectional communication protocol for field-mounted intelligent devices. It will be capable of operating over existing unshielded twisted-pair wiring as well as shielded twisted-pair wiring. The field bus would be used to connect the loops, devices, and elements at the lowest level of the batch model of Figure 4-7 with the controllers that reside at the unit and equipment module levels.

The SP50 Committee has adopted a "three-layer" architecture based on the ISO OSI reference model: the physical layer, the data link layer, and the application layer (Ref. 17). SP50 is focusing on two sets of requirements called H1 and H2. H1 is a digital replacement for existing 4-20 mA systems. It is intended for short distances, operates at low speeds, and uses low-cost wire in a star topology (Ref. 18). H2 is a higher-performance system suitable for logic applications; it uses a bus topology and provides support for longer distances.

Internetworking Bridges, routers, and gateways provide a way to interconnect different local area networks.

A *bridge* is used to connect two of the same kinds of networks together (see Figure A-17), e.g., two MAP broadband networks or a broadband network to a carrierband network. It is an intelligent device that monitors data on each of the connected LANs and makes decisions about which data packets should be transferred across LANs and which should remain on the LAN where they were generated. But a bridge does not implement a Layer 3 protocol, so it is used to interconnect two networks that have the same addressing scheme at Layer 2. It maintains a list of addresses on both networks. If the upper layers of the two networks are not compatible, the bridge will correctly transfer the information, but the end systems will not be able to communicate because the total information packet is not compatible (Ref. 19).

Figure A-16 shows the use of a *router* to connect the broadband network with the carrierband network. A router (also called a MAP network relay) connects two local area networks by implementing an OSI network Layer 3 protocol (see Figure A-18). It uses addresses in Layer 3 (Network Layer) to transfer and route information to the correct network. It has the ability to route around a malfunctioning part of the network and will operate between any two networks with identical layers above Layer 3. Routers are needed when there is a requirement for a node to be available to more than one other network.

A *gateway* (see Figure A-19) is used to connect a non-MAP network, e.g., a proprietary network, to a MAP network. It is a dual architecture device that supports the full 7-layer MAP protocol and another full communications architecture.

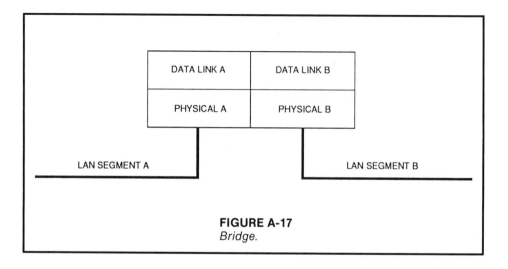

FIGURE A-17
Bridge.

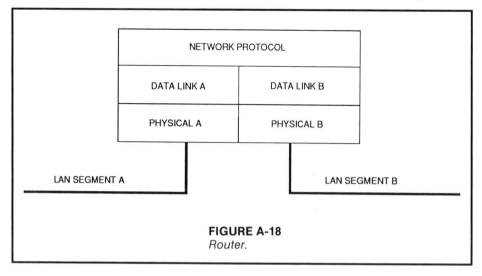

FIGURE A-18
Router.

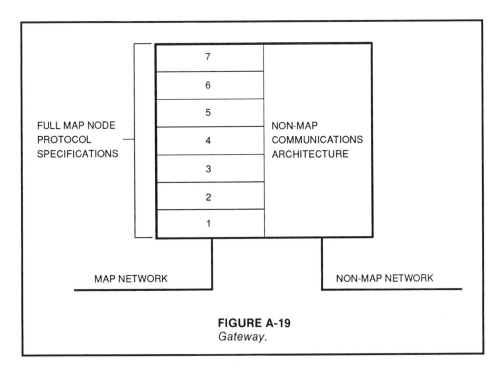

FIGURE A-19
Gateway.

A gateway is a device designed to link two incompatible communication networks. It takes messages and data from one highway, converts them into a form recognizable by the second network, and then sends this translated message to the second highway. An ideal gateway or interface would be capable of combining two incompatible systems without losing any data or execute any functions available in the second system and vice versa. In fact, the ideal gateway would appear to each network not as a gateway but rather as an extension of itself (Ref. 20). However, any real-world gateway is far from ideal. Some trade-off between functionality and performance always occurs. How large these trade-offs are typically depends on the degree of dissimilarity between the two systems. If the functions of the system vary greatly, it may not be possible to convert from one to the other.

A Total Plant Communications System

The batch process industry tends to be a very diverse industry and requires a wide range of equipment to perform its functions. This equipment includes (Ref. 21):

- field instruments that read raw process data;
- programmable controllers and distributed control systems that collect the raw data, perform control functions, and provide operator interfaces;
- departmental and MIS computers that use process data to provide management functions; and
- networks that tie all of the equipment together.

No single vendor can provide all the required equipment, so users and vendors must work in a multivendor environment.

Figure A-20 shows how a total plant communications system might be set up using open systems protocols. The backbone network that would run through the plant would be the MAP broadband network. The carrierband networks would be installed at several locations within the plant. For example, the plant may be broken down into various trains/lines. A carrierband network could be installed in each train/line. The connection between the carrierband network and the broadband network would be via a bridge or router. The Modbus and Data Highway networks shown are existing proprietary data highways. They would interface either to the MAP broadband network or to a carrierband network via a gateway. The field bus would be used at the lowest level of the hierarchy and would connect either to the unit controllers at the carrierband level or directly to the carrierband network via a bridge.

Some concerns must be addressed when networks are used for batch control systems in the process industries (Ref. 22). McCarthy provides these guidelines based on some of the concerns (Ref. 22):

1. Field digital sensor and actuator networks must conform to the ISA SP50 standard.

2. The real-time process control network must provide a migration path to the ISO standards in the MAP specification as well as to ISA-SP72.02 (for those process control systems that don't meet those requirements now).

3. Network redundancy and time synchronization must be available between the nodes of the process control network.

4. The process control system database must be structured to work with the MMS standards and accommodate the real-time collection needs of plant operations.

5. Plant information networks must use the ISO standards contained in the TOP or MAP specifications. Support for MMS as well as X.400 must be provided.

6. Data ownership and the security and integrity of the process control database must be maintained in the interconnections to plant-wide information systems.

7. The MAP X.25 connection must gain access to the enterprise network for business information.

Technical and Office Protocol (TOP)

TOP is a sister specification to MAP, intended for the engineering and office environments. Like MAP, TOP is a standards-based specification. The primary medium for TOP is a baseband cable running CSMA/CD. However, it also allows token-passing rings on shielded twisted-pair wiring, token-passing bus on a broadband cable, and broadband with CSMA/CD sub-network access. TOP uses the same protocols as

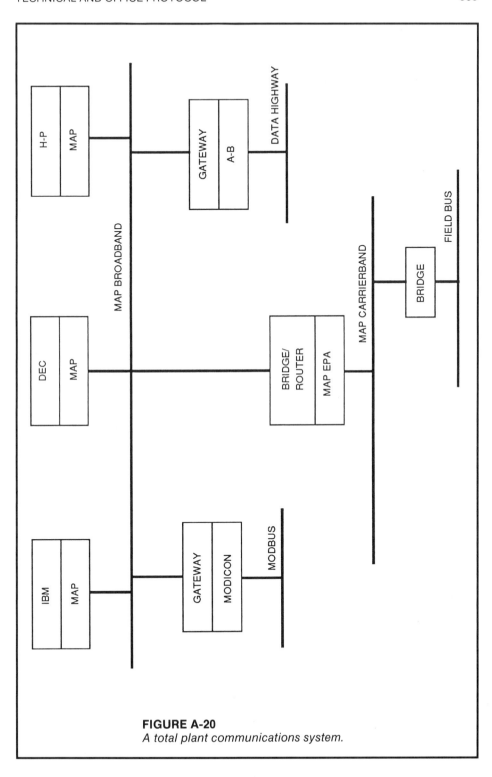

FIGURE A-20
A total plant communications system.

MAP in Layers 2 through 6. Some of the applications services supported by TOP are (Ref. 6):

- remote file access and transfer,
- electronic mail,
- remote terminal access,
- distributed CAD/CAM, and
- word processing and exchange of documents containing text and graphics.

MAP and TOP are complementary and are designed to work together in separate, but supportive, sectors of a multi-vendor computer network.

REFERENCES

1. EIA: RS-232-C, "Interface between Data Terminal Equipment and Data Communication Equipment Employing Serial Binary Data Interchange," Electronic Industries Association, 1969.

2. Alford, R. C., "Serial Interfaces in the Industrial Environment," *CONTROL*, February 1989.

3. Held, G., "The RS-232-C Interface," *Journal of Data and Computer Communications*, Winter 1989.

4. Britton, T., "LANs Get Islands of Automation Talking," *I&CS*, June 1983.

5. Owen, R., "Data Communications," *Interface Age*, March 1983.

6. *The Computer Integrated Organization: Some Business and Technical Issues for the OSI-MAP/TOP Solution*, Department of Trade and Industry, U.K., as edited by B. Thacker for the Society of Manufacturing Engineers, Dearborn, MI, 1988.

7. Pingry, J., ed., "Local Area Networks: A Primer for Manufacturing Facilities," Cutter Information Corp., Arlington, MA.

8. Freedman, D., "Fiber Optics Shine in Local-Area Networks," *Mini-Micro Systems*, September 1983.

9. Higham, J.; B. Kendall; and M. Gerdts, "The Data Freeway Network: A Coaxial Multi-Drop Management Control Bus," *Control Engineering*, September 1981.

10. Alford, R. C., "RS-485 Communications in the Plant Environment," *CONTROL*, July 1989.

11. Kaminski, M. A., Jr., "Protocols for Communicating in the Factory," *IEEE Spectrum*, April 1986.

12. Klein, M., and T. Balph, "Carrierband Is Low Cost, Single-Channel Solution for MAP," *Computer Design*, February 1, 1986.

13. Accampo, P. W., "MAP Pilots: Promises and Pitfalls," *CIM Technology*, Spring 1986.

14. Baur, P. S., "MAP and the Process Industries: Charting a New Course?" *InTech*, July 1986.

15. Mackiewicz, R., "An Overview of the Manufacturing Message Specification (MMS)," 40th Annual PetroChem Forum, The Foxboro Company, June 5–7, 1989.

16. Bader, F. P., "Getting Familiar with MAP in the Process Industries," Moore Products Company, Tech Paper 3917.

17. Sheng, R. S., "ISA Defines a New Fieldbus Standard," *Linkage*, Honeywell Inc., Vol. VI, Spring 1990.

18. Joseph, C. A., "Using LANs to Automate the Factory Floor," *CIM REVIEW*, Summer 1990.

19. Nadler, G., "Internetworking — Bridges, Routers, and Gateways," Enterprise Conference Proceedings, Society of Manufacturing Engineers, June 5-8, 1988.

20. Arnold, J. N., "Practical Techniques for Linking Foreign Devices to a Distributed System," ISA/87, Paper #87-1162.

21. "Open Communications in the Process Industries: A MAP/TOP Perspective," North American MAP/TOP Users Group and ISA's Open Systems Interconnection Division, October 23, 1989.

22. McCarthy, J. J., "The OSI Standards Challenge," *Control Engineering*, March 1989.

Appendix B
Database
Management
Systems

Introduction   In the 1980s, information has emerged as a major management issue in the manufacturing community. In many manufacturing companies, information is being viewed as a management opportunity for the enterprise as a whole. Many people now believe there is a direct relationship between the efficiency of information management and the efficiency and effectiveness of the overall manufacturing industry. This is especially true now with the increase in the amount of indirect labor and the decrease in the amount of direct labor. Manufacturing productivity is believed to be linked to the notion of shared or common data.

Data in a total plant automation system is spread across the various applications, and the goal is to integrate this data so that it is accessible to all who need it and to ensure its accuracy and timeliness. Many databases must be accessed throughout the organization.

The MAP and TOP specifications provide the first step toward plant integration. They take care of the problems of physical connectivity and make sure the data is represented in a common language. However, even with MAP and TOP, integrating the databases from the distributed process control system up to the plant-wide and company-wide databases will be a considerable challenge.

Although MAP/TOP can provide easy access to and interconnection with process control systems, plant management systems, departmental computers, and the like, the total communications problem cannot be solved until the databases in each of these systems are also integrated; there must be a common data structure/database. This will not be easy since databases have proliferated throughout today's industrial plants.

Database Management Systems   A database management system (DBMS) is a set of tasks that makes access to information stored in files more flexible and easier for the user to acquire. When the required functions can be planned ahead, file access requirements can be implemented once and then reinitiated as required. In other cases, the user must be able to access information based on the occurrence of a situation that might not have been previously planned for. With the right DBMS model, such a report can be constructed and requested on demand, using a high-level query access technique such as Structured Query Language (SQL). Then all of the information that is being stored can be accessed as needed.

There are three standard database models: the hierarchical model, the network model, and the relational model (Ref. 1, 2, and 3).

Hierarchical Databases In the hierarchical database, information is maintained in a tree structure that emphasizes relationships between superior and subordinate items (see Figure B-1). Each train/line has several units and equipment modules assigned to it, and each unit has many loops, devices, and elements assigned to it. The emphasis in a hierarchical database is on the relationships between higher- and lower-level items. A link connecting two record types, e.g., train/line and unit, represents a one-to-many relationship in the downward direction. Many-to-many relationships can be handled with a combination of hierarchies. The hierarchical database structure becomes cumbersome when multiple relationships are present among higher- and lower-level items.

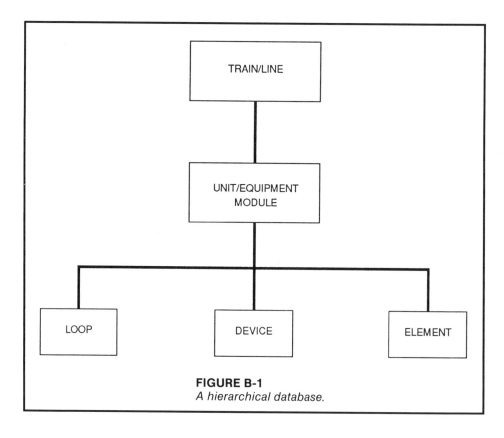

FIGURE B-1
A hierarchical database.

Networked Databases In the networked database, predefined links connect many leaves in a tree (see Figure B-2). It is similar to the hierarchical database, except that there are additional links interconnecting record types. As in the hierarchical case, each link between two record types in the network represents a one-to-many relationship, in the direction shown by the arrows in Figure B-2. It provides improved capability in recording relationships between items of information as compared to the hierarchical database. However, more complex processing is required for a given data manipulation operation.

In both cases, data is stored as records of different types, which are interconnected by pointers.

Relational Databases A relational database arranges information in a tabular format, which each table, or "relation," containing data that describes a particular type of object about which application programs require information (see Figure B-3). Individual fields containing the data item in each record are called attributes. All connections between tables are based on shared key values rather than on specialized link structures. Relational database technology is well accepted in the data processing world because it allows users to think of the data purely as tables, without paying particular attention to the method or location of data storage.

There is only one record for a given train/line, unit, loop, etc., because each of these items is unique. And since there is only one record, data acquired (such as process temperature, set point, etc.) appears only once. Therefore, there is no redundancy in data stored.

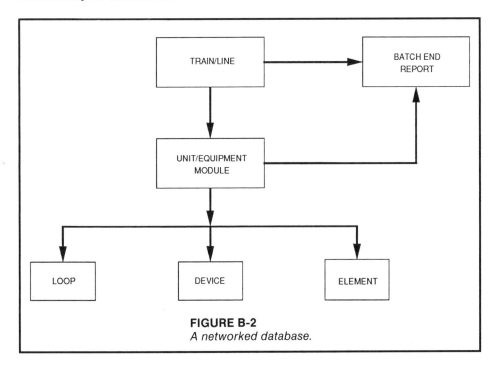

FIGURE B-2
A networked database.

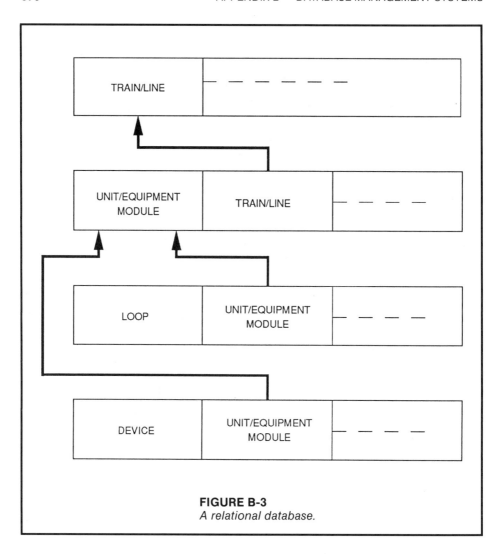

FIGURE B-3
A relational database.

The files in the relational database are independent, but there must be a way to integrate the data so that useful combinations of data from different files can be formed. This is accomplished by establishing links among the various files. For example, the unit/equipment module file contains a link to the train/line file. The link field stores the designated train/line number for each of the units/equipment modules; this establishes a relationship between the two.

Most of the databases used in today's process control systems are either hierarchical or networked types. However, relational databases are gaining popularity and are starting to appear in some process control systems. The following are some of the benefits of a relational database (Ref. 4):

1. Ease of use. The easiest way to represent most data to users not trained in the techniques of data processing is with two-dimensional tables.

2. Flexibility. Joint operations permit cutting and pasting of relations so that the different logical files wanted by different application programmers can be easily prepared in the form they want them.

3. Ease of implementation. The physical storage of flat files or two-dimensional tables is less complex than that of hierarchical and networked structures. Hardware devices to assist in rapid file searching are more feasible with files that avoid complex pointer linkages.

4. Data independence. Data independence can be achieved more easily with the logical structures in relational databases than with hierarchical or networked structures.

5. Security. Security controls can be more easily implemented, because sensitive attributes can be moved into a separate relation with its own authorization controls.

The biggest problem with the relational database is its lack of speed. This is the main reason that relational databases have been slow to catch on in process control systems, since speed is an important consideration in those applications. However, many sophisticated hardware and software techniques are being applied to enhance the performance of relational databases.

Although hierarchical and networked databases will continue to be used in control devices for some time, relational databases are the direction to move in for batch control systems of the future.

The Distributed Database Concept
A distributed database management system (DDBMS) is a network of computers in which each node supports database software. All the participating devices work together so that a user on any node can access data on the other nodes exactly as though the data were local. For this distribution of the database to be successful, the databases should appear to the user as a single database. This provides a more appropriate database structure because it locates the production databases physically at the area or unit that the data is being processed for, rather than in a central location (Ref. 5). Now, if there is a communication failure, the result will be some loss of capability. However, all of the production information for each area or unit will still be available for the operation of that part of the process. This provides a level of fault tolerance based on distribution of risk. It also matches the way in which humans deal with plant operations.

The relational database model is the only one that fits the concept of distributed databases. When a hierarchical or networked database is designed, the relationships (links) between records must be designed into the structure. This is important because accesses can be extremely slow when they are based on relationships that have not been designed into the structure.

The relational database meets the needs for ad hoc queries of data and permits the logical independence of the data from its physical location. It also allows the use of a high-level Structured Query Language (SQL) for nonprocedural, set-oriented access to the data. With SQL, users specify what is to be done, and the data is processed as sets of elements, rather than a record at a time.

Distributed database management systems are being developed as performance enhancements for relational systems to overcome the slow response of these systems.

One of the questions regarding the DDBMS is whether the data itself resides on multiple nodes throughout the network or whether access to the data is all that gets distributed. Although the distributed access approach is much easier to implement, it does require the use of a central server. This can end up being a bottleneck in the system because each network user ties up resources on the server. And if the server goes down, the entire network goes down. The distributed access network schemes are sometimes called "networking systems"; they are not true distributed database management systems (Ref. 1).

The Data Owner/Data User Concept (Refs. 6 and 7)   Data
and the ownership of that data are distributed among the various system components in a distributed system. For example, the process variables, set points, and modes associated with process-connected controllers are owned by the controllers. The owned data of a distributed component is also the key to any redundancy scheme that may be applied. It is the only data that must be maintained by a standby backup that has to take over on failure of the primary component.

A distributed component is also responsible for the integrity of the data it owns. Therefore, it must check store requests from other components to make sure that the values being stored are legitimate and consistent with other data in the component.

A data user will copy the process variables, set points, and so forth from the lower-level control for its internal use, but it does not own this data.

A Database Hierarchy   Most currently existing, isolated databases do
not easily interact. MAP/TOP addresses the ability to communicate between the islands of automation. However, the differing database structures inhibit effective use of "foreign" data within the islands.

Tools must be provided so that these databases can be used by multiple groups within the plant. McCarthy and McHugh (Ref. 6) suggest modeling these databases into hierarchical levels (refer to Figure 4-2 in Chapter 4). Then the needs of each department at each level can be considered; MAP and TOP can be applied to interconnecting the various levels.

Data is collected at each level of the hierarchy and is used to support the decision making that takes place there. The data typically becomes more compressed as it proceeds up the hierarchy. Although many plants now have these different levels of databases, there has been little integration between them. Part of that problem has been the difficulty of supporting intercommunications between them, and MAP and TOP provide the solution to that problem.

Even with MAP and TOP, a major challenge is still ahead. Along with the proprietary networks that have hampered communications among different systems, there are also proprietary data representation techniques that are used by most process control systems for their databases.

The accessing of data on a distributed processing system and the transmission of messages among components require a conceptual database structure supported by all. This involves specifying and generally standardizing the forms of data transmitted between the components.

McCarthy and McHugh (Ref. 6) suggest the following when planning integrated plant networks and databases:

1. Model the databases into a hierarchy of levels similar to the plant control layers. The lower layers will be structured for real-time performance, the upper layers for management information needs.

2. Have resident databases at all levels of the plant, from the field network to the corporate mainframe network. Each of these databases must be optimized to provide the different levels of information required for the various users.

3. Make sure that smart gateways to MAP and TOP have been developed that support interaction between the networks and their associated database entities at all levels of the plant hierarchy.

4. Look at the concept of data owners/data users so that data integrity, accuracy, and security can be maximized. Data owners control their portion of the distributed database and are responsible for the storage, maintenance, presentation, and updates of the data. Data users have varying levels of access to the data, but the data owner both controls access and structures the data to support uniform access rules by all system devices. In a true distributed system, data and the ownership of that data is distributed among the various system components. This means that each element of process data is owned and maintained by one, and only one, distributed component.

5. Make sure the functional requirements for plant-wide database linking are understood when planning for system integration. The high speed priorities of real-time process control must be maintained while supporting the information requirements of business-oriented databases.

Location of Functions

Although communications networks are becoming faster and faster, it will always be faster to access local memory than to access data from another component of the network. Therefore, data should not be shipped somewhere else to be operated on unless there is no other choice. However, this may be necessary when the function being done is one that coordinates and/or evaluates data from multiple distributed parts of the system.

Metzger and McCarthy (Ref. 7) list several things that determine the ideal location of a given function within the plant control hierarchy:

1. Scope. The ideal location is the lowest position in the hierarchy that is still equidistant from all its inputs and outputs. If the scope is a single controller, the function should be placed right with the controller. If the function involves information or coordination among various controllers, the function should not be forced down to a level where it is closer to some of its variables than to others.

2. Response needs. Higher levels in the plant control hierarchy inevitably have slower response to the data because of the layers of communication links

through which the requests and data must travel. If the need is for quick response, the function must be close to the process.

   3. Reliability needs. Because there is less equipment between lower levels of the plant control hierarchy and the process, they are inherently more reliable.

   4. Cost needs. Although this is changing somewhat, it typically costs more to put functions at lower levels. Large computers at the upper levels usually have a lower cost for a given amount of memory, storage, and computing power.

Key Characteristics of Database Management Systems

In considering the needs for a DBMS for integrating the control and information systems from throughout the plant, some key characteristics are suggested (Refs. 8, 9, and 10).

Real-Time Collection Data acquisition in today's process plants is primarily performed by the process-connected control, analysis, and monitoring systems. The values are used by the operators, and the control system is an inherent part of their operations. The most important characteristic of a real-time database management system at this level is its ability to provide guaranteed response for any data manipulation request for which there is a strict deadline. This predictability is essential to the real-time control of the process and plant.

   Traditionally, database management systems have not been utilized in control systems because their operation is just not fast enough. This constraint can be overcome by having real-time functions bypass the DBMS when updating the data. However, once the data is in the file, access to it can be via the DBMS.

Time-Tagged Records Time is an added dimension of the data acquired from the process. Time of occurrence is an important part of any process data so that the data can be analyzed at a later date. The closer the tagging of the data is to the data acquisition process, the more accurate and useful the data will be. If the process-connected data acquisition control system cannot provide the time tagging, the DBMS must support the adding of time values to data sets as well as synchronizing its time value with the data acquisition process.

On-Line Archiving Once the time-tagged data has been collected, the means for storing this data must be provided. The concern here is for timely storage in large volumes and for structuring the data for later access. However, the processing of the data into an elaborately structured database to allow easier access at a later time could take more time than the data acquisition cycle permits.

Multiple User Views Users at different levels in the organization have a need for different types of data. They may need data structured into different sets, across process units or plant areas, and across time. However, the control and display processing at the process-connected level determines the priorities and structure of the data acquisition process. The DBMS must be capable of supporting the types of access to the data needed by the various users.

Standard Query Language A high-level query language, such as SQL, greatly simplifies and expedites the task of manipulating data. It supports the collecting and storing of fields in multiple tables in a single operation. It also permits the user to define the data by its properties rather than by location so that the user does not need to know the location when the request for data is made.

Remote Database Access (RDA) Although SQL (Structured Query Language) has emerged as the accepted way to access relational databases locally, it is not suitable for accessing databases remotely over a network. RDA (Remote Database Access) will provide that standard. It will provide a standard way for data manipulation language statements (such as SQL) that are coming from a workstation to be encoded, sent over an OSI communication network, received by a database server, decoded, and executed (Ref. 9). RDA will also allow the database server to communicate its response back to the workstation.

RDA is on its way to becoming an international standard; ISO has elevated it to draft proposal status. ANSI (American National Standards Institute) has also formed a task group specifically dedicated to RDA.

RDA is based on the Client-Server relationship (see Figure B-4) (Ref. 10).

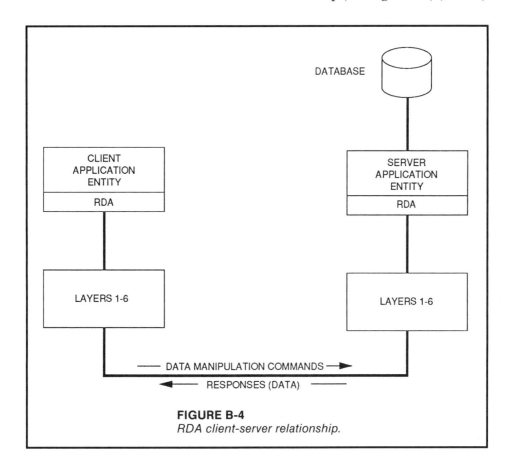

FIGURE B-4
RDA client-server relationship.

This is primarily a master-slave relationship where the Client behaves in an active role and initiates most of the activity. The Server acts in a passive role, and, in general, responds only to Client requests. The normal use of RDA is to support access from a Client (e.g., an intelligent workstation) to a physically remote database server. The Server accepts incoming messages from the Client and translates them into data manipulation commands than can be executed by the database. The results are relayed back to the Client using RDA.

RDA allows the system components of the Client and Server to be independent so that a Client can interact with any database that supports the RDA standard. This provides a platform for the implementation of a true heterogeneous distributed database system (Ref. 10).

Simplified Archive Retrieval A DBMS is needed that can handle the complex queries and extensive processing that may be needed to access the data collected and archived by the process-connected system. This data is normally structured according to the variable and unit to which it is connected, as well as time, which can make retrieval more difficult. Data that must be accessed immediately, such as for displays of process variable trends, needs simple access mechanisms for timely results.

Data Integrity The DBMS must be able to assure that all the data in a set are consistent. For example, if one block of the set has picked up some errors during transmission, it must be retransmitted. This means that the rest of the set is out of step with it and should not be used. When a data set is being updated, other users should be prevented from using the data until the update is complete.

Access Control The data owner at each level in the hierarchy must have some control over access to the database by other users. With multiple users able to access the database distributed across the plant, the ability of those external users to affect unit operations or plant operations based on that data becomes a concern. Access to lower levels, such as the data acquisition values, is usually restricted to the owner of the data.

Control Integrity Integrity, in the data processing world, refers to the ability of the system to perform predictably, to not crash, and to act responsibly in the presence of device failures or data corruption. This is especially important in a process management and control system. In fact, the integrity must extend beyond the system itself to the process equipment it controls. The control system must consider the constraints and failures of sensors and actuators so that it maintains the integrity of the control strategies, even if the database management system is operating normally and predictably.

REFERENCES

1. Winston, A., "A Distributed Database Primer," *UNIXWORLD*, April 1988.

2. "Types of Industrial Databases," *CONTROL*, January 1989.

3. Raines, W. F., and W. C. Muraski, "Use of a Relational Database in a Distributed Process Control System," ISA/87, Paper # 87-1180.

4. Chatha, A. S., "Next Generation of Plant Management Systems," *CONTROL*, January 1989.

5. Martin, P. G., "A Software Structure for Open Industrial Systems," Proceedings of the Fourteenth Annual Advanced Control Conference, September 19-21, 1988.

6. McCarthy, J. J., and A. E. McHugh, "Plant Data Bases and the Integration of MAP Networks," Honeywell, Inc., Phoenix.

7. Metzger, D. P., and J. J. McCarthy, "The Challenge of Integrating Hierarchical Control Across Distributed Processors on a Plant-Wide Network," Honeywell, Inc., Phoenix.

8. McCarthy, J. J., and K. Mikkilineni, "Considerations for Distributed Data Bases in the Computer Integrated Business," ISA/88, Paper # 88-1492.

9. Moad, J., "The Database Dimension," *DATAMATION*, May 15, 1989.

10. Gerhardt, R. W., "Remote Database Access," *GATEWAY*, May/June 1988.

Index